FROM CLASSICAL TO MODERN CHEMISTRY

SOME HISTORICAL SKETCHES

It is always safe and philosophic to distinguish, as much as is in our power, fact from theory; the experience of past ages is sufficient to show us the wisdom of such a course; and considering the constant tendency of the mind to rest on an assumption, and, when it answers every present purpose, to forget that it is an assumption, we ought to remember that it, in such cases, becomes a prejudice, and inevitably interferes, more or less, with a clear-sighted judgement.

M. FARADAY, *Experimental Researches in Electricity*, Vol. II (1844).

FROM CLASSICAL TO MODERN CHEMISTRY

SOME HISTORICAL SKETCHES

BY

A. J. BERRY, M.A.

Fellow Emeritus of Downing College Cambridge

CAMBRIDGE
AT THE UNIVERSITY PRESS
1954

PUBLISHED BY
THE SYNDICS OF THE CAMBRIDGE UNIVERSITY PRESS

London Office: Bentley House, N.W. 1
American Branch: New York

Agents for Canada, India, and Pakistan: Macmillan

Printed in Great Britain at the University Press, Cambridge
(Brooke Crutchley, University Printer)

CONTENTS

PREFACE

The purpose of the present work is primarily that of considering the historical development of certain branches of chemical science, which were either omitted from, or only adverted to in brief outline, in an earlier book, *Modern Chemistry—Some Sketches of its Historical Development*, published in 1946. The method of treatment, namely that of selecting particular topics and allocating them to separate chapters—that is, division according to subject-matter and not according to periods of time—has again been adopted. It may be added—as is indicated by the title—that somewhat greater emphasis has been given to certain of the older parts of the science.

Although the book is intended for the serious student of chemistry, the style of treatment is 'elementary' in the sense that it should appeal to others whose acquaintance with the subject is more limited, and whose chief interests may lie in altogether different kinds of study. It will doubtless be appreciated that in a book of this kind the sketches of individual topics must of necessity be somewhat impressionistic. But the selection of references appended to the several chapters should enable the reader to find the way to further and more detailed information.

In the opinion of the author, much of the history of chemistry—and particularly certain of its most interesting features—cannot be properly appreciated without giving some attention to the corresponding history of physics. The comprehensive works on chemistry of the early years of the nineteenth century, such as the *Lehrbuch* of Berzelius and Gmelin's *Handbuch*, contain lengthy sections devoted to heat, light, and electricity. Accordingly certain chapters have been written with this object in view, and with due regard to the relevance of these branches of physics to questions of more purely chemical interest.

The author considers himself as fortunate having regard to the valuable assistance he has received from several friends. Certain chapters have been read in typescript by Dr A. G. Sharpe, Fellow of Jesus College, and others by Dr F. Wild, Fellow of Downing

College, and the whole work has been read by Dr Moelwyn-Hughes. Information on particular points has been kindly given by Professor Partington and by Mr J. A. Chaldecott. To all the author would wish to express his sincere thanks, and particularly to Dr Sharpe for the additional work of reading the proofs. He desires also to record his sense of gratitude to his daughter, Mrs Claudine Walford, for help in connexion with the work of indexing. Finally the author would gratefully acknowledge the ever helpful co-operation of the staff of the University Press.

A. J. B.

CAMBRIDGE
Easter Term, 1954

CHAPTER I

SOME REMARKS ON THEORY IN CHEMISTRY

What is the significance of the term *modern* in connexion with the development of chemical and physical science? That the word is capable of a very wide interpretation is sufficiently obvious. Nevertheless, there has been a fairly general agreement, among writers on the history of chemistry, in dating the beginnings of modern chemistry from the time of Lavoisier. In their minds the downfall of the phlogistic theory was the determining event. But having regard to the extremely rapid progress of chemistry in recent times, as contrasted with the turmoil in the first half of the nineteenth century over atomic weights and formulae, some might prefer to date modern chemistry as starting with Cannizzaro's generalization which effected practically universal assent to Avogadro's principle. The position with regard to physics has been very different—in that science the dividing line between the classical and the modern parts of the subject has usually been drawn at the enunciation of Planck's quantum theory of radiation. The matter is very much one of emphasis, and it must be stressed that although some of the older work in chemistry and in physics is now superseded or viewed differently, much still remains which is of permanent value and importance.

Kopp's celebrated *Geschichte der Chemie* (1843–7), which dealt with the subject from the earliest times to those of the author, was written on the principle of division according to epochs. Of these the fourth period concerned the phlogistic theory, namely, from the middle of the seventeenth to the last quarter of the eighteenth century, and the fifth and last period was designated as the age of quantitative investigations. It is of interest to note that Kopp placed Cavendish in the fourth period—the era of the phlogistic theory—thereby giving more emphatic expression to his theoretical views than to his experimental accuracy. Historically the position thus assigned to Cavendish was of course correct, because of the well-known preference which Cavendish had expressed for the older theory of combustion, although he had a perfectly clear understanding of Lavoisier's views. It must, however, be added that Kopp fully appreciated the importance of those quantitative experimental researches which constituted the distinctive feature of the whole of Cavendish's work.

Kopp's discussion of the relation of chemistry to physics is of much interest. He pointed out that the methods of experimental physics began with astronomy in the early years of the seventeenth century, but in those times, chemists were occupied with the *qualitative* aspects of their studies. Thus the two sciences drifted apart, and for a time the separation between them became practically complete. Later as the study of chemistry became more and more quantitative, particularly as regards the properties of gases and the nature of heat, they came together again. The influence of Lavoisier was, according to Kopp, of particular importance in effecting this reunion; indeed he was, in a sense, to be regarded as the chief founder of physical chemistry.

The union of chemistry with physics, effected at the dawn of the nineteenth century, was not destined to remain unbroken, and for a time the contacts between the two sciences tended to diminish. More than one reason can be given to account for this. In the first place it should be remembered that the great advances in physics up to that time, and indeed throughout much of the nineteenth century, were accomplished by the avenue of mathematics. This mode of approach was a legacy from Newton, and was greatly extended by mathematicians of the French school, and particularly by Laplace. After the death of Lavoisier during the Revolution, Berthollet became the recognized leader of science in France. His *Essai de statique chimique*, which was published in 1803, was an attempt to discuss chemical phenomena on the principles of mechanics—in short, to apply to chemistry those principles which had led to results of outstanding importance in the domain of physics. The rudiments of the law of mass action are to be found in Berthollet's work, but in other respects the *Essai* had some fundamental errors: it was asserted that compounds were of variable and not of fixed composition. These mistakes were pointed out by Proust, who was able to show by accurate analytical work that compounds are of constant composition. Secondly, the publication in 1808 of the first part of Dalton's *New System of Chemical Philosophy* aroused widespread interest among chemists, who recognized the importance of the atomic theory for the future of chemistry.

The foundations of classical atomic theory, derived from Newton by Dalton, thus became the means whereby the composition and reactions of substances could be discussed. But, as formulated by Dalton, it was soon found to have serious limitations. Gay-Lussac's experiments on the simple proportions by volume according to which gases enter into combination were readily intelligible according to the hypothesis expressed by Avogadro in 1811, but not in terms of Dalton's theory. In a letter to Dalton, the distinguished Swedish chemist, Berzelius remarked: 'I think, however, that there are parts of this theory, much as science owes to you at present, which demand a little alteration. That part, for example, which obliges you to declare as inaccurate the experiments of Gay-Lussac, on the volumes of the gases which combine. I should have thought rather that these experiments were the finest proof of the probability of the atomic theory; and I confess to you, that I do not so easily think Gay-Lussac in fault, especially in a matter where the point is about measuring good or bad.' Fifty years were destined to elapse before the 'little alteration', namely, the acceptance of Avogadro's principle, was finally accomplished.

Notwithstanding the widespread confusion over chemical theory in the first half of the nineteenth century, great progress was being made on the experimental side of the science. Accordingly many chemists, possibly a majority and certainly including Bunsen, acquired a sort of dislike of theories; they were content to leave theories, especially such as were elaborated mathematically, to the physicists. Even after the doctrine of valency had been laid down by Frankland and Kekulé, the greater part of the progress in chemistry was for long effected with a minimum of theory. The separation of physics from chemistry was thus fairly evident. There were, however, always a few investigators, of whom Faraday was by far the most eminent, who cultivated the borderland between the two sciences, so that the separation between them never became complete; and towards the close of the century there was a very great increase of interest in the experimental side of physics, an interest which has become of ever-growing importance. As Norman Campbell remarked in his *Physics: the Elements* (1920), 'Nobody can hope to advance physical knowledge very greatly unless he has at his disposal, either in himself or in another, some portion of the skill of the mathematician; but neither can he hope to advance it to-day unless he has also at his disposal the skill of the glass-blower. It is hardly possible for a physicist to be wholly ignorant of mathematics—it is only if he is a Faraday that he can achieve that feat; but it is quite possible for a mathematician to be wholly ignorant of physics, especially in its more modern developments.'

Two departments of theoretical physics, namely, thermodynamics and the kinetic theory of gases, which were largely elaborated during the nineteenth century, were destined ultimately to exert very great influence on the progress of chemistry. It has been claimed for thermodynamics that results obtained by its means are independent of atomic and molecular considerations, and, as the two fundamental laws of that science are derived from experience, they constitute a better foundation for chemical and physical science than classical atomic theory. Ostwald was the most prominent expositor of this doctrine, and he claimed to be able to establish the fundamental laws of chemical combination on this basis. But Ostwald secured very few adherents to his views, and, it may be added, he eventually overcame some of his deeply rooted dislike of mechanical theories and admitted that the evidence forthcoming from such phenomena as the Brownian movement and radioactivity provided direct evidence of the reality of atoms and molecules. Regarding the dependence or otherwise of thermodynamics on molecular theory, it would be correct to say that the subject as treated in terms of the original methods of Carnot, Kelvin and Clausius is completely independent of any assumptions regarding the constitution of matter. But the discussion by Maxwell of the limitations of the second law was a tacit presupposition of the existence of molecules. It is indeed scarcely possible to enter upon a discussion of entropy without involving molecular considerations. All this is closely related to the problem of the distribution of molecular velocities according to the dynamical theory of gases, and consequently to that of the partition of kinetic energy. What has become known as the Boltzmann-Maxwell doctrine of the partition of energy arose in consequence of a publication by Maxwell in 1860, and became a highly controversial subject for many years afterwards. From first to last the doctrine was considered by Lord Kelvin as utterly unsound. Thus he expressed doubt regarding the conclusion drawn in 1895 by Rayleigh and Ramsay of the monatomicity of the molecules of argon from the ratio of the specific heats. Admitting that a value of 1·67 for this ratio, which was obtained later for the other inert gases, would seem to justify this conclusion according to elementary kinetic theory, Kelvin pointed out that the spectra of these gases contained a large number of lines, and if the Boltzmann-Maxwell doctrine were correct, the value for the ratio of the specific heats of a monatomic gas should be definitely less than 1·67. (This objection was raised long before modern electronic theories of the constitution of atoms were forthcoming.) However, the conclusions drawn by Rayleigh and Ramsay regarding the atomicity of the argon gases soon received universal assent. In more recent times the Boltzmann-Maxwell doctrine has secured general acceptance, and has assumed much importance in various directions, and notably in connexion with the kinetics of gaseous reactions.

Certain general principles of fundamental importance for the study of chemical equilibria and rates of reaction, namely, the law of mass action, the phase rule, and the theorem of Le Chatelier, came to be formulated in the course of the latter part of the nineteenth century. The law of mass action was first clearly stated by Guldberg and Waage in 1864, and again in more elaborate detail in 1867. The expression of this law was the outcome of experimental work carried out by these two Norwegian investigators themselves, but they also took account of the researches of others, notably those of Berthelot and of Péan de Saint Gilles on esterification, which had been carried out shortly before; they were, however, apparently ignorant of Wilhelmy's experiments in 1850 on the rate of hydrolysis of cane sugar. To Guldberg and Waage should be given the credit of having first given a clear definition of the concept of active mass as denoting molecular concentration, and of pointing out that the active mass of solids must be constant. The work of the Scandinavian investigators was very largely neglected, and so it happened that the law came to be established independently later by others. In this connexion the experiments of Harcourt and Esson in 1865 and 1866 on the kinetics of the reduction of potassium permanganate by oxalic acid and of the oxidation of hydriodic acid by hydrogen peroxide were of particular importance. It was also shown by van't Hoff that the law could be derived from thermodynamical principles and also from the molecular mechanical point of view. In 1879 Guldberg and Waage published a third paper in which they asserted their claim to priority, and entered into a discussion of further experimental work of their own and of others in support of the law.

The phase rule, derived between 1875 and 1878 by Willard Gibbs by the aid of his method of thermodynamic potential, is concerned with equilibria in heterogeneous systems. On account of the elaborate mathematical language in which the rule was first expounded, it received no attention from chemists. Some ten years later, however, its great value for the classification of equilibria was recognized by Roozeboom, and supported by a vast amount of careful experimental work. The principles of the phase rule are altogether independent of any considerations relating to the constitution of matter, and are concerned solely with the *number* of phases of a heterogeneous system which can co-exist under specified conditions. The actual determination of the nature of the various phases is a matter for experiment, and the work of Roozeboom and his successors, who might truly be termed the Dutch school of physical chemists, has gone far to confirm the importance of the law in the most diverse directions. In 1897 Bancroft published a valuable monograph on the phase rule, which dealt with the subject in a clear direct manner, without mathematical elaboration, and thus was of much influence on further experimental developments.

The principle governing qualitatively the effect of alteration of physical conditions on all kinds of equilibria, and usually termed the theorem of Le Chatelier, was developed chiefly and independently by van't Hoff and by Le Chatelier himself. In 1884 van't Hoff stated his principle of mobile equilibrium dealing with the effect of change of temperature on chemical equilibria. The principle was derived by invoking the aid of both thermodynamics and of molecular mechanics. In 1888 Le Chatelier published his *loi de stabilité de l'équilibre chimique*, which dealt primarily with the effect of change of pressure, but Le Chatelier also expanded his theorem so as to embrace any kind of alteration of physical conditions. In the course of his work Le Chatelier, without any knowledge at that time of Gibbs's work, discovered certain aspects of the phase rule. His derivation of the theorem was effected entirely by thermodynamics supported by much experimental work: as a follower of Sainte-Claire Deville he had no particular liking for molecular mechanics. The fundamental principles contained in Le Chatelier's theorem are really very much older, and are traceable in generalizations such as those of least action, enunciated by Maupertuis in the eighteenth century, and of least time, expressed by Fermat nearly one hundred years earlier in connexion with the refraction of light.

Some years after the phase rule had been accepted as a necessary theoretical principle for the discussion of heterogeneous equilibria, a question was raised in 1903 by Wegscheider regarding the definition of one of the fundamental concepts, namely, that of components. There were, of course, no difficulties over phases and degrees of freedom. He drew attention to a difference between two types of equilibria in which solid and gaseous phases are concerned, such, for example, as that of calcium carbonate, lime, and carbon dioxide, in contrast with that of ammonium chloride and its products of dissociation, ammonia and hydrogen chloride. Both are univariant systems, and yet there is an important difference between them. In the thermal dissociation of calcium carbonate the pressure of the carbon dioxide is solely dependent on the temperature, and as the composition of each phase can be constructed from two 'independently variable constituents' the system is clearly one of two components. But the pressure of the products of the thermal dissociation of ammonium chloride is a simple function of the temperature, only when these are present in equivalent proportions. If the composition of the vapour phase is altered by adding excess of either constituent, that is, if the composition of the vapour is represented as $x\mathrm{HCl}+y\mathrm{NH_3}$, the pressure depends not only upon the temperature but upon how much excess has been added. When this is done the system ceases to be univariant and becomes bivariant. Accordingly, the question arose whether the system of ammonium chloride in equilibrium with its dissociation products should be defined as of one or of two components. Another question considered by Wegscheider concerned the equilibria between solids and their saturated solutions in those special cases when separate dextro- and laevo-rotatory crystals are deposited. This question had been raised by van't Hoff in 1902 in a lecture delivered by him before the German Chemical Society. He pointed out that since the phase rule is founded upon thermodynamics, only such substances which differ in the thermodynamic sense can be considered as separate phases—'links- und rechts-drehende Verbindungen von üblichen Standpunkte identische sind'. Wegscheider concluded that if two solid phases separate from solution, which differ solely in the sign of their optical rotation, when only one solid should be expected according to the phase rule, the rule is to be extended if the optical antipodes are to be regarded as *one* independent constituent. But if they are to be considered as *two* independent constituents, then the ordinary phase rule remains valid. Wegscheider defined independent constituents as 'those substances which are necessary and sufficient, firstly to set up the conditions of equilibrium under the experimental conditions (limits of temperature, pressure and concentration), and secondly to express the composition of every separate phase at equilibrium'. Admittedly it is not easy to formulate a definition of components without difficulties arising in connexion with certain applications of the phase rule, but Wegscheider's attempt at a definition resulted in a somewhat acrimonious dispute with Nernst without any final conclusion being reached. The thermal dissociation of ammonium chloride may be regarded as a univariant system either of one component, or alternatively of two components, subject to the limitation that the ammonia and the hydrogen chloride are present in equivalent proportions.

The classification of the elements in periods according to their atomic weights was enunciated as a fundamental 'law of nature' by Mendeléeff in 1869, and a closely similar principle was expressed very shortly afterwards by Lothar Meyer. But beginnings in this direction had been made shortly before these publications by de Chancourtois and by Newlands. The reception given to the law of octaves, as Newlands termed it, was highly unfavourable: the Chemical Society refused to publish his paper. It is not altogether easy to account for this, but it may be mentioned that Newlands was not a good expositor of his ideas, and he failed to follow up the possibility of further developments. Mendeléeff, on the contrary, made successful predictions, notably the existence of hitherto undiscovered elements, and the necessity of correcting certain atomic weights which were at variance with the system. However, after the discovery of three new elements predicted by Mendeléeff, namely, scandium, gallium and germanium, the merits of Newlands's priority received some recognition. Public opinion in chemistry at that time was by no means particularly favourable to new theoretical ideas: even Bunsen did not consider the periodic law worth mentioning in his lectures. But Mendeléeff's prediction regarding the necessity of correcting certain atomic weights to bring them into harmony with the periodic classification was largely verified when the atomic weights came to be revised, except in the difficult case of the position of tellurium with respect to iodine. The results of the best determinations of the atomic weight of tellurium gave clear indications that its position constituted an irregularity in the system. Another defect was the impossibility of including the rare-earth elements in the table. It was thus realized that the periodic classification had some serious limitations, but hopes were entertained of discovering some means of effecting the necessary reconciliation. These hopes were destined to remain unfulfilled for over forty years, but were completely realized when a new basis of classification, namely, that of atomic numbers, was adopted.

In the last years of the nineteenth century a new era in experimental physics had its beginnings. The most far-reaching discoveries, namely, those of X-rays by Röntgen in 1895, and of radioactive phenomena by Henri Becquerel three years later, were eagerly pursued by numerous investigators, and were destined to effect a complete revolution of outlook on the nature of atoms. The first indications of the atomic nature of electricity were to be found in Faraday's work in the early part of the century and were followed in the nineties by the experiments of J. J. Thomson and his pupils on the cathode rays, culminating in 1897 with his determination of the mass of the cathode-ray particles—electrons. The recognition of electrons as universal constituents of matter led directly to the formulation of electronic theories of the constitution of atoms and of chemical combination. But it should be added that the development of modern atomic science was not wholly the work of physicists; the part played by chemists, though different, was of not less importance. The nature of X-rays was a matter of considerable discussion for a quarter of a century, but was settled in 1912 by Laue, Friedrich and Knipping. They showed that X-rays could be diffracted by crystals, just as light of ordinary wave-length is diffracted by a grating, and thus concluded that the wave-lengths of X-rays correspond to atomic distances within crystals. The extensive practical development of X-ray analysis was an immediate outcome of this discovery. In another direction the study of X-ray spectroscopy by Moseley in 1913 resulted in characterizing the elements in terms of their atomic numbers—a more fundamental basis than that of atomic weights. In the same year the displacement law of radioactive change was formulated independently by Soddy, Fajans and Russell. Closely connected with this subject was the idea that atomic weights might be average values, and in particular that the atomic weight of lead, 207, was an average of units of 206, derived from the disintegration of uranium atoms, and of 208 similarly derived from thorium atoms. This suggestion received experimental verification chiefly by Fajans and by Soddy. What is of particular importance was that a conception, namely, that of isotopes, originated in radioactivity and was extended to other elements by the method of positive-ray analysis, initiated by J. J. Thomson and improved by Aston.

The beginnings of electronic theories of the constitution of atoms were due chiefly to J. J. Thomson in 1904. His idea was that atoms consist of electrons within a uniform sphere of positive electrification. But in 1913 Rutherford showed that it was necessary to regard the positive electricity—to which the mass of the atom is attributed—as concentrated at the centre, with the electrons moving in orbits at distances which are considerable in comparison with the size of the nucleus. Bohr showed that such model atoms as understood by Rutherford would be in conflict with the principles of classical electrodynamics, but that by introducing Planck's quantum theory, consistency could be secured. According to the Rutherford-Bohr theory of atoms the chemical properties of elements are determined chiefly by the peripheral electrons, the nucleus being concerned with the mass and with the radioactive properties. In 1912 van den Broek suggested that the atomic number of an element is equal to the number of electrons in its atom, and in 1921 Bohr discussed the actual distribution of electrons in successive shells around the nucleus and the characterization of the electronic orbits from studies on spectral lines. Identical conclusions regarding the distribution of the electrons were reached in the same year by Bury starting from more purely chemical considerations. It is true that views regarding the structure of atoms, as consisting of protons and electrons, have been slightly modified since 1932 as a result of the discovery of two additional types of elementary particles, namely, neutrons and positrons. In that year Heisenberg ventured upon an explanation of the relation between atomic numbers and atomic weights, on the assumption that the nucleus consisted of protons and neutrons; and in particular he explained why, for the lighter atoms, the atomic weight should be double that of the atomic number, and suggested the reason of the gradual departure from this simple numerical ratio with increase of atomic mass. Nevertheless, the theory of atomic structure due to Bohr, when considered together with the results of X-ray spectroscopy, provided the means of predicting the nature of the then undiscovered element 72. In 1923 Hevesy and Coster pointed out that this element could not be a rare earth, but must be quadrivalent; and in the same year by working with these principles in mind they isolated from zirconium minerals the element which received the name of hafnium. An interesting example of the prediction, followed by the discovery, of an element (protoactinium) from a different principle, namely, the displacement law of radioactive change, was realized in 1918 by Hahn and Meitner, and independently by Soddy and Cranston. Both sets of investigators considered that the element would belong to the fifth group in the periodic classification and be chemically similar to tantalum, and as a result of careful work on tantalum residues obtained from pitchblende, the isolation of the element was accomplished.

The modern conception of the periodic classification of the elements thus represents a fundamental advance on the ideas of Mendeléeff. In the nineteenth century the possibility of subdividing atoms into smaller units was a subject with which chemists were not very seriously concerned. A few of them had ventured in somewhat speculative terms to discuss this idea. Thus Graham in 1864 remarked that 'it is conceivable that the various kinds of matter, now recognized as different elementary substances, may possess one and the same ultimate or atomic molecule existing in different conditions of movement. The essential unity of matter is an hypothesis in harmony with the equal action of gravity upon all bodies. We know the anxiety with which this point was investigated by Newton....' Very different were the views of Mendeléeff on this subject in the Preface to the last edition of his *Principles of Chemistry*, which he wrote in 1902. 'I may mention', he remarked, 'that the more I have thought on the nature of the chemical elements, the more decidedly have I turned away from the classical notion of a primary matter, and the hope of attaining the desired end by a study of electrical and optical phenomena....The return to electro-chemism which is so evident in the supporters of the hypothesis of "electrolytic dissociation", and the notion of a splitting up of atoms into "electrons", in my opinion only complicate and in no way explain so real a matter (since the days of Lavoisier) as the chemical changes of substances, which led to the recognition of the invariable and ponderable atoms of simple bodies.' The progress of chemistry during the last fifty years has given the most complete contradiction to every one of these remarks. Mendeléeff's success in founding the periodic classification upon the atomic weights was really fortuitous, and arose simply because, apart from the very few cases of inversion, namely, those of argon and potassium, tellurium and iodine, nickel and cobalt, and lastly of protoactinium and thorium, the numerical sequence of the atomic weights is identical with that of the atomic numbers.

The theories of classical physics were founded upon dynamics, and throughout the nineteenth century it was the established custom to offer mechanical explanations of physical phenomena. Poincaré pointed out that Maxwell, in connecting physical optics with electricity, did not give a mechanical explanation of electricity and magnetism, but confined himself to showing the possibility of an explanation of this kind. In a much more restricted sense mechanical explanations have found their way into chemistry. Davy seems to have thought that chemical phenomena might eventually be explained in terms of mechanics, because, in some notes of his impressions of various eminent French men of science, he adverted to a conversation which he had with Laplace on the subject. 'I remember the first day I saw him, which was, I believe, in November 1813. On my speaking to him of the atomic theory in chemistry, and expressing my belief that the science would ultimately be referred to mathematical laws, similar to those which he had so profoundly and successfully established with respect to the mechanical properties of matter, he treated my idea in a tone bordering on contempt, as if angry that any results in chemistry could, even in their future possibilities, be compared with his own labours. When I dined with him in 1820, he discussed the same opinion with acumen and candour, and allowed all the merits of John Dalton.'

Chemistry is particularly concerned with the *specific* properties of substances, and for that reason, if for no other, any attempts to discuss chemical reactivity in terms of mechanics are likely to meet with an extremely limited degree of success. A precise understanding of even such a simple reaction as the union of two gaseous molecules to form a compound is most difficult to secure. Striking differences in properties are by no means infrequently to be found associated with comparatively small differences in constitution, and considerable variations are known to exist among biological relations of optically isomeric substances. This subject figured conspicuously in Pasteur's work on the tartaric acids, and one of his methods of resolving racemic acid was based on the differential action of organisms on the dextro and laevo constituents. Much of Fischer's work on the sugars since 1894 was concerned with the action of enzymes on the optical isomerides of this group of substances. Later still, since 1904, Cushny investigated differences in the pharmacological action of the dextro and laevo forms of various drugs, notably of hyoscyamine. The subject was found to be highly complicated. He concluded that optical isomers differ in their pharmacological action proper, just as they differ in their action with enzymes and with substances of known constitution. All this goes to show how difficult it is to explain chemical phenomena on mechanical principles. It is, of course, true that a great deal of information has been accumulated concerning such physical conditions (temperature, pressure, influence of catalysts) which determine reaction, and it should be added that in certain directions, particularly in connexion with certain stereochemical problems, mechanical conceptions have been very helpful. Thus Baeyer's theory of strain in cyclic compounds, propounded in 1885, was a direct outcome of the tetrahedral conceptions of Le Bel and van't Hoff. According to this theory the angle between the bonds of a carbon atom is normally 109° 28′, and the degree of stability of a ring compound consists, in a general way, in the amount by which it departs from this angle. In 1876 Victor Meyer had stated that it was most unlikely that rings containing fewer than six carbon atoms in the molecule could be prepared, and in particular that all reactions which might be expected to give rise to rings with three carbon atoms had invariably resulted in the formation of isomeric open-chain compounds, and for the next few years Baeyer was evidently of the same opinion. But in 1882 W. H. Perkin (the younger) succeeded in convincing Baeyer that the subject was well worth experimental study. Having received sufficient encouragement from Baeyer, Perkin made a number of attempts to effect syntheses of this kind, and in 1884 he prepared trimethylenedicarboxylic ester, $\begin{matrix} CH_2 \diagdown & & \diagup CO_2Et \\ | & C & \\ CH_2 \diagup & & \diagdown CO_2Et \end{matrix}$, by condensing ethylene dibromide with the disodium derivative of ethyl malonate. Perkin expressly disclaimed this synthesis as the first example of the preparation of a trimethylene compound, because Freund had obtained trimethylene in an impure condition by the action of sodium upon trimethylene bromide. By heating the dibasic acid derived by hydrolysis, Perkin obtained the monobasic trimethylenecarboxylic acid, $\begin{matrix} CH_2 \\ | \\ CH_2 \end{matrix} \rangle CH.CO_2H$. A corresponding tetramethylenecarboxylic acid and, at a slightly later date, a pentamethylene compound were also prepared. The differences in stability of these substances were closely concerned with the working out of the strain theory. Support for this theory has been obtained from other sources, as, for example, by the action of heat upon dibasic carboxylic acids. It is well known that acids of the succinic and glutaric type readily give rise to anhydrides, thereby showing the readiness with which derivatives having five or six atoms in the ring are formed. The principles of the strain theory have been extended in various directions, as, for example, by Thorpe and Ingold since 1915, who provided evidence to support an idea of the possibility of varying the normal angle between the bonds of a carbon atom in such a way as to facilitate the formation of anhydrides; and by Ruzicka since 1926, who prepared various strainless cyclic compounds containing many carbon atoms in the rings.

The success of the strain theory—a thoroughly mechanical conception—is also to be seen in connexion with the formation, or non-formation, of cyclic compounds from geometrical and position isomerides. Thus it has long been known that while maleic acid readily forms an anhydride, its geometrical isomeride, fumaric acid, does not do so, although somewhat drastic treatment may result in the formation of small yields of *maleic* anhydride. Similar considerations are applicable to the three phthalic acids, of which only ordinary phthalic acid, the *ortho* compound, gives rise to an anhydride. These differences in behaviour are readily explained in terms of the relative positions of the carboxyl groups in space. As expressed in terms of projection formulae, the carboxyl groups in maleic acid $\begin{array}{c}HC.CO_2H\\ \| \\ HC.CO_2H\end{array}$, are contiguous, but in fumaric acid, $\begin{array}{r}HO_2C.CH\\ \| \\ HC.CO_2H\end{array}$, they are opposed. These acids differ also in other respects, and particularly as regards their ionization constants.

Since 1889 a great deal of information has been accumulated, chiefly by Ostwald and his collaborators, concerning the influence of the introduction of substituents into the chains of carboxylic acids on the dissociation constants. It was shown by Ostwald that the strengths of acids are affected not only by the nature of such substituents, but also by their positions with respect to the carboxyl groups. As regards dibasic acids the ionization is well known to proceed in two stages, $H_2X \rightleftharpoons H^+ HX^-$, followed by $HX^- \rightleftharpoons H^+ X^{2-}$, the first dissociation taking place to a much greater extent than the second. As the oxalic acid series is ascended, there is a progressive fall in the value of the first ionization constant, while that of the second remains more or less constant. In 1892 Ostwald gave a qualitative explanation of this phenomenon which has received fairly general acceptance from later investigators: he pointed out that while the introduction of a carboxyl group into the chain of a fatty acid should increase the strength of the acid, the presence of a carboxyl *ion* should have the opposite effect. Ostwald recognized the importance of the influence of distance, and remarked that his hypothesis explains why the ionization at the second stage of a dibasic acid takes place the less readily the closer the two doubly charged bivalent ions come together. The effect of distance is very clearly shown with maleic and fumaric acids, and with their monomethyl derivatives, citraconic and mesaconic acids. In both instances the *cis* acids are much stronger than the *trans* acids at the first stage, that is, as monobasic acids, but they are far weaker at the second stage, namely, as dibasic acids. For maleic acid the value of the ratio of the first, K_1, to the second dissociation constant, K_2, is about 50,000, while for fumaric acid the ratio K_1/K_2 is only about 36. For citraconic and mesaconic acids the contrast is not so extreme, but is nevertheless considerable, the values of K_1/K_2 being about 16,000 and 90 respectively. This subject presents a particular aspect of one of the essential features of the classical theory of ionization, namely, that of the existence of separately charged atoms or groups of atoms in solution, and rests ultimately on the fundamental principles of electrostatic attraction and repulsion, which are governed by the inverse square law first discovered by Robison in 1769. This law was also established by Cavendish in 1771, and independently by Coulomb in 1785, and the term *Coulomb forces* has come into general use. Cavendish also anticipated Faraday in the discovery of the property of specific inductive capacity, now more generally known as that of dielectric constant. In 1893 it was pointed out by J. J. Thomson, and independently by Nernst, that ionization should be promoted by a solvent such as water having a high dielectric constant, and the ions thereby kept apart. This idea, though formulated in connexion with the classical theory of electrolytic dissociation, is still valid, at least qualitatively, for the modern theory, according to which strong electrolytes are considered to be completely ionized at all concentrations.

The discussion of the course and mechanism of many reactions has been greatly assisted by attention given to stereochemical as well as to electrochemical considerations. The subject of steric hindrance really began with Menschutkin's experiments in 1879 on the influence of the constitution of alcohols as regards their capacity for esterification, but is more particularly identified with Victor Meyer's work in 1894 on the resistance to esterification of aromatic carboxylic acids having both *ortho* positions substituted by certain groups. At first experimental results appeared to support the fundamental idea, but exceptional cases, some of which were in direct conflict with it, were soon forthcoming, and accordingly the subject of steric hindrance lost much of its early popularity among organic chemists. Gradually the study of reactions between carbon compounds became more influenced by electrochemical considerations. Thus the work of Ostwald on the dissociation constants of dibasic acids, to which reference has already been made, has been greatly extended, on the theoretical side, notably by Bjerrum in 1923. Since 1926 much attention has been given to the subject, particularly by Lapworth, Ingold and Robinson, and in different ways they have discussed such reactions as nitration with a considerable degree of success. In his Faraday Lecture delivered before the Chemical Society in 1947, Robinson reviewed the subject at length, and dwelt on the importance of the older work on the dissociation constants of carboxylic acids, and on the possible modifying influence of steric conditions on the ionization of these acids.

CHAPTER II

VICISSITUDES OF THE THEORY OF HEAT

In the seventeenth century there were, broadly speaking, two altogether different views regarding the nature of heat. These have been termed the energetic and the materialistic conceptions respectively, and it has sometimes been stated that the physicists favoured the former view whereas the latter received support from the chemists. But such a manner of expressing the ideas of the men of science of that period must surely appear superficial. It must always be borne in mind that the masters of physical science at that time devoted attention to the study of both chemical and physical phenomena. But speaking in general terms it may be said that men whose interests were 'physical' rather than 'chemical', such as Boyle, Hooke, and particularly Newton, considered heat to be due to some kind of movement of the ultimate particles of matter as distinct from being itself a material substance. Thus Newton in the *Opticks* remarks: 'Do not all fix'd Bodies when heated beyond a certain degree emit Light and shine; and is not this Emission performed by the vibrating Motion of their parts?' It will be evident that Newton, usually a forceful advocate of the corpuscular theory of light, according to which optical phenomena are to be discussed in terms of minute particles cast off from a luminous object, had nevertheless clear ideas in attributing heat to some kind of movement of the particles of matter.

At that time, however, the views of those whose interests were primarily concerned with chemical phenomena were definitely materialistic regarding the nature of heat. Thus Boerhaave, one of Newton's contemporaries, considered heat to be a substance, to which the term *matter of heat* or *caloric* was assigned. It is by no means unlikely that ideas of this kind appealed to their minds in some such manner as Stahl's theory of phlogiston provided a very plausible means of explaining the phenomena of combustion.

As the thermal properties of gases are of such outstanding importance, it is of interest to note that Galileo, apparently about the year 1602, devised an apparatus which might be termed an air thermoscope. This consisted of a bulb blown on a long glass tube, the bulb containing some air and the lower open end of the tube immersed in water. According as the temperature rose or fell, the air expanded or contracted as shown by the movements of the water in the tube. Nearly two centuries later the quantitative law relating to the expansion of gases by heat was formulated by Dalton in 1801 and independently by Gay-Lussac in 1802. As is well known it has become customary to associate this law with the name of Charles, although his contribution to the subject is obscure. Clerk Maxwell, in a footnote to his *Theory of Heat*, remarks that Gay-Lussac stated 'that Citizen Charles had remarked fifteen years before the date of his memoir, the equality of the dilatation of the principal gases; but, as Charles never published these results, he had become acquainted with them by mere chance'.

In the eighteenth century discoveries of great importance were being made, which were destined to lead eventually to the downfall of the theory of caloric. Between 1757 and 1759 Black carried out his celebrated experiments on the melting of ice, which resulted in the discovery of what he termed *latent* heat. Independently, and apparently at a slightly later date, Cavendish was actively engaged on the same problems, and the Swedish physicist Wilcke was similarly occupied. Cavendish, as was his usual custom, carried out a great deal more experimental work on the phenomena of specific and latent heat than he ever published, and his thermal researches are therefore less well known than they deserve to be; but it now appears that the discovery of the appearance or disappearance of quantities of heat associated with changes of state was made independently by Black, Cavendish and Wilcke. In a paper which he published in 1783, Cavendish wrote: 'I am informed that Dr Black explains the above mentioned phænomena [latent heat] in the same manner; only instead of using the expression heat is generated or produced, he says latent heat is evolved or set free. But as this expression relates to an hypothesis depending on the supposition that the heat of bodies is owing to their containing more or less of a substance called the matter of heat, and as I think Sir Isaac Newton's opinion, that heat consists in the internal motion of the particles of bodies, much the most probable, I chose to use the expression heat is generated. Mr Wilcke, also, in the *Transactions of the Stockholm Academy of Sciences*, explains the phænomena in the same way, and makes use of an hypothesis nearly similar to that of Dr Black.' It is thus clear that Cavendish may be quoted as in favour of the view that heat is to be identified in some way with the kinetic energy of the ultimate particles of matter, and definitely against the idea that heat is a material substance.

Important developments in ice calorimetry were made between 1780 and 1784 by Lavoisier and Laplace. They acknowledged the priority of Wilcke in devising the method, but made no reference to the earlier work of Black and of Cavendish, which was done twenty years previously. As regards Black this neglect was not altogether surprising, as he was accustomed to making his discoveries known by quoting them in his lectures in the University of Glasgow without further publication. Although Cavendish published relatively little of his work on heat, it is more difficult to understand the failure of Lavoisier and Laplace to recognize his important discoveries. Unlike Cavendish, it would appear that Black adhered to the materialistic theory of heat; indeed, the word 'calorimeter' is suggestive of the theory of caloric. It is by no means easy to ascertain precisely what views Lavoisier and Laplace entertained on this subject. To them, however, must be assigned the credit of having foreshadowed the fundamental law of thermochemistry, namely, the law of constant heat summation (first clearly expressed by Hess in 1840), as the result of experiments which they carried out, such as the thermal effect of the mixing of sulphuric acid and water, and the heat evolved in the combustion of coal and sulphur, either in the presence of air or alternatively when mixed with an oxidizing substance such as potassium nitrate. Lavoisier and Laplace stated that 'toutes les variations de chaleur soit réelles, soit apparentes qu'éprouve un système de corps en changeant d'état, se reproduisent dans un ordre inverse, lorsque le système repasse à son premier état'. On the experimental side they made improvements in the ice calorimeter, an apparatus which was further improved by Bunsen in 1870, who estimated the mass of ice which was melted by measuring the resulting contraction in volume instead of by weighing.

In an attempt to follow the downfall of the theory of caloric, two names must be mentioned for their contributions of outstanding importance. In 1798 Benjamin Thompson, better known as Count Rumford, claimed to have demolished the caloric theory as a result of his studies on the heat generated by friction, particularly in the boring of cannon. In a *Historical Review of the Experiments on the subject of Heat*, Rumford quoted Berthollet, the author of the *Essai de statique chimique*, as not having established his point, namely, that his (Rumford's) experiments were consistent with the idea of caloric. Berthollet seemed to have supposed that the caloric was released during the disintegration of the metal. Rumford followed this up with some experiments on radiation, which he carried out in 1800–4, and which he regarded as having finally overthrown the materialistic theory. Then in 1799 Davy rubbed two pieces of ice together at 29° F. and thus melted them. As the temperature of these blocks of ice was below the melting-point, it is obvious that the cause of the melting must have been the heat generated by friction; in Davy's own words, 'It has thus been experimentally demonstrated that caloric or matter of heat does not exist.'

It might be supposed that these experiments of Rumford and of Davy would have led to the immediate abandonment of the theory of caloric and its replacement by something more logical, but, as we shall see presently, the theory of caloric, though possibly modified in the minds of its adherents, continued to command the support of a considerable number of men of science for many years. A comparison of the decline and fall of the phlogistic theory of combustion with that of the materialistic theory of heat exhibits some striking contrasts. When Lavoisier between 1777 and 1783 published his oxygen theory of combustion, the new views were eagerly accepted by most Continental men of science, but in this country Black alone abandoned the theory of phlogiston. Very interesting are some remarks which Cavendish appended to one of his papers entitled *Experiments on Air* in 1784: 'There are several memoirs of Mr Lavoisier published by the Academy of Sciences in which he entirely discards phlogiston, and explains those phænomena which have been usually attributed to the loss or attraction of that substance by the absorption or expulsion of dephlogisticated air; and as not only the foregoing experiments, but most other phænomena of nature, seem explicable as well, or nearly as well, upon this as upon the commonly believed principle of phlogiston, it may be proper briefly to mention in what manner I would explain them on this principle, and why I have adhered to the other.' Then after a short but very discerning analysis of the subject, Cavendish concluded: 'It seems, therefore, from what has been said, as if the phænomena of nature might be explained very well on this principle, without the help of phlogiston; and indeed, as adding dephlogisticated air to a body comes to the same thing as depriving it of its phlogiston and adding water to it, and as there are, perhaps, no bodies entirely destitute of water, and as I know of no way by which phlogiston can be transferred from one body to another, without leaving it uncertain whether water is not at the same time transferred, it will be very difficult to determine by experiment which of these opinions is the truest; but as the commonly received principle of phlogiston explains all phænomena at least as well as Mr Lavoisier's, I have adhered to that.'

It would thus appear that Cavendish had no difficulty in understanding the antiphlogistic theory of combustion, but for some reason he 'resented' it. Nevertheless, the views of Lavoisier rapidly secured universal acceptance; indeed, many men of science have dated the beginnings of modern chemistry from that time. Thus Wurtz, in an oft-quoted sentence in which his patriotic enthusiasm surpassed his scientific judgement, exclaimed: 'La chimie est une science française, elle fut constituée par Lavoisier.'

Very different was the downfall of the theory of caloric after the experiments of Rumford and Davy. Adherents of this theory were to be found many years afterwards, as anyone who has followed the early history of thermodynamics can testify. But in the case of both theories, there can be little doubt that there was a gradual change in the meanings attached to the words *phlogiston* and *caloric*. To Stahl the word phlogiston would have appeared to signify a subtle material having the property of combustibility, to later investigators, particularly to Cavendish, it was closely associated with hydrogen. The theory of caloric, or matter of heat as it was usually termed by its earlier partisans, was certainly not understood in the same sense by them as by Sadi Carnot and some of his immediate followers. Some physicists have even suggested that Carnot's caloric had something in common with the conception of entropy.

In 1824 Carnot published his celebrated *Réflexions sur la puissance motrice du feu*, which originated as a result of a study of the efficiency of the steam engines in use in this country as compared with those in France. This was emphasized by the sub-title of his treatise, *et sur les machines propres à développer cette puissance*. This brilliant theoretical work contained some of the fundamental principles of thermodynamics, in particular that all simple reversible engines have the same efficiency, which is solely a function of the difference between two temperatures, that of the source of heat and that of the refrigerator. In establishing this principle, Carnot adopted the materialistic theory of heat, which was still popular at that time, but some manuscript notes which were found after his death in 1832 show clearly how far he had advanced towards a more modern view of thermal motive power. These *Notes inédites*, which were later published by his brother, contain remarks such as 'La chaleur n'est autre chose que la puissance motrice, ou plutôt que le mouvement qui a changé de forme. C'est un mouvement dans les particles des corps. Partout où il y a destruction de puissance motrice, il y a, en même temps, production de chaleur.' In 1912 Callendar directed attention to the futility of criticisms which have at various times been levelled against Carnot's ideas on the ground that they were formulated in the language of the theory of caloric. Larmor in a paper entitled

On the nature of heat as directly deducible from the principle of Carnot, which appeared in 1918, pointed out that as the efficiency of a perfectly reversible engine is governed solely by a difference between two temperatures, questions regarding the *nature* of heat do not thereby arise.

The early history of thermodynamics, which is closely associated with the development of the conservation of energy, from the time of Carnot until the middle of the nineteenth century is somewhat complicated. Before attempting to discuss it in any detail, reference may be made to a short paper by Graham in 1826 entitled *On the heat of friction.* This was an attempt to effect some sort of reconciliation between the materialistic and the energetic conceptions of heat. Although no references were made to either Rumford or Davy, it is almost certain that Graham must have been familiar with their work, and is chiefly interesting as showing how widely the theory of caloric was held at that time. The discovery of thermo-electricity by Seebeck in 1821, and its further development by Peltier in 1834, greatly interested Faraday in connexion with his ideas regarding chemical action as the source of power in the voltaic pile. He pointed out that, in a voltaic circuit, 'the situation of antimony and bismuth varies according as one or another fluid conductor is used. Antimony being negative to bismuth with the acids, is positive to it with an alkali or sulphuret of potassium; still we find that they come *nearly together* in the middle of the metallic series. In the thermo series, on the contrary, their position is at the *extremes*, being as different or as much opposed to each other as they can be.'

The beginnings of the idea of the conservation of energy are to be found in the works of some of the older investigators, such as those of Galileo, Newton, Huygens and Leibnitz, the conception of *vis viva* or kinetic energy being correctly understood. It was not, however, until the years 1842–7 that a more general establishment of this important principle was effected. In 1842 Mayer announced the principle of the mechanical equivalent of heat. Between 1840 and 1843 Joule published several papers on the heating effects of currents, including an important one entitled

On the electric origin of the heat of combustion. In 1843 Joule established the principle on a sound experimental foundation and obtained a value for this constant of 798 foot-pounds per British thermal unit, the modern figure being 779 in these units or $4{\cdot}19 \times 10^7$ ergs per calorie. To both Joule and Mayer is due the credit of having established the principle of an exact proportionality between the quantities of mechanical energy transformed and of heat produced. The transformation of mechanical energy into heat can be shown to be strictly quantitative, but not so the reverse process. Only a certain fraction of the heat taken in at the source at the higher temperature in a reversible engine and given out to the refrigerator at the lower temperature is transformed into work. This apparent conflict between the principle of Joule and that of Carnot had some interesting consequences in the further development of thermodynamics, and was finally resolved by the independent work of William Thomson (afterwards Lord Kelvin), Clausius and Rankine in 1850.

Even before the time of Carnot, it had been recognized that there were processes (which have since been designated as adiabatic) in which heat does not enter or leave a system, and that there must be a difference in the values of the specific heat of a gas according as the determination is made at constant pressure or at constant volume. The square root of the ratio of these two values was applied by Laplace in 1816 to correct the expression for the velocity of sound in air as given by Newton, and the ratio has subsequently figured in many developments of the theory of gases in widely different directions in physical chemistry.

The reconciliation of the principles of Joule and of Carnot, together with the establishment of the mechanical theory of heat upon a satisfactory foundation, was effected in the years immediately following the enunciation of the principle of the conservation of energy in a clear and general way by Helmholtz in 1847.

In 1849 Kelvin published an analysis of Carnot's doctrine, which he had derived, not from the original work as it was not readily accessible, but from an exposition published ten years later by Clapeyron in which the cycle was discussed with the aid of graphical diagrams. Kelvin immediately appreciated the great value of Carnot's principle, but at that time he was unable to reconcile it with Joule's theorem of the equivalency of work and heat, as he still adhered to the doctrine of the materialistic nature of heat, probably because Carnot's doctrine was formulated in terms of that theory. Kelvin in discussing the possibility of abandoning Carnot's axiom remarked: 'If we do so, however, we meet with innumerable other difficulties—insuperable without further investigation, and an entire reconstruction of the theory of heat from its foundations. It is in reality to experiment that we must look either for a verification of Carnot's axiom and an explanation of the difficulty we have been considering, or for an entirely new basis of the theory of heat.' So for a year or two Kelvin neglected Joule's principle, in order, as he thought, to rescue that of Carnot.

A prediction was made in 1849 by James Thomson, using Carnot's reasoning, that since ice has a greater specific volume than liquid water at the freezing-point, increase of pressure should lower the melting-point. In his theoretical reasoning James Thomson formulated the familiar latent heat equation, an equation which has also been attributed to others, for instance, to Clapeyron and to Clausius. It has been employed in many subsequent developments in physics and chemistry, particularly by Kelvin, Rankine, and later by Willard Gibbs, van't Hoff and Le Chatelier. Thomson was thus able to calculate the expected degree of lowering of the freezing-point for any particular pressure. The correctness of his reasoning was very shortly afterwards verified experimentally by Kelvin, who actually obtained values for the amount of lowering in close agreement with the predicted figures. Then in 1850 Clausius published an important paper, written with a knowledge of Carnot's principle, as quoted by Clapeyron, and of the theoretical and experimental work on the freezing of water, in which a satisfactory reconciliation of the principles of Carnot and of Joule was effected. Two years before the publication of Clausius's paper, Kelvin pointed out the possibility of constructing an 'absolute' scale of temperature based on the principle of the Carnot cycle. Such a scale would have the advantage of being independent of the nature of the working substance, and would also provide a means of establishing the absolute zero of temperature as a physical reality, since, if the temperature of the source has a finite value and the temperature of the refrigerator is taken as zero, the whole of the work done in the cycle will be equal to the heat taken from the source.

The conception of the property termed 'entropy' by Clausius and 'the thermodynamic function' by Rankine has been of fundamental importance in the development of the science of energetics, and it is intimately connected with the formulation of the second law, a theorem which has been stated in several different ways—by Clausius, by Kelvin, by Rankine, and by others, objections having been raised to each of them. The expression of Clausius, namely, that *heat cannot by itself pass from a colder to a warmer body* is, perhaps, as satisfactory as any. In discussing reversible cycles with the aid of indicator diagrams, Rankine at first used the expression *curve of no transmission* and afterwards introduced the term *adiabatic* which has since come into general use. The first formal treatise on thermodynamics was published by Rankine in his *Manual of the Steam Engine and other Prime Movers* in 1859, and this work has had far-reaching consequences in the study of that subject by engineers. As it is only in strictly reversible processes that constancy of entropy is preserved, adiabatic lines may, as Willard Gibbs suggested, be termed *isentropic* lines; but this terminology has not become popular. In all irreversible processes the entropy must increase, or, what comes to the same thing, the available energy, that is, the energy practically convertible into work, must diminish. Clausius in 1865 expressed this by his much-quoted remark: 'Die Energie der Welt ist constant, die Entropie der Welt strebt einem Maximum zu', and this statement was used by Gibbs as a motto at the beginning of his celebrated memoir, *On the Equilibrium of Heterogeneous Substances*, published in four parts between 1875 and 1878. In this paper the conception of thermodynamic potential was introduced for the first time. Later still, in 1882, the doctrine of free energy was more formally developed by Helmholtz.

At what stage of its development did the science of thermodynamics assume a molecular aspect? Although the general principles of the subject, as usually formulated, are in no way concerned with theories relating to the constitution of matter, it would seem that molecular considerations are inseparably connected with the energetic theory of heat. The early beginnings of the kinetic theory of gases are much older than the *Réflexions* of Carnot, and are to be found in the writings of Huygens and of Daniel Bernoulli; but the modern development of that theory, chiefly associated with the names of Clausius and Clerk Maxwell, did not come about until after the middle of the nineteenth century. But in 1845 a paper entitled *On the physics of media that are composed of free and perfectly elastic molecules in a state of motion* was submitted to the Royal Society by Waterston in which many of the fundamental properties of gases were discussed in terms of the *vis viva* of the molecules. Most unfortunately this paper received unfavourable reports at the hands of the referees, and publication was refused. Nearly fifty years later the paper was discovered by Lord Rayleigh in the Archives of the Society, who immediately recognized its value and took steps to secure its publication. It was accordingly published in the *Philosophical Transactions* in 1892. Had Waterston's paper been published at the time when it was submitted, the subsequent progress of thermodynamics and of kinetic theory—the corner-stones of modern physical chemistry—might have followed a somewhat different path. But, viewed in historical perspective, some of the conclusions reached by Waterston are most interesting. Thus he showed that Graham's square-root law relating to the diffusion of gases followed at once from his reasoning. He was also able to give a fairly clear exposition of Dalton's law of partial pressures. In discussing the value of the ratio of the specific heat of a gas at constant pressure to that at constant volume Waterston considered that the ratio should be 4:3. Lord Rayleigh pointed out that Waterston's figure was marred by an arithmetical error, and that on his own showing the ratio should have been 5:3. In 1819 the ratio was determined experimentally for air by Desormes and Clément who obtained a value of 1·35, and very shortly afterwards

Gay-Lussac and Welter, using their method, obtained a figure of 1·37. These figures were familiar to Laplace and were quoted by him in the *Mécanique céleste* in giving support to his well-known formula for the velocity of sound in air. All this was known to Waterston, and, as was pointed out by Lord Rayleigh, since the experimental value for the ratio for air was not very different from 4:3, this probably prevented him from discovering his mistake.

The introduction of molecular conceptions into thermodynamics followed shortly after the establishment of the second law by Clausius and Kelvin. It may be noted that Rankine employed the term 'molecular vortices' to express some of his ideas. It would appear by no means unlikely that at that time many physicists, although familiar with and interested in kinetic theory, were anxious to develop the science of energetics, as free as possible from any hypothetical ideas concerning atoms and molecules. By far the greater part of nineteenth-century physics was built up on the idea that matter was to be regarded as a continuum; the development of chemistry was altogether different—in that science progress without the aid of atoms and molecules would have been as good as impossible.

In Gibbs's celebrated memoir, already referred to, of which the phase rule is the most valuable legacy to chemists, reference was made to experiments on the thermal dissociation of compounds like nitrogen tetroxide, those, for example, of Playfair and Wanklyn in 1861 and of Deville and Troost in 1867. Thermal dissociation is a subject very much concerned with molecules, while the phase rule deals with equilibria in heterogeneous systems, that is, with problems altogether apart from molecular considerations. In his *Populäre Schriften* Boltzmann remarked that 'Gibbs bei Begründung seiner Sätze sicher molekulare Vorstellungen machte....Erst später wurden die Sätze von ihrer molekularen Begründung getrennt und als reine Tatsache hingestellt.' It is therefore by no means difficult to understand that an attempt should have been made by Ostwald at the beginning of the twentieth century to establish a school of physical chemistry, based upon energetics as opposed to the atomic theory. The attempt, though interesting, was foredoomed to failure, as was indeed recognized later by Ostwald himself. The first to appreciate the limitations of the second law of thermodynamics was Clerk Maxwell. In the later editions of his *Theory of Heat*, Maxwell was careful to point out that the second law is limited to matter in bulk and cannot apply to individual molecules. He stated that 'it [the second law] is undoubtedly true as long as we can deal with bodies only in mass, and have no power of perceiving or handling the separate molecules of which they are made up. But if we conceive a being whose faculties are so sharpened that he can follow every molecule in its course, such a being whose attributes are still as essentially finite as our own, would be able to do what is at present impossible to us. For we have seen, that the molecules in a vessel full of air at uniform temperature are moving with velocities by no means uniform, though the mean velocity of any great number of them, arbitrarily selected, is almost exactly uniform. Now let us suppose that such a vessel is divided into two portions, *A* and *B*, by a division in which there is a small hole, and that a being, who can see the individual molecules, opens and closes this hole, so as to allow the swifter molecules to pass from *A* to *B*, and only the slower ones to pass from *B* to *A*. He will thus, without expenditure of work, raise the temperature of *B* and lower that of *A*, in contradiction to the second law of thermodynamics.' This imaginary being, capable of dealing with individual molecules, soon became known as Maxwell's Demon. Neither Maxwell nor anyone else at the time supposed that the machinations of any such demon would be possible to observe experimentally until Gouy began his investigations on the Brownian movement in 1888. According to Gouy the microscopic particles which constitute the Brownian movement differ in their individual content of kinetic energy, and thus do not individually obey Carnot's principle. In the words of Henri Poincaré, 'One can almost see Maxwell's demon at work'.* It should be added that the correctness of Gouy's theory of the

* 'On croirait voir à l'œuvre le démon de Maxwell.' *La Science et l'hypothèse*, Paris, 1902, p. 209.

Brownian movement has received the most ample confirmation as the result of the fine experimental work of Perrin since 1908.

In more than one of his writings, Larmor has considered that the concept of energy is not an ultimate one and that the basis of thermodynamics is really molecular. Thus in a short note entitled *The Carnot-Kelvin aspect of thermodynamics*, which was published in 1937, he asks: 'What is the foundation of the Clausius theorem of increasing entropy? This involves a correlative enquiry, What is heat; is it even a definite entity? Clapeyron, the earliest expositor of Carnot, explored graphically the case of cyclic working with a perfect gas..., but by an error in the elementary algebra he managed to conform to the prevalent postulate of caloric, which required that no aggregate of heat is lost when the gas does work in the manner of a cyclic engine. This apparent violation of conservation of total energy was easily put right by Clausius in a paper which has held a prominent place in the science: it is, however, only an elucidation, far from a universal proof, of the deep-seated cyclic presumption or postulate of Carnot....

'This concept of entropy is most readily illustrated from systems constituted molecularly, such as in the simplest case of a gas. But the slightest consideration of biological phenomena surely shows that molecular structure does not penetrate to the bottom of things, is only the surface generality that in the simpler range of occurrences is skimmed off into a physical science. The question remains whether or how far the entropy of Clausius, which need not be confined to molecular structures, and so may go far deeper, is adequate for a universal formulation.'

It should be noted that until thermodynamics received support from kinetic considerations there was no really satisfactory understanding of the second law, or, indeed, of the concept of entropy. Neither Clausius nor Kelvin in the middle of the nineteenth century was able to understand why thermal energy should be different from mechanical energy, or, in other words, why there cannot be complete conversion of heat into mechanical work, while there is complete convertibility of mechanical work into heat. The question may be formulated by inquiring why the conversion of heat into work is an irreversible process. No answer can be given to this question by invoking the principles of classical mechanics, because these deal only with strictly reversible processes, but hints on how the problem might be attacked are to be found in the works of Clerk Maxwell. Reference has already been made to Maxwell's view that the second law of thermodynamics fails when attempts are made to apply it to individual molecules as distinct from matter *en masse*, and Boltzmann has emphasized the view that heat consists essentially in the *irregular* motion of the molecules. Boltzmann applied the laws of probability to the movements of the molecules, and thus established the second law on a statistical basis. Gibbs in his later papers elaborated a science of statistical mechanics, which was largely founded on Boltzmann's ideas in which entropy was regarded as a measure of the degree of molecular disarrangement of the system under consideration.

Very shortly after the enunciation of the law of constant heat summation, which is really a special case of the first law of thermodynamics, by Hess in 1840, a number of investigators were attracted to the experimental study of thermochemistry. Of these the most prominent as regards the early development of the subject were Graham, Andrews, and Favre and Silbermann. The reactions which were studied were mostly those which readily take place at moderate temperatures, such as the heats of neutralization of acids, and the heats of hydration of salts, and a considerable mass of valuable experimental data was accumulated as a result of their labours. A little later two other investigators of note entered upon this work, namely, Julius Thomsen and Berthelot, the inventor of the well-known bomb calorimeter for determining heats of combustion, both of whom made many valuable additions to the stock of thermochemical knowledge, but a theorem, the law of maximal work, which they formulated, independently and in slightly different terms, was destined to give rise to considerable confusion for many years.

As has been pointed out by Duhem and others, up to the middle of the nineteenth century every exothermic reaction was regarded as a combination, while every decomposition was regarded as an endothermic process. In 1854 Thomsen, regarding the quantity of heat produced in a chemical change as a measure of the affinity of the reacting substances, summed up his theoretical ideas in the statement that *every reaction, simple or complex, of a purely chemical character, is accompanied by an evolution of heat.* In 1865 Berthelot published his first paper of a series on the general principles relevant to the heat liberated in chemical reactions. He assumed equivalence between the quantities of heat and what he termed the *travail moléculaire* of the reactions. Berthelot at first professed to recognize the principles laid down by Clausius in 1850 as being valid throughout the domain of chemistry. After a number of further publications, in which much valuable experimental material was subjected to discussion, unfortunately, however, without keeping the doctrine of Clausius before his eyes, Berthelot in 1873 announced what he termed the third principle of thermochemistry, according to which *every chemical change, accomplished without the intervention of external energy tends to the production of that substance or system of substances which evolves the maximum quantity of heat.* To this statement Berthelot gave the name of the *principle of maximum work.*

In 1873 Thomsen administered a sharp rebuke to Berthelot for never having once quoted his name in his numerous publications on thermochemistry, and particularly for having neglected to acknowledge his (Thomsen's) paper of 1854 according to which every reaction of a purely chemical character is accompanied with an evolution of heat. To this Berthelot gave a vigorous reply in which he described Thomsen's principle as neither original, nor based on phenomena, nor identical with his own law of maximal work. This controversy has been analysed by Duhem in his *Introduction à la mécanique chimique* (1893), who concluded that Berthelot was mistaken in regarding Thomsen's principle as lacking originality, but regarding its identity or otherwise with Berthelot's law of maximum work he practically left the matter an open question.

In some of his later publications, such as his *Essai de mécanique chimique fondée sur la thermochimie* which appeared in 1879, Berthelot continued to uphold his principle of maximum work, but, bearing in mind the difficulties associated with endothermic reactions and reversible reactions generally, he found it necessary to introduce reservations of an unsatisfactory character. Thus in the *Essai* the following statement is appended to the principle: 'Toute réaction chimique susceptible d'être accomplie sans le concours d'un travail préliminaire et en dehors de l'intervention d'une énergie étrangère à celle des corps présents dans le système se produit nécessairement, si elle dégage de la chaleur.' The study of reactions at high temperatures, particularly those on thermal dissociation associated with Grove and with Sainte-Claire Deville and others of the French school, led Duhem to point out that Berthelot's third principle of thermochemistry can be reduced to the valueless expression: 'Toute réaction qui n'absorbe pas de chaleur en dégage.' The unsoundness of the law of maximum work has been demonstrated in more than one way.

Horstmann in 1872 was one of the first to introduce the principles of thermodynamics into chemistry. He relied upon Kelvin's doctrine of the dissipation of energy and, what comes to the same thing, Clausius's doctrine of the tendency of entropy to increase, in framing a theory of thermal dissociation based on these principles, thus showing the fallacies inherent in Berthelot's law. A little later, in 1882, Helmholtz showed it to be utterly unsound. At the outset, Helmholtz pointed out that while the first law of thermodynamics can afford useful quantitative information regarding heats of reaction and of formation in any chemical change which can be studied experimentally, such is not the case with the second law. This latter law is only applicable to processes which are strictly reversible and can be brought through a complete cycle, and the number of reactions which can be thus dealt with is relatively small. Certain voltaic cells, however, fulfil the condition of strict reversibility, and to Helmholtz is due the credit of having first placed the theory of such cells on a satisfactory thermodynamic basis. In 1851 Kelvin made a calculation of the electromotive force of the Daniell cell, on the assumption that the total thermochemical effect corresponding to the chemical changes taking place within the cell and associated with the transfer of a definite quantity of electricity would give a measure of this. He obtained a value of 1·085 volts, remarkably close to the observed value of 1·09 volts. This calculation was later shown by Helmholtz to be deficient because no account was taken of change in the electromotive force with temperature when the cell is yielding current. The necessary correction was supplied by an equation derived by Helmholtz and independently by Willard Gibbs, both of whom showed that it is only the *free* energy, as distinct from the total energy, associated with the chemical changes in the cell which is concerned with maintaining the current.

The real fallacy underlying Berthelot's law of maximum work consists in regarding the heat evolved in a reaction strictly as a measure of the work obtainable if the changes could be effected according to a thermodynamically reversible process. One necessary consequence of this would be that the heat of reaction would be independent of the temperature, a conclusion altogether at variance with the results of experiment. It should be noted that the departure from observation is most pronounced at high temperatures, whereas Berthelot's principle is by no means infrequently true in an approximate sense at the ordinary temperature —a condition of affairs which Nernst described as comparable with the expectation of bad weather from a fall of the barometer. In order that the law of maximum work should be strictly true, conditions would require to be such that the whole of the work done in a Carnot cycle would be equal to the heat taken from the source. For this equality to be realized the temperature of the refrigerator should be absolute zero; in other words, Berthelot's law should be valid at that temperature.

Nernst has pointed out that all results obtained by thermodynamics may be derived by cyclic processes, although many authors seem to imagine that the conceptions of entropy, thermodynamic potential, or free energy may furnish more convincing proofs. He regarded the particular method of demonstration as purely a matter of individual choice, but added that 'die Propheten *ex eventu* der Thermodynamik' have almost without exception preferred the more abstract approach, whereas investigators have mostly used the original methods of Carnot and Clausius as being more direct.

The publication of Maxwell's electromagnetic theory of light in 1865 gave rise to fresh interest in the study of radiation phenomena, and one important consequence of it was the theory that radiation must exert pressure. In 1879 Stefan enunciated his law relating intensity of radiation to temperature, according to which the intensity of total radiation from a perfectly black body is proportional to the fourth power of the absolute temperature. In 1884 Boltzmann, by adopting Maxwell's theory that radiation exerts pressure, deduced Stefan's law by thermodynamic reasoning. Experimental evidence of the correctness of Maxwell's ideas regarding radiation pressure was provided at the beginning of the twentieth century independently by Lebedew and by Nichols and Hull. The Boltzmann-Stefan law deals with the total energy of radiation, but is not concerned with the distribution of energy throughout the spectrum. This latter problem was first investigated theoretically by Wien in 1893, who showed that the wave-length of maximum emissivity is inversely proportional to the absolute temperature, and consequently that the maximum emissivity is proportional to the fifth power of the absolute temperature. Experimental investigation of the distribution of energy in the spectrum by Lummer and Pringsheim gave results in partial agreement with the requirements of Wien's law, but were nevertheless inconsistent with the requirements of classical thermodynamics. In 1900 Planck showed that the difficulties could be removed by assuming that energy is discontinuous like matter, and is radiated in definite units known as quanta. This quantum theory has been of very great value in widely different directions in physics and chemistry. As regards chemistry, two problems of outstanding interest which have been resolved with the aid of Nernst's heat theorem and Planck's quantum theory are Berthelot's law of maximum work and the atomic heat law of Dulong and Petit, the latter having been enunciated as long ago as the year 1819.

Broadly speaking, classical thermodynamics was the means whereby the theory of chemical equilibria was placed on a satisfactory basis, as, for example, van't Hoff's deduction of the law of mass action in 1884, together with his equation connecting the effect of temperature on equilibrium constants with the heat of reaction. It was about this time that van't Hoff formulated his law of mobile equilibrium and Le Chatelier stated a corresponding theorem relating to the effect of pressure. Shortly afterwards Le Chatelier demonstrated the general applicability of the principle to the effect of change of physical conditions, whether of temperature or pressure, on physical and chemical equilibria. Classical thermodynamic doctrine may be summarized by the equation $A-U=T\frac{dA}{dT}$, which was largely associated with Helmholtz. In this equation A is the maximum work obtainable in an isothermal reversible process at a temperature T, and U the corresponding decrease in the energy of the system $A-U$, or the heat withdrawn from the surroundings. This may be expressed verbally by saying that the excess of maximum work of an isothermal process over the decrease of total energy, that is, the latent heat, is equal to the absolute temperature multiplied by the temperature coefficient of the maximum work.

The fundamental error in Berthelot's law of maximum work was the supposed identity of the thermal quantities A and U at all temperatures. The question now arises whether anything further can be done with the Gibbs-Helmholtz equation or, in other words, what (if any) relation exists between the total and the free energies. This problem was attacked from somewhat different standpoints by Nernst and by Richards, and both investigators showed that the values of dA/dT and dU/dT tended towards nought as the absolute zero of temperature was approached, and consequently at that temperature A must be equal to U.

In 1902 Richards published a paper entitled *The relation of changing heat capacity to change of free energy, heat of reaction, change of volume, and chemical affinity*, the experimental part of which was concerned primarily with the change of specific heat during transformation, and the temperature coefficient of electromotive force in reversible cells. This work received favourable attention by van't Hoff, who elaborated the theoretical ideas in further detail in a paper which was published in the *Boltzmann Festschrift* in 1904. This was followed by the first of a long series of publications by Nernst and his pupils in 1906, in which his heat theorem was formulated. The essential doctrine of this theorem is expressed by the equation $\lim dA/dT = \lim dU/dT = 0$, when $T = 0$; and it involves the demonstration of the impossibility of the practical realization of the absolute zero. In the same year Nernst delivered a course of lectures on the subject in Yale University under the auspices of the Silliman Memorial Trust. In one of these lectures Nernst made a reference to Richards's work in the following ironical terms: 'In 1902 a very interesting paper was published by T. W. Richards, in which he pointed out very clearly that the question whether $A > U$ or $U > A$ above absolute zero (where $A = U$) depends upon whether the heat capacity is increased or diminished during the chemical process, and I am very glad to be able to state that our formulae agree qualitatively in many cases with the conclusions of Richards. I do not wish to enter here into a discussion of the differences in the quantitative relations.' In a paper published in 1914, dealing with his hypothesis of compressible atoms, Richards adverted to this question of the relation between the free and total energies of a system and referred to two principles which he had established in the publication of 1902, namely, (1) when the heat capacity of a system does not change during a reaction, and concentration influences are balanced, the free energy and total energy changes of the reaction are equal and unchangeable with the temperature, and (2) the sign and magnitude of the difference between the free and total energy changes is dependent upon the sign and magnitude of the change of heat capacity of the system. Richards then continued: 'All these ideas were afterwards (1906) adopted unchanged by Nernst in his recent development of the "Wärmetheorem" usually named after him'; and finally with renewed emphasis he concluded: 'Qualitatively the Nernst proposition, especially in its recent more complex form, is identical with the older American one from which it was derived, the only essential differences is the assumed quantitative formulation.' In this memoir Richards quoted Nernst's remarks in the Silliman lectures as evidence of his (Nernst's) recognition of the essential identity of the two sets of theoretical ideas. Nernst would have none of it. In Chapter XVI of the English edition of the *New Heat Theorem*, Nernst delivered a violent attack upon Richards for presuming to consider himself as the real discoverer of *his* heat theorem and for misunderstanding the meaning of the cautious words already quoted, in his lecture, which he said were intended as a hint of unsound reasoning on the part of the American author. After some further discussion in which reference was made to 'thermodynamical oddities and vague results' in Richards's paper, Nernst pointed out that van't Hoff's extension of this work would lead to the limiting value of dA/dT being equal to $\pm\infty$ instead of 0, for $T=0$ as required by his heat theorem.

At an early stage in the formulation of his theorem, Nernst was able to indicate the general form of the curves which would be obtained by plotting the A-values and the U-values together as ordinates against the temperatures down to absolute zero. Both curves approach each other tangentially, the one being concave the other convex to the temperature axis, but they show clearly that the values of A and U become practically equal *before* absolute zero is indicated. In order to place the heat theorem on a sound experimental basis, Nernst with the aid of his pupils carried out an elaborate series of studies of the properties, especially the specific heats, of crystalline substances at low temperatures.

The law of Dulong and Petit holds an honoured place in the history of chemistry as one of the means by which the atomic weights of many solid elements were decided. Its extension to compounds by Neumann in 1831, and in more general detail by Kopp in 1865, seemed to indicate that the elements preserve their individual specific heats whether in the free or in the combined state. Nevertheless, there seemed no very obvious reason at the time either for the approximate value of 6·3 for the atomic heats, or for the exceptionally low atomic heats of certain light elements, such as boron, carbon and silicon. A number of experimenters were able to show that there was a marked rise in the value of the atomic heats of these somewhat exceptional elements at high temperatures. The uncertainty regarding the atomic weight of beryllium was removed by Nilson and Pettersson by determining the specific heat of the metal at high temperatures. The results obtained in this way were in agreement with the values obtained for the vapour density of the anhydrous chloride and confirmed the bivalency of the element. The general trend of investigations carried out during the nineteenth century indicated clearly that the law of Dulong and Petit was valid if the determinations of specific heats were made at temperatures not far distant from the melting-points. This conclusion is very relevant to the subsequent theoretical development of the subject at the hands of Planck, Einstein, Nernst, Debye and others.

The correct approach towards an understanding of the phenomena of specific heat is undoubtedly by considering certain aspects of molecular agitation. Diffusion phenomena in the gaseous state may be discussed in terms of the kinetic theory, and Graham's discovery of the diffusion of dissolved substances at once suggested that the cause of diffusion is to be sought in the movements of the molecules. The question thus arose whether molecular agitation ceases altogether when the crystalline state is reached, or whether diffusion can still, although on a greatly restricted scale, take place even in the solid state. The answer to this question—a definite affirmative—was given by the investigations of Roberts-Austen. For upwards of a century the manufacture of steel from wrought iron by the cementation process had raised the question of the means whereby carbon penetrated to the interior of bars of iron covered with powdered charcoal, although the temperature was far below the melting-point. Broadly speaking there were two theories on the subject, namely, absorption of the carbon as carbon monoxide and direct absorption by diffusion. It was, however, difficult to establish a satisfactory experimental proof of solid diffusion on account of the difficulty of eliminating effects due to the intervention of gas. In 1889, however, it was shown by Roberts-Austen that carburization of iron can be effected by diamond *in vacuo* at a temperature far below the melting-point of iron, and under conditions which completely preclude the presence of occluded gas. In 1900 he showed that when disks of gold were clamped to cylinders of lead and set aside for four years at the ordinary temperature, the precious metal actually diffuses into the lead to an extent sufficient for its recognition by assaying. There is thus convincing experimental evidence that molecular movement can take place in the solid state.

By elementary dynamical theory it has been shown that the kinetic energy of an atom, such as that of a monatomic gas, has a value of $\frac{3}{2}RT$, and Boltzmann in 1871 showed that the mean kinetic energy of the atoms of solids must be as large as that of the atoms of a monatomic gas. From such considerations it follows that the atomic heat of an elementary solid substance should have a value of 5·96, which is not very different from the average figure according to the law of Dulong and Petit. This law may therefore be claimed as having support based on the kinetic theory as regards values of atomic heats determined at ordinary and at higher temperatures. At lower temperatures, however, atomic vibrations would be expected to become much more restricted, and finally vanish altogether at absolute zero. All experimental work at very low temperatures, such as the determinations of the atomic heats by Dewar in 1913 at the temperature of liquid hydrogen, supports this view. In 1907 Einstein developed a theory of specific heats which correlated atomic vibrations with Planck's quantum theory of radiation. In 1911 Nernst and Lindemann began an elaborate investigation of specific heats at low temperatures, the primary objects of which were to ascertain the cause of the very rapid fall of atomic heats below the value of $3R$, and also the range of temperature within which the law of Dulong and Petit is valid. They found that it was impossible to discuss this in terms of the classical principle of the equipartition of energy, but by adopting Einstein's ideas they were able to introduce the quantum theory with a considerable degree of success. According to this theory, an atom can only receive or impart energy in definite units, each having a value of $h\nu$, in which h is Planck's constant and ν the frequency of vibration. Nernst and Lindemann have elaborated somewhat complicated formulae, based upon the quantum theory, for calculating the specific heats of solids from the lowest temperatures upwards and beyond the range at which the law of Dulong and Petit is obeyed. An improved formula depending upon the same principles was shortly afterwards derived by Debye. Experimental work by Nernst and his pupils on specific heats determined at temperatures from 35° absolute upwards have shown remarkably close agreement with the values calculated according to the theory over very wide ranges of temperature. In the case of silver, agreement with the requirements of the Dulong-Petit law was first observed in the neighbourhood of 200° absolute, above which there was a slow rise over a range of some 200°. With diamond the theoretical and experimentally determined values of the atomic heat are practically zero at all temperatures below 200° absolute, after which there is a steady rise, but the law of Dulong and Petit is not obeyed until a temperature of 1169° absolute is attained. Nernst and Lindemann have given a clear explanation of the general behaviour of the elements as regards this law. According to their reasoning, the exceptionally low atomic heats of carbon and other similar elements is due to their low atomic weights and very high melting-points. On the other hand, lithium, a light element, follows the law closely at the ordinary temperature because of its low melting-point. It may be added that the value of 6 for the atomic heat is generally exceeded as the melting-point of an element is approached, because of the increased vibratory motion of the molecules under such conditions, or more correctly, according to Lindemann, because at the temperature of the melting-point the amplitudes of the vibrations of the atoms become commensurable with the atomic distances; it is the collisions between the atoms which effects the destruction of the crystals.

It will thus be seen that these researches on atomic heats at very low temperatures have given rise to a much clearer understanding of the meaning of the law of Dulong and Petit—formerly regarded as no more than a purely empirical generalization. It may be noted that Debye's formula requires the value of the atomic heats at these low temperatures to be directly proportional to the cube of the absolute temperatures. Experimental proof of the accuracy of this conclusion was given by Eucken and Schwers in 1913, and again by Kamerlingh-Onnes and Keesom in the following year. Shortly before this, actually in 1911, Lindemann showed how *accurate* values of atomic weights could be derived from specific heats by the aid of a modified Dulong-Petit formula, and it is of interest to note that he obtained a value of 107·55 for the atomic weight of silver, as compared with the 'chemical' value of 107·88. Nernst has claimed that this adaptation of the law of Dulong and Petit to the determination of accurate atomic weights of solid elements will bear comparison with the determination of accurate values for the molecular weights of gases by the method of limiting densities, which is based on the principle that Avogadro's rule is strictly accurate for a perfect gas.

In reviewing the theory of heat since the seventeenth century, it may be remarked that the discovery of latent heat near the close of the following century, and the experiments of Rumford and others on the heat of friction were of particular importance in leading to the development of more modern views. It is of course true that the foundations of the science of thermodynamics, which were laid down by Carnot, were expressed in the language of the older theory of caloric. The prediction of the effect of pressure on the lowering of the melting-point of ice by James Thomson and the experimental verification of this by Kelvin were the means whereby a reconciliation of the experiments of Joule, on the mechanical equivalent of heat, with the theoretical ideas of Carnot was effected. The later development of classical thermodynamics by Clausius and others, and the establishment of the theory of entropy on statistical principles by Maxwell, Gibbs and Boltzmann, provided a secure theoretical foundation for thermochemistry. The study of radiation towards the close of the nineteenth century led eventually to Planck's theory of energy quanta. In the early years of the present century the quantum theory and Nernst's heat theorem led to a clearer understanding of the time-honoured law of Dulong and Petit. These newer theoretical ideas have also provided the means of illuminating one of the dark chapters of chemistry, namely, Berthelot's law of maximum work.

REFERENCES

SIR ISAAC NEWTON. *Opticks*. Reprinted from the fourth edition (1730) with a foreword by A. Einstein and an introduction by E. T. Whittaker. London, 1931.

HON. HENRY CAVENDISH. *Scientific Papers*, vol. I, *The Electrical Researches*. Edited by Sir Joseph Larmor; vol. II, *Chemical and Dynamical*. Edited by Sir Edward Thorpe and others. Cambridge, 1921.

A. L. LAVOISIER and P. S. DE LAPLACE. *Zwei Abhandlungen über die Wärme*. Ostwalds Klassiker der exakten Wissenschaften, no. 40. Leipzig.

SADI CARNOT. *Réflexions sur la puissance motrice du feu et sur les machines propres à développer cette puissance*. Paris, 1824. Reprinted 1924.

SIR JOSEPH LARMOR. *Aether and Matter*. Cambridge, 1900.

Mathematical and Physical Papers. Two volumes. Cambridge, 1929.

Origin of Clerk Maxwell's Electric Ideas. Cambridge, 1937. This work contains a note on the Carnot-Kelvin aspect of thermodynamics.

T. GRAHAM. *Chemical and Physical Researches*. Edinburgh, 1876.

J. P. JOULE. *Scientific Papers*. Published by the Physical Society of London. Vol. I, 1884; vol. II, 1887.

P. G. TAIT. *Sketch of Thermodynamics*. Edinburgh, 1868. Second edition, 1877.

W. J. MACQUORN RANKINE. *A Manual of the Steam Engine and other Prime Movers*. First edition. London, 1859.

Miscellaneous Scientific Papers. London, 1881.

R. CLAUSIUS. *The Mechanical Theory of Heat*. Edited by T. A. Hirst. London, 1867.

E. MACH. *Die Principien der Wärmelehre*. Leipzig, 1896.

G. F. FITZGERALD. Helmholtz Memorial Lecture. *J. Chem. Soc.* 1896, vol. LXIX, p. 885.

J. CLERK MAXWELL. *Theory of Heat*. Ninth edition. London, 1888.

SIR WILLIAM THOMSON (LORD KELVIN). *Mathematical and Physical Papers*. Six volumes. Cambridge, 1882–1911.

PIERRE DUHEM. *Introduction à la mécanique chimique*. Gand, 1893.

L. BOLTZMANN. *Vorlesungen über Gastheorie*. Leipzig, 1896–8.

J. WILLARD GIBBS. *Collected Works*. Two volumes. New York, 1928.

A Commentary on the Writings of J. Willard Gibbs by several authors. Two volumes. Yale University Press, 1936.

W. NERNST. *Experimental and Theoretical Applications of Thermodynamics to Chemistry*. London, 1907.

The Theory of the Solid State. London, 1914.

The New Heat Theorem. Translated from the second German edition. London, 1926.

O. SACKUR. *A Text-book of Thermochemistry and Thermodynamics*. Translated by G. E. Gibson. London, 1917.

M. Planck. *Theory of Heat* (vol. v of his *Introduction to Theoretical Physics*). English edition. London, 1932.

L. Boltzmann. *Populäre Schriften.* Leipzig, 1905.

J. S. Haldane. *The Collected Scientific Papers of John James Waterston.* Edinburgh, 1928.

H. L. Callendar. *British Association Report.* Presidential Address to Section A. Dundee, 1912.

CHAPTER III

SOME ASPECTS OF CLASSICAL ELECTRICITY AND ELECTROLYSIS

The beginnings of the study of electrical phenomena, apart from some interesting empirical observations which can be dated to certain early Greek philosophers, can be assigned to Gilbert of Colchester in the reign of Queen Elizabeth I. Gilbert made numerous experiments with magnets and greatly extended the list of substances which can be electrified by friction. In the seventeenth century the names of Boyle and of Otto von Guericke, familiar for their experiments on atmospheric pressure, should be mentioned, the former for having noted that the electric forces of attraction and repulsion can be observed through a vacuum, and the latter for having constructed the first frictional electric machine. This machine consisted of a sulphur ball which was rotated by a winch and produced electricity by friction with the hand. A somewhat similar machine having a glass globe instead of a sulphur ball was constructed about the year 1709 by Hauksbee, who observed that sparks could be drawn from it. About the same time Hauksbee observed that flashes of light were produced by shaking mercury in a dry vessel, but it seems doubtful if he regarded this phenomenon as electrical since he described it as *mercurial phosphorus*.

In the eighteenth century discoveries of outstanding importance were made in England, on the Continent and in America. These included the distinction between conductors and insulators by Stephen Gray in 1729, and the recognition of two kinds of electrification, vitreous and resinous, by more than one observer, but usually attributed to Dufaye. A third discovery, that of electrostatic induction, arose in more than one way, namely, as the result of some experiments carried out by Canton in 1753, and also in consequence of the great interest which was aroused in 1746 when Cuneus and Musschenbroek in Leyden received a severe shock while attempting to charge water, contained in a glass flask, with electricity. This accidental discovery marks the date of the beginnings of studies connected with the properties of dielectrics. In the words of Priestley, who made some interesting contributions to the experimental study of electrical phenomena before he became more interested in chemistry, 'the year 1746 was famous for the most surprising discovery that has yet been made in the whole business of electricity'. The discovery of the Leyden phial or jar appears to have been made independently at about the same time by Kleist in Pomerania. The study of condensers attracted many experimentalists, of whom particular mention must be made of Cavendish, Aepinus and Benjamin Franklin. It was shown by Franklin that the seat of the charge in a condenser, such as a Leyden jar, is not in the metallic coatings but in the glass. Another noteworthy discovery due to Franklin was his demonstration of the identity of the electric spark and the lightning flash in the year 1752. This identity had occurred to others, of whom mention may by made of the Abbé Nollet, since it was well known that the destructive effects of lightning could be imitated on the small scale by electric sparks and that combustible substances could be inflamed by such means. Franklin demonstrated the identity by collecting electricity from a thundercloud by means of a kite, and his work was afterwards confirmed by Canton.

Theories attempting to explain the fundamental phenomena of electricity were forthcoming soon after the recognition of vitreous and resinous electrification, and the terms 'positive' (to denote the former) and 'negative' (the latter) soon came into general use. The two-fluid theory, chiefly associated with the name of Dufaye, was perhaps less successful than a one-fluid theory especially identified with Franklin, and developed mathematically by Aepinus in 1759, and independently and in much more elaborate detail by Cavendish in 1771. Although the views of these physicists of the eighteenth century differed in detail as to any properties which the 'electric fluid' might possess, there was general agreement in regarding it as some sort of continuum. Such a conception though valuable at the time would not be in accordance with modern ideas. It is interesting, however, to note that after the atomic character of electricity had been demonstrated, chiefly as the result of the work of J. J. Thomson, Lord Kelvin in 1901 published a paper entitled *Aepinus atomized*, in which he stated 'my suggestion is that the Aepinus fluid consists of exceedingly minute equal and similar atoms...much smaller than the atoms of ponderable matter'; and he showed that the one-fluid theory as expounded by Aepinus could be discussed on such a basis.

The electrical researches carried out by Cavendish greatly surpassed, both in quality and in accuracy, those of any other experimentalist of that time. Although Cavendish published only two papers on electricity, namely, one entitled *An attempt to explain some of the principal phænomena of electricity by means of an elastic fluid* which appeared in 1771, and the other, *An account of some attempts to imitate the effects of the torpedo by electricity* which was published in 1776, his manuscript notes, which eventually came into the hands of Clerk Maxwell just a century later, were found to contain records of a vast amount of experimental work carried out between 1771 and 1781, including important discoveries which were attributed to subsequent investigators. The publication of these researches by Maxwell in 1879 showed in no uncertain terms how far Cavendish was ahead of the other men of science of his time.

One of the first subjects which Cavendish investigated was the variation of the electric forces of attraction and repulsion with distance. He relied upon the reasoning employed by Newton in the *Principia*, according to which gravitational attraction should be zero within a uniform spherical shell of gravitating matter on the assumption of an inverse square law. Cavendish accordingly reasoned that if it could be shown that there is no electric force within a closed spherical conductor, the law relating to electrostatic attraction must be in accordance with inverse proportionality to the square of the distance. He accordingly devised what has been termed his 'globe and hemispheres experiment', by which he was able to show the complete absence of any appreciable electric force within the closed conductor. Considering that the tests were carried out with the aid of a pair of pith balls as his electrometer, the result which he secured was little short of marvellous. 'We may conclude', wrote Cavendish, 'that the electric attraction and repulsion must be inversely as some power of the distance between that of the $2+\frac{1}{50}$ and the $2-\frac{1}{50}$, and there is no reason to think that it differs at all from the inverse duplicate ratio'. In the course of his editorial work, Maxwell repeated the experiment using a Kelvin quadrant electrometer and verified the inverse square law with an accuracy of one part in 21,600.

In 1785 Coulomb discovered the inverse square law relating to electric attraction and repulsion by an altogether different method, namely, that of the torsion balance. This consists of an apparatus for measuring the attractive or repulsive force by its effect in twisting a fine wire or fibre and noting the angle through which the wire has to be turned for the restoration of equilibrium. Coulomb displayed much ingenuity in devising his apparatus, and, considering the experimental difficulties which must have attended the measurements, his realization of the inverse square law must be described as remarkable. The principle involved in the torsion balance as regards its mechanical aspect did not, however, originate with Coulomb, but he was doubtless an independent discoverer of the principle. The first suggestion of measuring small mechanical forces by their torsion effects was made by Michell, who actually constructed an apparatus for the purpose about the year 1768. After Michell's death this apparatus came into the hands of Cavendish, who used it in his celebrated experiment by which he determined the mean density of the Earth in 1798.

Cavendish devoted a great deal of attention to the study of the capacity of condensers. He investigated the subject both mathematically and experimentally, and it is no exaggeration to say that he laid the foundations of this subject. In the course of his experiments he not only discovered that the capacity of a condenser depends on the nature of the dielectric and thus anticipated Faraday, but actually made some comparative measurements of its value for a few substances. Faraday's investigations on specific inductive capacity or dielectric constant, as the property is now usually termed, were published in 1837, but as the experiments of Cavendish had remained unpublished Faraday was unaware of their existence. They were, however, known to Snow Harris, whose name is familiar in connexion with much experimental work on electrostatics and with lightning conductors, and through whose hands Cavendish's manuscripts passed before they were edited by Clerk Maxwell. In his *Treatise on Frictional Electricity* which was published in 1867, Snow Harris adverted to this subject as well as to certain other discoveries made by Cavendish but withheld from publication. It has been truly said that the 'modern' science of electricity is concerned with the relations between electricity and matter in contradistinction to the older science which was occupied primarily with the properties of electrified substances, and if this division is accepted Cavendish must be designated as the founder of the newer aspects of the science. The importance of the interrelationship between electrical and chemical phenomena was, however, foreseen by Priestley as far back as the year 1767. In his *History and Present State of Electricity with Original Experiments* he writes: '...for chymistry and electricity are both conversant about the latent and less obvious properties of bodies; and yet their relation to each other has been but little considered, and their operations hardly ever combined....'

The paper which Cavendish published in 1776 on the imitation of the effects of the torpedo by electricity had been preceded by a memoir by Walsh three years previously in which that author concluded that the shocks given by the fish are produced by electricity. Cavendish regarded the evidence which Walsh had adduced was, on the whole, fairly convincing; but he considered it desirable to investigate the matter much more thoroughly by means of an apparatus designed to imitate the effects of the animal artificially, and after a most elaborate series of experiments he concluded: 'On the whole, I think, there seems nothing in the phenomena of the torpedo at all incompatible with electricity; but to make a compleat imitation of them, would require a battery much larger than mine....' Throughout his researches Cavendish frequently used the phrase *degree of electrification*, which Maxwell pointed out is precisely what would now be termed potential, and he clearly indicated that the phenomena of the torpedo could be explained as consistent with the discharge of a large quantity of electricity at a low potential.

The paper on the torpedo contains a reference to 'some experiments, of which I propose shortly to lay an account before this Society,* that iron wire conducts about 400 million times better than rain or distilled water; that is the electricity meets with no more resistance in passing through a piece of iron 400,000,000 inches long than through a column of water of the same diameter only one inch long. Sea water, or a solution of one part of salt in 30 of water, conducts 100 times, and a saturated solution of sea salt about 720 times better than rain water.' Cavendish never carried out his intention of publishing an account of these experiments, but they were none the less accepted by the scientific world at the time. As Maxwell pointed out, no one seems to have had any idea of the means by which Cavendish obtained these results 'more than forty years before the invention of the galvanometer, the only instrument by which anyone else has ever been able to compare electric resistances'. The invention of the galvanometer did not take place till after Oersted's discovery in 1820 of the deflexion of a magnetic needle by a wire carrying an electric current when held above or below it, whereas the whole of Cavendish's experiments on electric resistance were conducted between 1773 and 1871. 'We learn from the manuscripts now first published', wrote Maxwell, 'that Cavendish was his own galvanometer. In order to compare the intensity of currents he caused them to pass through his own body, and by comparing the intensity of the sensations he felt in his wrist and elbows, he estimated which of the two shocks was the more powerful.'

The experiments which Cavendish carried out in 1777 on the resistance of electrolytes by his method of discharging Leyden jars through them and measuring the intensity of the shocks are of much chemical interest. In this series of experiments Cavendish employed solutions of various acids, alkalis and salts containing equivalent quantities of the substances. He left no record regarding

* The Royal Society.

the source from which he obtained his equivalent weights, and Maxwell was doubtless right when he stated that they must have been determined by Cavendish himself, particularly as Richter's *Anfangsgründe der Stöchyometrie* was not published until 1792. In his paper on 'Factitious air' published in 1766 Cavendish made a number of experiments on the quantity of carbon dioxide evolved by the action of hydrochloric acid on various carbonates by the method of loss of weight. These were all referred to the quantity of the gas obtainable from 1000 grains of marble. From the results recorded in this paper and from experiments described in a paper entitled *Experiments on Rathbone Place water* published in the following year, it appears that Cavendish recognized the principle of equivalency as regards neutralization of acids; but he must have made additional experiments to have furnished himself with all the necessary material for the determinations of the resistance of electrolytes. Some of the actual values which he obtained are of great interest and bear comparison with the results obtained by Kohlrausch a century later by using the Wheatstone bridge method with alternating currents to avoid polarization. It will be seen that there is rough agreement between the values for the equivalent weights determined by Cavendish and the modern values. Maxwell was unable to discover the actual concentrations employed by Cavendish, but concluded that dilute equivalent solutions must have been employed. In comparing the figures obtained by Cavendish for the conductivity with those of Kohlrausch it may be noted that the effects of polarization would scarcely arise in Cavendish's experiments because of the small quantities of electricity which would be involved in discharging his condensers through the solutions. All the figures for the conductivity are referred to sodium chloride as unity:

	Equivalent weight		Conductivity	
Substance	Modern	According to Cavendish	According to Cavendish	According to Kohlrausch
Potassium chloride	74·6	74	1·08	1·21
Sodium sulphate	71	69	0·696	0·95
Sodium nitrate	85	89	0·887	0·91
Ammonium chloride	53·5	51	1·13	1·17
Sulphuric acid	49	48	0·783	1·23

Among the numerous interesting results which Cavendish obtained in the course of his studies on the conductivity of electrolytes was the variation of resistance with temperature. Thus he found that a salt solution conducted '1·97 times better in heat of 105° [F.] than in that of 58½° [F.]'. According to Kohlrausch the ratio for this interval of temperature should be 1·59. He also found that the resistance of water was the greater the higher its degree of purity; thus the resistance of pump water was found to be 4⅙ times less than that of rain water. He also discovered that the conductivity of distilled water was increased by the presence of dissolved gases: he stated that 'distilled water impregnated with fixed air from oil of vitrol and marble conducted 2½ times better than the same water deprived of its air by boiling'.

Cavendish obtained one of his most remarkable results in 1781, when he attempted to ascertain 'what power of the velocity the resistance is proportional to'. Maxwell pointed out that by the term 'resistance' Cavendish intended to signifiy the whole force which resists the current, and by 'velocity' the strength of the current through unit of area of the conductor. By discharging his condensers through salt solutions all of the same concentration but contained in tubes of different dimensions and estimating the intensity of the shocks, Cavendish concluded that 'resistance is directly as velocity'. This highly interesting result is a definite anticipation of the fundamental law of electric resistance, namely, Ohm's law, which was first published in the year 1827.

It would appear that the whole of Cavendish's electrical researches were completed in 1783, though he continued some important chemical investigations after that date. But even his published work was largely unknown to his contemporaries. Had some of these researches, particularly those on specific inductive capacity and on the resistance of electrolytes, been known and understood, the history of electrochemistry might have been profoundly modified. The beginnings of the study of the chemical effects of electricity were all made in investigating reactions between gases brought about under the influence of sparks. Thus Priestley exploded mixtures of hydrogen and oxygen in 1781, and in the same year Cavendish repeated this work with every refinement to secure accurate measurements of the combining volumes of the gases. The now celebrated experiments on the union of nitrogen and oxygen when subjected to prolonged sparking were first published in 1785 and extended in 1788. But the subject of electrolysis had its beginnings at a later date, namely, after the discovery of current electricity, associated more particularly with the name of Volta.

In 1790 it was observed by Galvani that when the legs of a recently dissected frog were placed in the vicinity of an electrostatic machine, violent contractions took place whenever sparks were produced. Precisely similar effects were also observed under the influence of atmospheric electricity. Galvani also found that when two conductors of different metals were attached, the one to the nerve and the other to the muscle, of a frog's leg, contractions were produced as soon as the wires were allowed to touch each other. Galvani regarded this experiment as in some respects similar to the charging and discharging of a Leyden jar, the source of the electricity being in the animal preparation—he had, in short, considered the phenomenon as due to animal electricity. There the subject was left, but it soon attracted the attention of Volta, who repeated the experiments with various modifications. Volta gradually found that it was possible to obtain electrical effects, such as had been observed by Galvani, by establishing contact between two dissimilar metals separated by a moist conductor and without using any animal preparation whatever. His two most important publications on this subject were in 1792 and in 1796, in which he finally showed that although the frog preparations were highly sensitive *detectors* of electricity, the *source* of that electricity was to be found in the contact effects between the dissimilar metals, and could not possibly be of animal origin. Volta was thus the discoverer of contact electricity, a subject around which a great deal of controversy took place during the subsequent century regarding the source of the electromotive force in voltaic cells.

In order to gain a clear understanding of the import of Volta's discoveries, a few remarks must be added regarding the improvements which were made in the means of detecting and measuring electrostatic charges since the work of Cavendish and Coulomb. Various modifications in the pith-ball electroscopes (or electrometers as they became to be called when they were adapted to obtain some quasi-quantitative indication of the magnitude of the electric charge) were made by some contemporary experimentalists. The most important improvement in this direction was undoubtedly the invention of the gold-leaf electroscope by Bennet in 1787. The sensitiveness of the instrument was greatly increased by combining it with a Volta condenser, an apparatus which had been devised some years previously by its inventor. Volta had devoted much attention to the study of electrostatic induction and devised his electrophorus—the forerunner of the more modern influence machines—in 1775. This was followed in 1782 by the condenser, which was really an adaptation of the electrophorus for use in conjunction with an electroscope.

In his earlier experiments, the purpose of which was to discover the cause of the phenomena observed by Galvani, Volta found that the contractions which took place in frog preparations were a highly sensitive means of detection of electricity from any source, more sensitive indeed than the best electroscopic apparatus which he could then arrange. By means of these frog preparations he was able to show the production of electricity by contact of dissimilar metals. Later he confirmed the correctness of his conclusions by the use of the condensing electroscope. About a century later the gold-leaf electroscope, in a modified form due to C. T. R. Wilson, became an important form of apparatus for the study of radioactive phenomena.

In 1800 Volta devised his celebrated pile, and shortly afterwards the more convenient 'crown of cups'—two forms of apparatus which were destined to lead to discoveries of the greatest importance. Voltaic, or as some have termed it, galvanic, electricity was recognized. Both the pile and the crown of cups aroused very great interest and immediately attracted the attention of a number of experimentalists. Most of the early researches were concerned with electrochemical decompositions. Thus in 1800 Nicholson and Carlisle effected the decomposition of water, and in 1807 Davy isolated the alkali metals by the electrolysis of the fused hydroxides. These spectacular results soon gave rise to a number of subjects for experimental inquiry, particularly the nature of the mechanism of the electrolytic processes and the source of the electricity generated by batteries, whether by contact or by chemical action. This latter subject necessitated a solution of the problem regarding the identity of electricity from whatever source it was derived, a question which occupied the attention of several investigators and was finally settled by Faraday in 1832.

The identity of animal electricity and 'common' electricity was established as regards the torpedo by Cavendish, and although Davy did not appear to be altogether convinced, the experimental evidence adduced by Cavendish was considered satisfactory by Faraday. Greater difficulty was experienced in establishing the identity of voltaic and frictional electricity. In 1801 Wollaston claimed to have effected experimental proofs of electrolysis by frictional electricity. Thus he placed the ends of silver wires, which were completely insulated except for the tips, in a drop of cupric sulphate solution. On passing the electricity from a frictional machine through this apparatus, he found that one wire acquired a minute coating of copper. Other experiments carried out by Wollaston consisted in passing electricity generated by friction through papers moistened with various solutions such as potassium iodide or through moist litmus or turmeric paper containing sodium sulphate, so that the occurrence of chemical change could be readily visible. In such experiments Wollaston was satisfied regarding the production of chemical change. Faraday repeated these and other similar experiments with great care and pointed out that some of Wollaston's conclusions were not altogether justified. With regard to the reddening of moist blue litmus paper, Faraday remarked as follows: 'In all experiments of electro-chemical decomposition by the common machine and moistened papers, it is necessary to be aware of and to avoid the following important source of error. If a spark passes over moistened litmus and tumeric paper, the litmus paper (provided it be delicate and not too alkaline) is reddened by it; and if several sparks are passed, it becomes powerfully reddened.... These effects must not be confounded with those due to the true electro-chemical powers of common electricity, and must be carefully avoided when the latter are to be observed.... The effect itself is due to the formation of nitric acid by the combination of the oxygen and nitrogen of the air, and is, in fact, only a delicate repetition of Cavendish's beautiful experiment. The acid so formed, though small in quantity, is in a high state of concentration as to water, and produces the consequent effects of reddening the litmus paper; or preventing the exhibition of alkali on the turmeric paper; or, by acting on the iodide of potassium, evolving iodine.'

In the course of repeating Wollaston's experiments, Faraday found that it was necessary to make certain modifications so as to avoid the possibility of chemical change arising in consequence of sparking, and thus to ascertain whether genuine electrolysis by frictional electricity could take place. In the method finally adopted, composite pieces of litmus and turmeric paper were moistened with a solution of sodium sulphate and arranged so that each paper was connected with the next one in series by platinum wires. The papers with the communicating wires all rested on a glass plate. The first paper was connected with the prime conductor of a frictional machine, and the last one with the discharging train. On working the machine, Faraday observed that acid was evolved 'at *all* the poles by which the electricity entered the solution and alkali at the other poles by which the electricity left the solution'. Faraday concluded this series of experiments by stating that 'there cannot be now a doubt that Dr Wollaston was right in his general conclusion that voltaic and common electricity have powers of chemical decomposition, alike in their nature, and governed by the same law of arrangement'. The identity of thermo-electricity and of magneto-electricity with frictional electricity was also demonstrated by him, and this was followed up very shortly afterwards by quantitative experiments on the effects of electricity derived from various sources on a galvanometer.

Faraday was soon able to distinguish between what he termed *quantity* and *intensity* as applied to electricity, or what in modern phraseology would be designated as *current* and *difference of potential*, and this led on to the discovery of his well-known laws of electrolysis in 1833 relating to electrochemical equivalency. Faraday was greatly impressed with what he termed the 'absolute quantity of electricity associated with the particles or atoms of matter'. 'What an enormous quantity of electricity,' remarked Faraday, 'therefore, is required for the decomposition of a single grain of water! We have already seen that it must be in quantity sufficient to sustain a platina wire 1/104th of an inch in thickness, red hot, in contact with the air, for three minutes and three-quarters....' These experiments doubtless gave rise to the now universal recognition of the atomic nature of electricity, though much had still to be done before it could be regarded as established. Thus Clerk Maxwell, in the chapter on electrolysis in his *Treatise on Electricity*, which appeared in 1873, spoke of 'a molecule of electricity', but he qualified his idea with the words: 'This theory of molecular charges may serve as a method by which we may remember a good many facts about electrolysis. It is extremely improbable, however, that when we come to understand the true nature of electrolysis that we shall retain in any form the theory of molecular charges, for then we shall have obtained a secure basis on which to form a true theory of electric currents.' It would thus appear that Maxwell had doubts of extending atomic or molecular conceptions to electricity. Helmholtz in his Faraday Lecture to the Chemical Society in 1881 was much more definite. Adverting to electrochemical equivalency he stated: that 'If we accept the hypothesis that elementary substances are composed of atoms, we cannot avoid concluding that electricity also, positive as well as negative, is divided into definite elementary portions which behave as atoms of electricity.' How brilliantly have the ideas of Helmholtz been verified by the work on the conduction of electricity through gases!

A brief reference may now be made to an interesting controversy, which arose as one of many consequences of Faraday's electrochemical researches, regarding the possibility or otherwise of conduction of electricity through an electrolyte without simultaneous decomposition. Faraday himself in 1834 ventured the opinion that very feeble currents could be carried in this manner, and experiments by others at first seemed to support this view. In 1853 opposite opinions on this subject were expressed by Foucault and by Buff; the former insisted that there is such a phenomenon as 'physical' as distinct from 'chemical' conductivity, and thus upheld the views of Faraday, while the latter maintained that conduction by an electrolyte cannot take place without chemical decomposition. It should be added that Foucault always regarded the 'physical' conductivity as very small in comparison with the 'chemical' one. The controversy between these two investigators continued for some years, and indeed the subject was by no means easy to settle experimentally. Others entered upon this line of inquiry; thus between 1854 and 1856, Despretz brought forward experimental evidence in support of the views of Foucault, whereas those of Buff found an advocate in Andrews. Modern views on this subject would, in general, support the view that conduction by an electrolyte necessarily involves some decomposition, in short, that ions of whatever kind or however generated must be present to carry the current.

Theories regarding the source of the electricity in voltaic cells began to be formulated very shortly after Volta's fundamental discoveries. Broadly speaking there were two schools of thought on this subject, namely, the 'contact' theory, of which Volta was the chief exponent, and the theory of chemical action, which was advocated by a number of investigators, notably by Faraday, Becquerel, de la Rive and Schönbein. A lively controversy on this subject continued for the greater part of a century, and viewing the subject in retrospect it may seem strange how a question of this kind should have presented so many difficulties. The answer is chiefly to be sought in the different experimental methods adopted by the respective adherents of the two theories, but it should also be borne in mind that the modern doctrine of energy had not been formulated with precision until about 1850 when Kelvin was able to correlate Joule's experimental results with the principles laid down by Carnot in 1824, and the introduction of the conception of entropy by Clausius. At the same time it should be added that Faraday in 1839 and Grove in 1842 saw clearly that the maintenance of a current without chemical action would involve the possibility of perpetual motion.

Davy's attitude to this question was very remarkable. At first he expressed himself in favour of the 'chemical' theory, and this is scarcely surprising in view of his brilliant experimental work on electrolysis. In his first Bakerian Lecture he remarked that 'the relation of electrical energy to chemical affinity is, however, sufficiently evident. May it not be identical with it and an *essential property of matter*?' Gradually however Davy abandoned this point of view and became impressed with the contact theory. Ostwald in his *Elektrochemie: ihre Geschichte und Lehre* considered that Davy's change of view is to be ascribed to the influence of Volta: 'Es giebt vielleicht kein auffallenderes Beispiel für die Gewalt, welche Volta auf die wissenschaftlichen Anschauungen seiner Zeitgenossen ausübte, als der Umstand, dass er auch Davy zu der Annahme der Idee von der Berührungselektricität brachte.' Ostwald may possibly have been right in his conjecture, but if so it may be noted that Volta's influence, far-reaching as it doubtless was, failed to convince certain other contemporary workers on electrochemistry such as Berzelius and their immediate followers, particularly Faraday and Schönbein. Both of these last-named investigators and also Becquerel constructed numerous and varied types of cells all of which were found to yield currents, so long as there was any difference either in the electrodes themselves or in the liquids surrounding them. Some of Schönbein's experiments are of great interest. In connexion with his investigations on the passivity of iron in concentrated nitric acid, Schönbein in 1842 constructed a cell consisting of two iron plates, one being immersed in dilute sulphuric acid and the other in concentrated nitric acid, the two liquids being separated by a porous partition. This arrangement was found to be a satisfactory source of current.

At an early stage of his work, Volta established his principle of a contact electromotive series of metals. This principle consisted in arranging the metals in such a way that if any two were connected with each other and also with a liquid conductor, such as a solution of a salt, a current would flow from the metal higher in the series through the liquid to the other. It was noted by Ritter that the order of contact in electromotive series, as understood by Volta, was identical with the order in which the metals precipitate one another from solutions of their salts. And as long ago as the year 1801 it was observed by Wollaston that if a piece of zinc and one of silver were immersed in dilute sulphuric acid, without being allowed to touch, the zinc dissolved slowly with evolution of hydrogen, but if the two metals were brought into contact the zinc dissolved more rapidly and the evolution of hydrogen took place at the surface of the silver. Thus arose what Volta considered as the order of the metals according to his ideas of contact electricity, but what would, according to others at the time and certainly according to more modern conceptions, be the potential or electrochemical series of the metals.

From the year 1833 onwards Faraday regularly determined quantities of electricity by measuring the volumes of hydrogen and oxygen obtained in the electrolysis of dilute acid in a given time. It was observed by him and by others that the simple forms of cell then in use soon languished, and that the rate of evolution of gas as measured in the voltameters was greatly reduced. Faraday soon became aware of the cause of the failure of these cells. Thus he found that if the acid in the battery was stirred from time to time after it had become defective, the battery recovered much of its activity. In further experiments he was able to recognize the existence of what amounted to an opposing electromotive force within the cells—he had indeed discovered the phenomenon of electrolytic polarization. The outcome of these observations was to direct attention to the construction of cells of constant electromotive force—a problem which was solved in different ways by Daniell in 1836 and by Grove in 1839, and was of much importance in various directions of electrical research, more particularly in connexion with certain aspects of electrical measurements.

The beginnings of quantitative experiments with electric currents, apart from the historical measurements of electrostatic charges by Cavendish to which reference has already been made and which were unknown to his contemporaries, are centred around Ohm's law. The voltameter figured largely in the researches of Hittorf on the migration of ions, carried out between 1853 and 1859, and before that time important beginnings had been made in the development of methods for the comparison of resistances and the measurement of electromotive force. In 1843 Wheatstone devised his well-known bridge method for comparing resistances, which he had derived from an idea due to Christie some years previously. In measuring the resistance of electrolytes, satisfactory results cannot be obtained by the use of direct currents; but Kohlrausch between 1869 and 1874 showed how this difficulty could be avoided by the use of alternating currents in conjunction with a Wheatstone bridge with a telephone as the detector. The well-known potentiometer method for comparing electromotive forces was devised as long ago as the year 1841 by Poggendorff, and improved by others, notably by Latimer Clark, at a later date. In passing it may be noted that while it is a simple matter to make a resistance of any desired value, it is not possible to construct a cell of any desired electromotive force. All that can be done is to take the most constant cell which may be available, measure its electromotive force once for all, and use that value as a standard.

In both the Daniell and the Grove cells the chemical reactions in the vicinity of the electrodes are kept separate by the use of porous partitions. Polarization in the Daniell cell is avoided electrochemically, while the cell is yielding current, by precipitation of copper on the copper electrode from the cupric sulphate solution, while zinc in equivalent quantity is dissolved from the zinc electrode. This cell was formerly used as a standard of electromotive force, but other cells involving the principle of electrochemical replacement, such as those of Latimer Clark and of Weston have been found more satisfactory. In the Grove cell, polarization is obviated by a different method. While that cell is yielding current, the hydrogen generated by the action of the zinc on the dilute sulphuric acid is not evolved, but is oxidized by the nitric acid surrounding the platinum electrode. The electromotive force of the Grove cell is considerably higher than that of the Daniell cell when the nitric acid is concentrated, but it gradually falls as the acid becomes diluted with its reduction products. The depolarizing action of nitric acid is complicated, and is almost certainly connected with the presence of nitrous acid. In 1842 Millon discovered that certain metals such as copper and silver will not dissolve in nitric acid in the absence of nitrous acid—an observation confirmed and extended some fifty years later by Veley, and certainly relevant to a correct understanding of the chemistry of the Grove cell. The recognition of the importance of oxidation potentials has redirected attention to this subject, and an interesting investigation on the effect of concentration of the nitric acid on the electromotive force of the Grove cell was carried out by Ihle in 1896. He studied the electromotive force of the cell $Pt/HNO_3/ZnSO_4/Zn$ under various conditions, and found that with a volume concentration of nitric acid exceeding 95% the electromotive force attained a value of just over 2 volts. As the concentration of the nitric acid was reduced there was a corresponding fall in the electromotive force, the latter falling to a value of 1·89 volts when the volume concentration of the acid was as low as 35%. Ihle found that the presence of nitrous acid depressed the oxidation potential, but at the same time it increased the velocity of the oxidizing action of the nitric acid. This interesting research can, however, be regarded only as in the nature of an approximation to a full understanding of the chemistry of the Grove cell, since the various reduction products of the nitric acid were unspecified.

The question of contact electricity as the source of the electromotive force in voltaic cells received continued support from many physicists as improvements were being made in electrostatic methods of investigation. Lodge in 1885 published an elaborate report entitled *On the seat of the electromotive forces in the voltaic cell*, in which he stated that 'whenever electrostatic methods were employed, and where the electroscope was the instrument of research, contact theorists had it all their own way..., but when electric currents were dealt with and the galvanometer used, then the chemists had their turn, and they showed most conclusively that no mere contact could maintain a current unless heat disappeared or chemical action occurred: a fact obvious enough to us to-day on the principles so laboriously and finally established by Joule'. Lodge added that 'from 1860, the invention of the quadrant electrometer put into the hands of the electrostatic experimenters a far more refined and delicate instrument than could have been thought possible a few years before...'.

Most of the improvements in the construction of sensitive electrometers in the nineteenth century were due to Lord Kelvin. His divided ring electrometer, which was devised in 1857, was followed a year or two later by the quadrant electrometer, which was really an improvement of the former instrument and figured largely in various directions of electrical research. In 1897 Lord Kelvin repeated the fundamental experiments by which Volta had claimed to have discovered contact electricity of dissimilar metals. He used an apparatus consisting of two disks, one of zinc and the other of copper, forming an adaptation of a Volta condenser in conjunction with a quadrant electrometer. The results were perfectly definite. 'We conclude', wrote Kelvin, 'that in the separation of two disks of copper and zinc, the copper carries away resinous electricity and the zinc vitreous electricity....The reason of this unmerited neglect of a great discovery regarding properties of matter is that it was overshadowed by an earlier and greater discovery of its author, by which he was led to the invention of the voltaic pile or crown of cups, or voltaic battery, or, as it is sometimes called, the galvanic battery.' There can be no doubt that Kelvin demonstrated the genuineness of Volta's discovery of contact electricity. A much more difficult problem is the question of correlating the values of the contact difference of potential between metallic surfaces with their physical condition, that is, how far the magnitude of the effect is determined by the presence of a very thin film of oxide or of gases adsorbed on the surfaces.

A further question, to which a great deal of attention has been given, is connected with the differences of potential which exist between a metal and a solution containing its own ions. One approach towards a solution of problems arising in this way has been by way of using dropping electrodes. This method appears to have been first used by Lord Kelvin in connexion with investigations on atmospheric electricity from about the year 1860. He employed an apparatus for allowing drops of water to fall continuously from a conductor connected with an electrometer in order to determine the difference of potential between the earth and any point in the atmosphere. In 1868 he employed the flame of a lamp instead of a water dropper for experiments of this kind. The capacity of flames for discharging conductors had, however, been recognized long before that time, and since the beginning of the present century the subject of thermionics has received a great deal of attention from a number of experimentalists, of whom mention may be made of J. J. Thomson, O. W. Richardson and H. A. Wilson.

As regards attempts towards an understanding of the production of electric currents by voltaic cells a brief reference to electro-capillary phenomena must first be made. Lippmann in 1875 made an elaborate investigation of the relation between potential and surface tension at a mercury/water interface. It had long been known that the curvature of a mercury surface in contact with an aqueous solution may be varied with the state of electrification, and Lippmann applied this principle to devising a highly sensitive capillary electrometer, an instrument which has been much used in electrochemical research. The theory of these electro-capillary phenomena is complicated and difficult, and was first discussed by Helmholtz in 1882 in terms of the electrification at the interface resulting in the production of a condenser of very small capacity with its parallel faces oppositely charged. This is known as the theory of the Helmholtz double layer, and is essentially electrostatic in outlook. In 1889 Nernst put forward his theory of electrolytic solution pressure, which is an attempt to give expression to the equilibrium which should arise between the tendency of a metal in contact with a liquid to give rise to positive ions and the oppositely directed osmotic pressure of those ions. The immediate effect of this will be that the solution must become positively and the metal negatively charged, with formation of a Helmholtz double layer of electricities of opposite signs. Nernst's theory has been applied, with a considerable degree of success, to the discussion of the production of voltaic currents, and the calculation of the electromotive force of such cells as are reversible in the thermodynamic sense, including the theory of concentration cells. It also provides a useful means of discussing such phenomena as the precipitation of one metal by another from a solution containing its own ions and the evolution of hydrogen by the dissolution of metals in acids. As applied to the study of dropping electrodes, some experiments carried out by Palmaer between 1898 and 1901 are most instructive. He allowed mercury to flow drop by drop through an extremely dilute mercurous solution into a mass of mercury at the bottom of a vessel. The solution pressure of mercury is extremely low, and consequently mercurous ions tend to be deposited as metal on each drop, but as the drops reach the mass of mercury at the bottom they lose their charge and give back the mercurous ions to the solution. The upper regions of the solution would thus be expected to become more dilute and the lower regions more concentrated with respect to the mercurous salt. Such changes in concentration were indeed observed by Palmaer, which thus gives strong support to Nernst's theory of dropping electrodes.

According to Nernst's theory of electrolytic solution pressure, the electromotive force of a concentration cell should be directly proportional to the logarithm of the ratio of the osmotic pressures of the ions in the concentrated and in the dilute solutions respectively. By assuming proportionality between osmotic pressure and concentration, the expression for the electromotive force could be rewritten with the logarithm of the ratio of the concentration of the ions. The agreement between the observed and the calculated values of the electromotive force is fairly good, and in many cases it may be said that the theory of these cells, as formulated by Nernst, is approximately though not exactly followed. It should, however, be noted that Nernst's theory rests upon the classical theory of ionization formulated by Arrhenius in 1887, according to which the electromotive activity of ions should be proportional to their concentration. The limitations of the classical theory of ionization are, however, now generally recognized, and it has been found necessary to introduce certain deviation coefficients, as has been shown by Bjerrum and others since 1907 to give a more accurate account of concentration cells and of other electrolytic phenomena.

Much experimental work has been done on concentration cells of a different type, namely, those having a single electrolyte with different concentrations of the electrodes. A very interesting cell depending upon this principle was studied in 1892 by des Coudres. It consisted of a long and a short column of mercury each separated from a solution of a mercurous salt by parchment paper, which is impervious to mercury in bulk but permits mercurous ions to pass easily. The source of the electromotive force of this cell is the difference in pressure due to the difference in the height of the columns. Mercury dissolves from the long column and is precipitated beneath the short one, a current meanwhile passing through the solution. The values of the electromotive force as calculated from the difference in height of the mercury columns were in good agreement with the observed values.

The theory of concentration cells has been extended into many other departments of electrochemical research. Thus it has been applied by Nernst and others to discuss the electromotive force of chemical cells which are reversible in the thermodynamic sense. Of perhaps more immediate chemical interest is the elaboration of a method devised by Cohen in 1894 for determining transition points. The principle of the method may be illustrated with reference to the determination of the transition point between the hexahydrate and the heptahydrate of zinc sulphate. A cell consisting of the combination, $Zn/ZnSO_4,7H_2O/ZnSO_4,6H_2O/Zn$, in which the solid phases are present in great excess and contact between the two divisions of the cell is made by a saturated solution of zinc sulphate, was set up together with a resistance and a galvanometer. Since the two solutions of zinc sulphate in the vicinity of the two electrodes are saturated with respect to different solid phases, the concentration of zinc ions is different, and there will therefore be a source of current. When the transition temperature is attained, however, the concentration of zinc sulphate in the two compartments of the cell will become equal, and the electromotive force disappears. In this way Cohen found the transition temperature for these two hydrates to be 39° C., which was in good agreement with determinations made by other methods. A somewhat similar principle was applied by the same author in an investigation of the allotropy of tin. The electrolytic solution pressures of grey and white tin are different, and therefore a cell consisting of electrodes of the two phases of the metals and a solution of a tin salt has a measurable electromotive force which vanishes at the transition point. Cohen determined this temperature for the two allotropes of tin to be 18° C.

The determination of single potential differences between a metal and a solution of its own ions has been the subject of very numerous experiments, and is indeed of much importance in connexion with the general study of the chemistry of the metals. Determinations of this kind are carried out potentiometrically by using a 'half-cell' consisting of the metal and electrolyte under investigation in conjunction with a standard electrode, such as a hydrogen or calomel electrode, a solution of an indifferent electrolyte, sometimes known as a 'salt bridge', being interposed between the 'half-cell' and the standard electrode. In terms of the classical theory of ionization it was considered that in experiments of this kind, so long as the solutions were sufficiently dilute for the ionization to be complete, the values of the electrode potentials should be independent of the nature of the acidic ion, provided always that the formation of complex ions was excluded. This subject was investigated by Neumann in 1894, who found that for some twenty thallous salts, mostly of organic acids, when examined in centinormal concentration, the values of the electrode potential were independent of the anion. With salts of other metals, however, there were marked differences, which would appear to indicate appreciable tendency towards the formation of complex ions.

The discovery of complex ions is dated from the classical work of Hittorf between 1853 and 1859 on the migration of ions; he showed that when solutions of salts such as potassium ferrocyanide or potassium platinichloride were electrolysed, the heavy metal migrated towards the anode and its deposition on the cathode arose as the result of secondary reactions. Since that time the existence of complex ions has been recognized by a variety of methods, and it is now generally agreed that the distinction between double salts and complex single salts is one of degree, and is not fundamental, but determined by the stability or otherwise of the complex ions. Thus in the ferrocyanides and ferricyanides the anions are so stable that none of the usual analytical reactions of ferrous and ferric ions are obtained, whereas in salts such as the ferrioxalates the distinctive reactions of ferric ions are readily observed because of the very limited stability of the ferrioxalate ions. Hittorf in 1892 returned to the subject in an interesting study of the electromotive forces of various voltaic combinations, in which particular attention was devoted to cells consisting of metallic electrodes capable of giving rise to complex anions with the solutions surrounding them. In this way he found that the relative electrochemical properties of certain metals, notably of copper and zinc, could be reversed as regards their usual position by the action of potassium cyanide. Thus in the cell $Cu/KCN/K_2SO_4/ZnSO_4/Zn$, Hittorf found that copper dissolves as a complex cuprocyanide ion and zinc is withdrawn in the ionic condition from the zinc sulphate solution and deposited on the zinc electrode. The current thus flows in the opposite direction to that of a Daniell cell. The reason for the reversal is to be sought in the exceedingly small concentration of copper cations corresponding to the very great stability of the complex anions.

Ever since the early beginnings of electrochemical investigation the evolution of gases at the electrodes has given rise to a variety of problems. As early as the year 1830 de la Rive showed that impure zinc dissolves in dilute sulphuric acid much more rapidly than the purer metal, and that highly pure zinc dissolves with considerable difficulty. This was correctly explained in terms of 'local cells' and was a matter of much importance in connexion with the practical use of voltaic cells. At about the same time it was shown by Kemp and by Sturgeon that if impure zinc is amalgamated with mercury its electrochemical properties approached those of pure zinc, and amalgamated zinc was thereupon brought into general use in batteries by Faraday and others. The effect of amalgamating a plate of impure zinc on its resistance to acids was correctly understood by Faraday as due to the production of a much more homogeneous surface. When a cell is on open circuit hydrogen is not evolved at the surface of an amalgamated electrode, but when the circuit is closed the zinc dissolves easily and a current is produced. In the electrolysis of an aqueous solution such as dilute sulphuric acid it was soon observed that a certain minimum potential had to be applied to the electrodes before gases were evolved at the electrodes with the passage of a current of appreciable magnitude. Above this critical potential electrolysis occurred freely with evolution of the gases. This phenomenon was misunderstood by many of the earlier experimentalists, who regarded it as supporting the older theory which regarded the electrolytic process as consisting primarily in decomposition of the molecules of the electrolyte followed by transference of the products to their respective electrodes. A correct understanding of these phenomena began after the discovery of the gas battery by Grove in 1842. This apparatus consists of an ordinary sulphuric acid voltameter with platinum electrodes projecting upwards into the hydrogen and oxygen gases collected from the electrolysis. The gas cell furnishes a secondary electromotive force due to polarization amounting to about 1·07 volts, and can generate a current with simultaneous recombination of the gases.

The phenomena of polarization have received a great deal of attention from experimentalists, particularly from Le Blanc, since 1891. He found that the minimum electromotive force required to decompose an aqueous solution such as dilute sulphuric acid using bright gold or platinum electrodes approximated to 1·7 volts. Since the secondary electromotive force due to polarization is 1·07 volts, it is clear that the evolution of gas at a bright electrode of an unattackable metal is an irreversible process. Le Blanc also found that, if platinum electrodes are covered with a deposit of platinum black, electrolysis can take place without evolution of gas with an applied electromotive force of 1·07 volts. The effect of coating the electrodes with platinum black is thus to render the process reversible, because the platinized electrodes adsorb the gases during the passage of the current without the formation of bubbles. Under these conditions, therefore, the system becomes capable of being studied thermodynamically and the logarithmic formulae of Nernst are applicable.

The evolution of hydrogen by the action of metals on acids has received much experimental study in more modern times. Thus Ericson-Auren and Palmaer made many quantitative experiments on the rate of evolution of hydrogen from zinc and dilute acids between 1901 and 1906. On the basis of the theory of local cells, and, by making certain assumptions, they claimed that the rate of evolution of hydrogen from zinc containing lead as the impurity in hydrochloric acid of different concentrations was in agreement with the requirements of the electrochemical theory. The whole problem is, however, far from simple. A general theory of velocity of reaction in heterogeneous systems, more particularly as applicable to the rate of dissolution of solids in liquids, was formulated by Nernst in 1904. This theory is based on the assumption of extreme rapidity of reaction at the surface of separation in the absence of the impeding effects of the products of the reaction. With sufficiently vigorous stirring it is assumed that a layer of constant thickness is maintained in contact with the solid and thus causes diffusion. The rate of reaction is therefore determined solely by diffusion phenomena. This theory has received a considerable amount of support from experiments on the rate of dissolution of substances such as magnesium oxide or calcium carbonate in dilute acids; but such reactions are simpler than where metals are concerned, because complications due to polarization do not arise. It should be added that Nernst's theory of regarding such reactions as being governed primarily by diffusion has received a certain amount of criticism.

It has been observed that when some metals are dissolved in acids, the evolution of hydrogen assumes a periodic character. This phenomenon is particularly characteristic of chromium, and was first studied by Ostwald in 1900. The rate of evolution of hydrogen when the metal is dissolved in hydrochloric acid at first increases, reaches a maximum, and finally diminishes. The periodic evolution of the gas continues throughout the dissolution of the metal, and the form of the velocity curve is determined by the presence of impurities and other factors. Brauer in 1901 investigated changes of potential which occur when chromium is dissolved in hydrochloric acid, using a self-recording apparatus, and found that the variations in the electromotive force synchronized with the periods in the evolution of hydrogen. Phenomena of this kind are really highly complicated, and it would appear that chromium, like other metals can readily assume a temporarily passive condition. The subject of passivity, first observed by Keir in the case of iron as long ago as the year 1790, has been the subject of a very great number of investigations. As already mentioned, it attracted attention from Schönbein and Faraday in the early years of the nineteenth century. Broadly speaking three different theories have been advanced with the object of explaining the phenomena of passivity. Faraday favoured the view of the formation of a protective film of oxide. Hittorf, who was familiar with the passivity of chromium, regarded the passive and active forms of the metal as allotropic. Le Blanc considered that passivity was in some manner caused by electrolytic polarization. As regards iron and certain other metals, there can now be no doubt that Faraday's explanation of a protective film of oxide is the correct one. The existence of such a film was demonstrated experimentally by Evans in 1927.

It has been noted that the values of the electrode potentials of the metals are, in general, independent of the nature of the acidic ion which may be present, so long as the formation of complex ions does not arise. It would accordingly follow that the order of the metals, as set forth in the electrochemical series, should provide definite information regarding the capacity of any particular metal to displace another metal from a solution of its salts, and also regarding its behaviour with acids as to whether hydrogen is or is not evolved. This is in general the actual state of affairs: the reactivity of a metal with an acid accompanied by liberation of hydrogen is determined according as the metal is or is not above hydrogen in the potential series. But the position is different if complex anions can be formed. As long ago as the year 1857 it was observed by Odling that finely divided copper can be dissolved in boiling concentrated solutions of the halogen hydracids with liberation of hydrogen. This behaviour would appear to be anomalous, since copper comes below hydrogen in the potential series. Odling's observation has been confirmed by subsequent experimenters, and has been shown to be due to the formation of complex cuprobromic or cuprochloric acids with evolution of a quantity of hydrogen corresponding to the *cuprous* equivalent of the metal.

It is instructive to review in very brief historical perspective how much modern views regarding acids, bases and salts have been influenced as the results of studies on electrolytic phenomena. The idea of oxygen as the fundamental unit of acidity was due to Lavoisier. The work of Davy in the early years of the nineteenth century resulted in the recognition of basic oxides as well as acidic oxides. In 1819 Berzelius enunciated his celebrated dualistic theory of the constitution of acids and salts, which regarded salts as compounds of an acidic and a basic oxide and acids as compounds of water with an acidic oxide. This dualistic electrochemical theory was of much value in its day in dealing with oxy-acids and their salts, and has even some interest at the present time in connexion with silicates. Its downfall in the early years of the nineteenth century was due primarily to the discovery of the elementary nature of chlorine by Davy in 1810 and of iodine by Gay-Lussac in 1814, thereby showing that oxygen is not a universal constituent of salts. A second and important contributing influence was the discovery by Dumas in 1834 that in many organic compounds hydrogen could be replaced by chlorine without effecting any very profound changes in the properties of the resulting products—the chloracetic acids, for example, are very similar to acetic acid.

The steps by which Daniell came to abandon the dualistic theory in favour of what he termed the *binary* theory of salts are most interesting as an early example of the value of electrolytic methods of investigation. All Daniell's work on electrolysis was, as he stated, inspired by Faraday's electrochemical researches. Between 1839 and 1843 Daniell electrolysed solutions of various salts using divided cells, and he showed that in the electrolysis of a salt, such as sodium sulphate, the hydrogen and oxygen liberated at the cathode and anode respectively were secondary products of the reaction. He considered that results of this kind were inconsistent with the views of Berzelius, according to which the ions would be the basic and acidic oxides which constituted the salt. Daniell preferred to regard the ions as the metallic and acidic residues of the salt. He embodied these views in his *Introduction to the Study of Chemical Philosophy*, the second edition of which appeared in 1843. In this work Daniell discussed the modifications of phosphoric acid in terms of the dualistic and binary theories. The celebrated researches of Graham on the arsenates and phosphates and on the modifications of phosphoric acid were published in 1833, and Graham formulated the various salts in terms of the dualistic theory, using a curious notation due to Berzelius: oxygen atoms were represented by dots written above the symbols of the elements with which they were combined. As rewritten by Odling, the formulae of *ortho*-, *pyro*- and *meta*phosphoric acids, according to Graham's views, were $3HO.PO_5$, $2HO.PO_5$ and $HO.PO_5$. Daniell, using the dualistic system, formulated them as $3HO.P_2O_5$, $2HO.P_2O_5$ and $HO.P_2O_5$, the difference between his formulae and the original ones of Graham being due to taking different values for the atomic weights. After discussing the acids and the salts derived from them, in which Daniell recognized that Graham's formulae gave a representation of the differences in basicity of the acids, he pointed out that if electrolytic phenomena were taken into consideration the *ortho*-, *pyro*- and *meta*phosphoric acids could more appropriately be formulated as $P_2O_8+H_3$, $P_2O_7+H_2$ and P_2O_6+H, which he regarded as a better means of giving expression to the differences in basicity of the three acids. It is thus evident that the emphasis on the fundamental properties of acids was transferred from what might be termed the 'oxygen' to the 'hydrogen' point of view. Liebig at about this time revived an idea due to Davy that the saturation capacity of an acid for a base is determined by the hydrogen it contains, and considered that Graham's discovery of the different phosphoric acids was of theoretical value in building up a general theory of polybasic acids, but as Liebig's ideas were formulated almost simultaneously with those of Daniell, it is uncertain whether he was much influenced by the electrochemical ideas of the latter chemist.

Although the dualistic theory of Berzelius and the binary theory of Daniell were fundamentally different as regards the *nature* of the ions, they had a basis in common of regarding salts as additive products of electropositive and electronegative constituents. With the rapidly growing interest in organic chemistry in the early years of the nineteenth century, it is not surprising that attempts were made to formulate theories relating to the composition and structure of compounds based on other considerations. In 1848 Gerhardt published a short work entitled *Introduction à l'étude de la chimie par le système unitaire.* In this work molecules were considered first and atoms afterwards. 'Nous considérons tout corps, simple ou composé, comme un édifice, comme un système unique, formé par l'assemblage, dans un ordre determiné mais inconnu, les particules infinément petites et indivisibles, appelées atomes.' Gerhardt strongly condemned Berzelius's dualistic system, partly because of its failure with organic compounds and also because it could admit of the formulation of salts in more than one way. Gerhardt pointed out that barium sulphate, which he wrote as Ba_2SO_4, could be represented as $Ba_2O.SO_3$, or as $Ba_2O_2.SO_2$, or even as $Ba_2S.O_4$. These attempts towards the foundation of a comprehensive system of chemistry were all made, however, at a time when Avogadro's theorem had not been generally accepted, and when the theoretical side of the science might be described as 'chemistry at the cross-roads'.

After the work of Hittorf, the extensive experimental determinations of the conductivity of aqueous solutions of electrolytes by Kohlrausch, when considered alongside the osmotic properties of solutions, culminated in the electrolytic dissociation theory propounded by Arrhenius in 1887. For upwards of twenty years the 'classical' school of physical chemistry founded by Ostwald on the principles laid down by van't Hoff and Arrhenius enjoyed a great measure of success. A great deal of the experimental work which was done by the workers in that school was directly based on the theory that the properties of acids and of bases are fundamentally the properties of hydrogen and of hydroxyl ions. Thus numerous experiments were made in correlating the catalytic activity of acids with the concentration of hydrogen ions. Thus the theory of indicators and many of the aspects of analytical chemistry received a logical, and, on the whole, a fairly satisfactory explanation in terms of the classical theory of ionization. Gradually, however, developments arose which necessitated modifications in the theory as formulated by Arrhenius.

One of the serious flaws in the classical theory was its failure over the position of strong electrolytes with regard to the law of mass action, a matter which was finally put right by the introduction of the conception of complete ionization due to Bjerrum, Hantzsch, Milner and later in a much more elaborated form by Debye and Hückel in 1923. Somewhat more subtle difficulties were encountered over problems connected with the catalytic action of acids in reactions involving hydrolysis. It was recognized in a broad general way that the catalytic action of an acid was a function of its available hydrogen ions, but more refined investigation showed that molecules would require consideration as well as ions. This was particularly important in attempting to gain an understanding of the mechanism of the reactions of hydrolysis and esterification. An important investigation on the function of hydrogen chloride in esterification was undertaken by Lapworth in 1908. He showed that the introduction of water into alcohol containing hydrogen chloride must necessarily reduce the number of available hydrogen ions, or, in other words, the amount of available hydrochloric acid. This was a definite indication of the basic properties of water. Long before that time it was known that anhydrous hydrogen chloride was devoid of acid properties, though a solution of the gas in water was a strong acid. Lapworth's conceptions of the function of hydrogen ions in esterification and hydrolysis are, in a sense, an anticipation of the modern generalized theory of acids and bases, which was put forward independently by Lowry and by Brönsted in 1923.

At the beginning of the twentieth century Hantzsch put forward his theory of pseudo-acids and pseudo-bases. This valuable conception arose as a result of the investigations carried out with the assistance of his pupils on compounds such as the nitroparaffins and nitrophenols. As formulated by Hantzsch, a pseudo-acid is an electrically neutral compound which can undergo reversible isomeric change, the isomeride having well-defined acidic properties. Similar considerations are applicable to pseudo-bases. It is no impossible step to apply this conception to the halogen hydrides, by regarding them as compounds which by the addition of water give rise to ionizable compounds having acidic properties. On various grounds it had become evident that many ions, and the hydrogen ion in particular, were hydrated. Thus Washburn in 1908 in his determination of what he termed 'true' as distinct from 'Hittorf' transport numbers obtained direct evidence of the migration of the solvent together with the ions. The hydrogen ion was accordingly formulated as the hydroxonium ion H_3O^+. An interesting and direct confirmation of these considerations was obtained by some elegant electrolytic experiments carried out by Bagster and Cooling in 1920. They showed that dry solutions of hydrogen bromide in liquid sulphur dioxide were practically non-conducting, but the addition of a little water enabled the current to flow easily, with evolution of hydrogen at the cathode together with transference of water from the anode to the cathode. By conducting the electrolyses in series with a silver voltameter they were able to show that one equivalent of water is transported to the cathode for every equivalent of silver liberated. The interpretation to be given to these experiments is expressed by the equation: $HBr + H_2O \rightleftharpoons H_3O^+ + Br^-$. At the cathode the hydroxonium ion loses its positive charge with evolution of hydrogen and formation of water.

The modern generalized conceptions advanced in 1923 by Lowry and by Brönsted may be expressed in the simple form: acid $\rightleftharpoons$ base + proton. But since a free hydrogen ion cannot exist in the presence of other molecules, this equation does not represent a process which can be observed practically. The actual acid-base equilibria which are studied are concerned with what the authors of the theory have termed 'corresponding' acids and bases. This theory has extended the original conceptions of acids and bases so as to include substances which ordinarily would not have been regarded as belonging to these classes of compounds. Thus the amphoteric properties of water are shown by its reaction with acetic acid giving rise to hydroxonium ions, and with ammonia producing hydroxyl ions thus: $CH_3CO_2H + H_2O \rightleftharpoons H_3O^+ + CH_3CO_2^-$, and $NH_3 + H_2O \rightleftharpoons NH_4^+ + OH^-$.

Much modern work on acids and bases has been discussed in terms of these newer conceptions. The ionic concentrations have been measured not only by electrometric and conductometric methods, but also by methods involving kinetics of reactions, especially the rate of decomposition of ethyl diazoacetate, and by the use of indicators. In the hands of Brönsted since 1927 the theory has been concerned with some highly interesting researches on the acidic properties of substances such as the aquocobalt ammines and other similar compounds. Brönsted obtained good experimental evidence for regarding the acidic dissociation of chromic chloride hexahydrate as taking place according to the equation: $[Cr(H_2O)_6]^{3+} \rightleftharpoons [Cr(H_2O)_5OH]^{2+} + H^+$. These investigations led Brönsted and Ross Kane in 1931 to investigate anew the very old subject of the dissolution of metals in acids. Under ordinary conditions electrolytic reactions take place due to the setting-up of local cells arising from the heterogeneous character of the metals. Brönsted and Ross Kane extended this work to the problem of pure metals. They studied the action of acids upon dilute sodium amalgam, prepared with great care to ensure a homogeneous material, by measuring the rate of evolution of the hydrogen. Their conclusions indicated that the dissolution of a pure metal in an acid solution is the result of a reaction between an electron in the metal and a molecule of the acid. This was in complete accordance with the extended theory of acids and bases, and was strongly supported by their observation that solutions of aquo-pentammine cobaltic perchlorate were found to react very rapidly with sodium amalgam. This salt contains the tervalent roseo cation $[Co(NH_3)_5(H_2O)]^{3+}$ which according to Brönsted dissociates in aqueous solution as follows:

$$[Co(NH_3)_5(H_2O)]^{3+} + H_2O \rightleftharpoons [Co(NH_3)_5OH]^{2+} + H_3O^+,$$

and would thus have a strong attraction for the electrons of the metal because of its high positive charge.

REFERENCES

HON. HENRY CAVENDISH. *Scientific Papers.* Two volumes. Cambridge, 1921.

M. FARADAY. *Experimental Researches in Electricity.* Three volumes. 1839–55. Electrolytic sections republished by Messrs J. M. Dent in Everyman's Library.

W. HITTORF. *Die Wanderung der Ionen.* Ostwalds Klassiker der exakten Wissenschaften, nos. 21 and 23. Leipzig.

SIR WILLIAM SNOW HARRIS. *A Treatise on Frictional Electricity.* Edited by C. Tomlinson. London, 1867.

A. and E. BECQUEREL. *Résumé de l'histoire de l'électricité et du magnétisme.* Paris, 1858.

J. PRIESTLEY. *The History and Present State of Electricity with Original Experiments.* London, 1767.

W. OSTWALD. *Elektrochemie: ihre Geschichte und Lehre.* Leipzig, 1896.

G. W. A. KAHLBAUM and F. V. DARBYSHIRE. *The Letters of Faraday and Schonbein (1836–62).* Bale and London, 1899.

SIR WILLIAM R. GROVE. *The Correlation of Physical Forces.* London, 1843. Sixth edition 1874.

A. VOLTA. *Collezione delle opere.* Firenze, 1816.

SIR WILLIAM THOMSON (LORD KELVIN). Reprint of *Papers on Electrostatics and Magnetism.* London, 1872.

Mathematical and Physical Papers. Six volumes. Cambridge, 1882–1911.

Baltimore Lectures. Cambridge, 1904.

J. F. DANIELL. *An Introduction to the Study of Chemical Philosophy.* Second edition. London, 1843.

O. J. LODGE. On the seat of the electromotive forces in the voltaic cell. *British Association Report,* 1884. Also *Phil. Mag.* 1885, vol. XIX (v), pp. 153, 254, 340 and Appendix 487.

G. WIEDEMANN. *Die Lehre von der Elektricität.* Erster Band 1882. Zweiter Band, Braunschweig, 1883.

J. CLERK MAXWELL. *A Treatise on Electricity*. Two volumes. Oxford, 1873. Third edition revised by J. J. Thomson, 1892.

W. C. D. WHETHAM. *A Treatise on the Theory of Solution, including the Phenomena of Electrolysis*. Cambridge, 1902.

H. VON HELMHOLTZ. On the modern development of Faraday's conception of electricity. *J. Chem. Soc.* 1881, vol. XXXIX, p. 277.

H. E. ARMSTRONG. Presidential Address. *J. Chem. Soc.* 1895, pp. 1122 et seq.

P. WALDEN. *Salts, Acids, and Bases*. New York, 1929.

R. P. BELL. Acids and Bases. *Annual Reports of the Chemical Society*, 1934, vol. XXXI, p. 71.

J. N. BRÖNSTED and N. L. ROSS KANE. On the dissolution of metals in acids. *J. Amer. Chem. Soc.* 1931, vol. LIII, p. 3624.

SIR EDMUND WHITTAKER. *A History of the Theories of Aether and Electricity. The Classical Theories*. 1951.

CHAPTER IV

PHYSICAL OPTICS AND CHEMISTRY

It has sometimes happened that in the development of certain branches of physical science practice has preceded theory, and the history of physical optics, particularly in the seventeenth century, shows that the invention of instruments, such as the telescope and the microscope, had been made before there was any really satisfactory progress in optical theory. Thus the fundamental law of refraction, attributed to Snell, according to which the ratio of the sines of the angles of incidence and of refraction is constant for any two media, is usually dated as the year 1621; but Galileo had constructed refracting telescopes, on a principle which may still sometimes be seen in opera glasses, some ten years before this date.

The beginnings of physical optics in contradistinction to purely geometrical optics as a subject of study are by no means easy to trace. Thus the phenomena of colour had attracted attention from very early times, and in 1637 Descartes attempted to formulate a theory of the rainbow on the principles of geometrical optics. Descartes seems to have regarded the colours of the rainbow as produced in some manner by the refracting action of the drops of water, but the composite nature of white light was first clearly demonstrated by Newton in 1666. This celebrated discovery arose as a result of Newton's attempts to minimize chromatic dispersion in lenses, and was made by separating the constituents of white light with the aid of a prism. Newton was able to recombine the prismatic colours and thus obtain white light. These experiments were published in 1672. Newton's experiments did not lead to a solution of the problem of avoiding chromatic aberration in lenses, probably because he considered that deviation and dispersion were strictly parallel. The construction of an achromatic combination by using lenses of different kinds of glass was made at a much later date. Disappointment with his failure to obtain achromatic lenses resulted in Newton's abandonment of refracting telescopes; but in 1668 he devised a reflecting instrument containing a concave mirror, which was found to be satisfactory, since the focal length of such a mirror is independent of the colour of the light and consequently chromatic aberration does not arise.

Meanwhile experimental studies on optical phenomena were being made by others. Thus about the year 1665 it was observed by Father Grimaldi that when a small opaque object was placed in the path of a ray of sunlight, admitted through a very small aperture into a darkened room, coloured fringes could be seen at the borders of the shadows. Grimaldi is thus the discoverer of diffraction phenomena, a subject to which a great deal of attention has been devoted by subsequent investigators. At about the same time Hooke made some experiments on the colours of thin films—a phenomenon known to Boyle—including the means of producing such colours by means of an air film between two lenses of large radius of curvature. This subject was investigated in much greater detail by Newton, who made careful measurements of the rings, and after a lengthy discussion of his results in the *Opticks* in which a somewhat curious blending of the corpuscular and the wave theories can be traced, he summed up his views by stating that 'the returns of any Ray to be reflected I will call its *Fits of easy Reflexion*, and those of its disposition to be transmitted its *Fits of easy Transmission*, and the space it passes between every return and the next return, the *Interval of its Fits*'. Newton considered that the lengths of these intervals was supposed to depend on the colour of the light, being greatest for red light and least for violet, and he elaborated his theory of the colours of thin plates on the basis of this idea of 'fits'.

The phenomenon of double refraction was first observed with Iceland spar by Bartholinus in 1669, and studied in much greater detail by Huygens some twenty years later. In 1690 Huygens published his *Traité de la lumière*, in which he propounded an undulatory theory of light. He seems to have had remarkably clear ideas of the different modes of propagation of sound and light, and referred to 'particles qui nagent dans une matière beaucoup plus simple...'. The *Traité*, in the words of Larmor, contains 'a remarkable conception of the kinetic origin of aereal pressure, much more vivid than anything given by Daniel Bernoulli, as well as a correct view of the nature of the elasticity of homogeneous media, and the consequent uniformity of velocity of all pulses whether intense or weak'. Huygens attempted to discuss the various phenomena of light on his wave theory, in which the existence of an aether of some kind was assumed for the propagation of the disturbances. But, as regards the discussion of double refraction, considerable difficulties soon began to arise. On this subject Newton (Query 28 in the *Opticks*) remarked: 'To explain the unusual Refraction of Island Crystal by Pression or Motion propagated has not hitherto been attempted (to my knowledge) except by Huygens, who for that end supposed two several vibrating Mediums within that Crystal. But when he tried the Refractions in two successive pieces of that Crystal..., he confessed himself at a loss for explaining them....To me, at least, this seems inexplicable, if Light be nothing else than Pression or Motion propagated through Aether....'

The *Opticks*, which embody the results of over twenty years of Newton's researches on light, first appeared in 1704, and later editions were published in 1717, 1721 and 1730. In that work it is not difficult to trace a gradual preference for an emission theory as opposed to an undulatory theory of light. Apart from the difficulty of explaining the rectilinear propagation of light on the wave theory, the phenomena of diffraction and of double refraction appeared to Newton to present insuperable difficulties of discussion on such a basis. So Newton begins Query 29 by asking directly 'Are not the Rays of Light very small Bodies emitted from shining substances?' Throughout this work Newton's ideas regarding an atomic constitution of matter are clearly evident. Refraction was considered by Newton to be capable of discussion in terms of a theory of attraction, according to which a ray of light in passing from a rarer into a denser medium was attracted downwards into the latter. Such an idea would imply that the velocity of light should be greater in the more dense medium; this result was shown to be erroneous by direct experiment at a much later date, and has been frequently quoted as the *experimentum crucis* in deciding against the emission theory. The first successful measurement of the velocity of light was made by Römer in 1676 as a result of inequalities which he observed in the eclipses of the satellites of Jupiter. These eclipses were found to appear earlier or later than the calculated times according to the relative positions of the Earth and Jupiter with respect to the Sun, and were attributed by Römer to the finite time taken by light to travel from the Sun to the Earth—about eight minutes—and his result became known to both Newton and Huygens. In 1728 Bradley determined the velocity of light by a different astronomical method, namely, that of aberration. He reasoned that if light consists of corpuscles moving towards an observer with a definite speed the apparent direction from which they come must be affected by the motion of the observer. Having noted certain apparent displacements in the position of the fixed stars, Bradley concluded that these could be explained on the basis of the movement of the Earth in its orbit, and his calculation of the velocity of light gave a value similar to that obtained by Römer.

Astronomical methods afford no information regarding the velocity of light in media other than air, but after Bradley's work, Father Boscovich ventured the opinion that the phenomena of aberration might be examined in water by using a telescope with its tube filled with that liquid to see whether this would make any difference in the amount of aberration actually observed. But Fresnel in a letter to Arago in 1818 expressed the view that negative results were to be expected from experiments of this kind, and that in any case they would not be of any value in attempting to discriminate between the emission and the undulatory theories. Arago, however, in 1838 suggested the adaptation of Wheatstone's revolving mirror experiment, which had been made four years previously, to the problem of the velocity of light in water; and in 1850 Foucault, using a suitable modification of Arago's idea, determined the velocity of light in water and found it to be less than in air—a result which finally established the superiority of the undulatory theory.

Newton's optical researches provided a rich harvest of results, most of which were garnered in the nineteenth century. Thus although Newton assumed parallelism between the refractive and dispersive properties of media, and, as has been seen, this led him to abandon refracting telescopes, he ventured to give expression to some sort of proportionality between the densities of various substances and their refractive properties: 'the Refraction of Camphire, Oil Olive, Linseed Oil, Spirit of Turpentine, and Amber, which are fat sulphureous Bodies, and a Diamond, which is probably an unctuous Substance coagulated, have their refractive powers in Proportion to one another as their densities without any considerable Variation.' In this statement it is possible to trace one of the first beginnings of the study of the relations between optical properties and composition, a subject which was destined to become of much interest to chemists. As regards the immediate development of optical research after Newton's time, the chief interest is centred around the work of Young and of Fresnel.

The outstanding contributions associated with Young are undoubtedly those concerned with the production of colours by interference and diffraction. Young repeated and extended many of Newton's experiments and discussed them on the basis of an undulatory theory. In developing his ideas Young was doubtless largely influenced by the theoretical ideas of Huygens; and in contrasting the propagation of sound and light, they realized that whereas sound is not propagated through a vacuum but light is readily transmitted through a space devoid of air, the presence of some medium for the propagation of the waves of light would seem to be a necessity. The gradual establishment of an undulatory theory of light was beset with considerable difficulties, chiefly concerned with the nature of the medium and of the manner of the wave motion, and was the gradual outcome of the work of Young and of Fresnel, which rested on the foundations laid by Newton and Huygens.

Most of Young's optical researches were carried out between 1800 and 1804, and one experiment of particular interest to chemists should be mentioned. Newton's work on the colours of thin plates and films was extended by Young, and he devoted much attention to making measurements of the wave-lengths of Newton's rings. Having become aware of the chemically active but invisible rays—later known as ultra-violet light—discovered independently by Ritter and Wollaston—Young determined their wave-length by causing them to act upon silver nitrate. He arranged a Newton's ring experiment in which the illumination was effected by ultra-violet light, and projected a real image of the rings on to a piece of paper impregnated with silver nitrate and thus obtained an actual impression of the rings. The action of light on silver salts had been known long before this time; indeed, the darkening of silver chloride under the influence of light was familiar to Boyle, and Scheele found that blue or violet rays were more efficient chemically than red light; but Young's experiment must be regarded as one of the earliest examples of experimental photography.

Several of Young's discoveries were made independently and at a slightly later date by Fresnel, who generously recognized their priority and importance. But Fresnel, whose work dates from about the year 1814, carried his investigations much further afield; and by his development of an undulatory theory in which he assumed the vibrations to take place transversely to the direction of propagation, was able to discuss not only reflexion and refraction, but diffraction, double refraction and polarization on a satisfactory basis. Throughout his writings Fresnel assumed matter to possess a molecular composition: expressions such as *molécules lumineuses* are frequently to be found in his book *De la Lumière* which appeared in 1822, the last paragraph of which emphasizes his ideas: 'Si la lumière n'est qu'un certain mode de vibrations d'un fluide universel, comme les phénomènes de la diffraction le démontrent, on ne doit plus supposer que son action chimique sur les corps consiste dans une combinaison de ses molécules avec les leurs, mais dans une action mécanique que les vibrations de ce fluide exercent sur les particules pondérables, et qui les oblige à de nouveaux arrangements, à de nouveaux systèmes d'équilibre plus stables, pour l'espèce ou l'énergie des vibrations auxquelles

elles sont exposées. On voit combien l'hypothèse que l'on adopte sur la nature de la lumière et de la chaleur peut changer la manière de concevoir leur actions chimiques, et combien il importe de ne pas se méprendre sur la véritable théorie pour arriver enfin à la découverte des principes de la mécanique moléculaire, dont la connaissance jetterait un si grand jour sur toute la chimie. Si quelque chose doit contribuer puissamment à cette grande découverte et révéler les secrets de la constitution intérieure des corps, c'est l'étude approfondie des phénomènes de la lumière.' Molecular considerations characterize the writings of Young as well as those of Newton and of Huygens, but in a broader and somewhat different sense from that adopted by Dalton and Avogadro and their more immediate followers. Broadly speaking the physicists up to the early years of the nineteenth century postulated a granular or discontinuous structure for matter to enable them to discuss optical phenomena without being much concerned with the nature of the ultimate particles; on the other hand, the chemists concentrated their attention towards an understanding of reactions between atoms and molecules. But towards the middle of the century new discoveries in physical optics were being made which were destined to become of great importance to chemical science.

In the course of his studies on the refracting properties of substances, Newton adopted the expression $\frac{n^2-1}{d}$ (where n is the index of refraction and d the density) for what he termed the 'absolute refractive power', and Laplace in the *Mécanique céleste* made use of the same formula, which he regarded as a specific property for a given substance. This expression is based on the emission theory of light, and was assumed to be nearly independent of temperature. But with the gradual development of the undulatory theory in the hands of Fresnel, particularly when it was found that the formula was by no means independent of temperature, it was soon abandoned. The first successful attempt to establish a relation between the refracting properties of substances and their densities was made by Gladstone and Dale in 1858, who replaced Newton's formula by the simpler empirical expression $\frac{n-1}{d}$, which they found to be nearly independent of temperature. In 1863 Gladstone and Dale extended their work with the object of establishing some relation between the specific refractive energies and their composition, and work on similar lines was carried out at about the same time by Landolt. The results of this work showed that the molecular refraction of a compound may be regarded as the sum of the values of the refractive powers of its elements, but modified according to the manner of combination. The property is therefore primarily additive but also partly constitutive. In 1870 Gladstone observed that certain compounds, particularly benzene and some terpenes, were found to have higher values for the molecular refractive power than the calculated values. This led shortly afterwards to an elaborate study of the optical properties of unsaturated compounds by Brühl.

Before the year 1880 the study of the refractive power of substances was largely without any theoretical foundation, but in that year an improved formula for expressing molecular refractive power was introduced independently by H. A. Lorentz and by L. Lorenz. Maxwell had shown in 1865, in his celebrated paper on the electromagnetic theory of light, that the dielectric constant of a medium should be equal to the square of the index of refraction for light of infinite wave-length; and Lorentz's formula was directly due to Maxwell's theory. Lorenz derived the same formula, namely, $\frac{n^2-1}{n^2+2} \cdot \frac{M}{d}$, by starting for a conception of dielectrics due to Mossotti in 1850, and frequently quoted as the Clausius-Mossotti theory of dielectrics. This expression is much superior to the simpler one of Gladstone and Dale, not only on account of its theoretical foundation, but because it has been found to be even better as regards independence of temperature. Eykman in 1895 claimed to have improved the formula in this latter respect by substituting the term 0·4 for 2 in the denominator, but the original expression has been preferred on theoretical grounds and has accordingly come into general use. Brühl employed the Lorentz-

Lorenz formula throughout his numerous and elaborate investigations on molecular refraction, and greatly extended the earlier observations of Gladstone and Dale. By taking the values of the refractive power of compounds in various homologous series, he was able to assign values for the individual elements and for the mode of linking, including the values for unsaturated linkages in the molecule. It was thus possible to calculate the molecular refractive power of any particular compound, and also to adapt the results to the determination of problems of constitution.

In numerous cases the study of molecular refraction has given valuable aid to problems of this kind, but sometimes the results have been far from conclusive. In the latter part of the nineteenth century, opinion was divided fairly evenly as regards the relative merits of Kekulé's formula for benzene and the centric formula for the compound, associated with the names of Armstrong and Baeyer. Support to Kekulé's formula was certainly given at first by the value for the molecular refraction, which was nearly equal to that for six atoms of carbon, six of hydrogen, together with three double bonds. But in 1907 Brühl discovered that compounds having conjugated double bonds in the molecule had abnormally high values for the molecular refractive power—a phenomenon known as optical exaltation. This peculiar optical property at once gave rise to uncertainty regarding the constitution of benzene: it was generally held that no conclusions on that subject could be drawn from considerations of the molecular refractive power.

Molecular refractive power is always determined with reference to light of some particular wave-length, e.g. the D line of the sodium spectrum or one of the lines of the hydrogen spectrum in the visible region; and by taking the differences in the values for any two wave-lengths, e.g. as between the γ (violet) and the α (red), or between the β (blue-green) and the red hydrogen lines, the molecular dispersion is obtained. This property is more subject to constitutive influences than molecular refraction, particularly to the effects of unsaturated linkages. When optical exaltation due to the presence of conjugated double bonds has been found to arise, there has in general been a correspondingly more pronounced degree of molecular dispersion.

Regarding the value of spectrochemical methods for investigating questions of constitution, historically it must be recognized that the vast collection of data due to the labours of Brühl and others has been useful for suggesting means of settling such questions rather than for effecting final decisions. Since Brühl's time the values for the atomic refractions of the elements, and particularly of those which vary according to the mode of combination such as oxygen and nitrogen, have been revised, notably by Auwers and by Eisenlohr since 1910. It has become recognized that conclusions drawn by considering similarly constituted compounds are usually reliable, but that it is very important to avoid making comparisons between classes of compounds which are not closely related. In particular, it has become abundantly clear that spectrochemical methods should always be controlled by purely chemical investigation. The modern way of approach has been particularly valuable in connexion with the chemistry of the terpenes and camphors. Much of the older work of Brühl, dating from the year 1886, has been corrected by Wallach on purely chemical grounds. As an example of the difficulties which have arisen in interpreting the results of measurements of molecular refraction, reference may be made once again to the constitution of benzene. The molecular refraction of this compound corresponds fairly closely to the requirements of the Kekulé formula, but without any optical exaltation. Brühl in 1907 gave values of 25·93 and 26·31 as the observed and calculated molecular refractivities of this compound, showing therefore a slight optical *depression*. That ring formation *per se* does not affect the optical properties of elements can be judged from the observed and calculated values for cyclohexane, 27·67 and 27·62, as determined by Wallach and by Willstätter in 1907. In the same year Sir William Perkin determined the molecular refraction of hexatriene, $CH_2{=}CH{-}CH{=}CH{-}CH{=}CH_2$, and obtained a value of 30·58 as compared with the calculated value of 28·52, showing therefore an optical exaltation of 2·06 units. The effect of the conjugated double bonds in the molecule of hexatriene is thus clearly marked; but if the Kekulé formula of benzene is accepted, the absence of optical exaltation is difficult to understand, and has indeed been urged as affording evidence against the Kekulé formula. Brühl, however, having regard to the general chemical properties of benzene, considered the conjugated double bonds in the molecule as forming a stable 'neutral' system and therefore not inconsistent with acceptance of the Kekulé formula. It is now well recognized that it is impossible to represent the molecule of benzene by any single formula: indeed, Kekulé himself regarded his formula as a dynamic, not a static one; and in 1897 Collie suggested a more elaborate dynamic formula in which the Armstrong centric formula was represented as an intermediate phase, and at the present time the constitution of benzene is expressed in terms of the theory of resonance.

At various times since Newton's unsuccessful attempt to construct achromatic lenses, the attention of physicists has been directed towards establishing some sort of relation between refraction and dispersion. As early as the year 1830 Cauchy became interested in this subject, and in 1836 he suggested a formula connecting refractive index with wave-length in terms of Fresnel's theory, and some kind of molecular structure of matter was assumed. Cauchy's theory represents the dispersion of many substances with a fair degree of accuracy, but it has been criticized because the molecular structure of matter, as ordinarily understood, is too fine-grained to produce more than a small fraction of the dispersion which is actually realized. According to this view dispersion depends essentially upon the ratio of the wave-length to the distance between adjacent molecules of matter. About the year 1842 Neumann and O'Brien independently drew a more precise distinction between aether and ponderable matter, and attributed dispersion to an interaction between them. In particular O'Brien derived a formula which represents what has since been termed *anomalous* dispersion, and he connected this with the presence of absorption bands in the spectrum. On the experimental side much attention has been given to studies on the relations between the refractive index and absorption of light. In the case of transparent substances the refractive index increases with decrease of wave-length, but at different rates in different substances. With substances which exhibit selective absorption, there is usually some reversal of the order of the colours when they are used as prisms. One of the important early discoveries in this connexion was made by Le Roux in 1862. He found that a prism containing iodine vapour deviated the red rays more than the blue ones, the index of refraction for the former colour being actually greater than for the latter. Le Roux is usually regarded as the first discoverer of anomalous dispersion, though the claim for priority has also been made for Fox Talbot. It was also observed by Christiansen in 1870 for solutions of fuchsine, one of the triphenylmethane dyestuffs. Since 1903 anomalous dispersion has been studied in elaborate detail by R. W. Wood, particularly with reference to *p*-nitrosodimethylaniline and to sodium vapour, with the object of testing a dispersion formula suggested by Sellmeier in 1872. This formula has been regarded as the best expression of refractive index in terms of wave-length according to classical theory, but it should be added that an identical expression had been derived by Maxwell three years previously. The Maxwell-Sellmeier theory has received much support from the experimental work of Wood and of others.

The study of molecular volumes has been approached from several points of view since the classical work of Kopp. In 1885 it was shown by Exner that the Lorentz-Lorenz expression for molecular refractive power can provide the means of measuring the relative magnitudes of molecules apart from the aether surrounding them. This idea appealed to Traube, who studied molecular volumes between 1895 and 1899, but his approach was different from that of Kopp. Kopp compared the molecular volumes of liquids at their boiling-points—a fortunate choice since the comparisons were made at approximately corresponding temperatures according to van der Waals. Traube, on the other hand, preferred comparison at the ordinary temperature, and stressed the idea of space partly occupied by matter and partly devoid of it. He also regarded molecular volumes as consisting of the sum of the atomic volumes together with a constant which he termed the co-volume. It was pointed out by van't Hoff that Traube's assumption of a constant value for the co-volume can neither be proved nor disproved. In 1907 Traube showed that when Brühl's values for the molecular refractive power of compounds were divided by the total number of valencies in the molecules a constant, having a value of 0·78–0·79, was obtained. He also identified the molecular co-volume with the expression $(v-b)$ in the van der Waals equation. As the quantity b in that equation is regarded as equal to four times the actual volume of the molecules, assuming them to be spherical, Traube drew some conclusions regarding certain relations between refractive power and molecular volume. Historically Traube's ideas on valency are of interest as being nearly contemporaneous with those of le Bas, who showed that, when the molecular volumes of the normal paraffins, as determined at their melting-points, are divided by the total number of valencies in the molecules, a constant is obtained. Very similar ideas are to be found in Barlow and Pope's theory of valency volumes, which was formulated in 1908. Although ideas of this kind have been abandoned, the study of molecular refraction is nevertheless still of much importance. In 1926 Fajans and Knorr discussed molecular refraction in terms of the Lewis-Langmuir theory of atomic structure, and showed that departure from additive relations could be calculated on the assumption of displacement of the electron shells by the proximity of other atoms.

The relations between magnetic and optical phenomena were first studied by Faraday in 1845. In the following year he published his great discovery in magneto-optics, namely, that when a ray of plane-polarized light is caused to pass through an isotropic substance having high refractive power, such as dense flint glass, in a direction parallel to the lines of force, the plane of polarization is rotated. There is a fundamental distinction between this *magnetic* rotation of polarized light, and the rotation brought about by optically active substances, first studied by Biot about 1815, and afterwards and in great detail from 1848 onwards by Pasteur. The distinction between the two kinds of rotation was clearly understood by Faraday, but has sometimes been confused by subsequent workers. *All* transparent substances can be made to rotate plane-polarized light by the action of powerful magnetic fields, whereas optically active substances must possess molecular dissymmetry to produce this effect. Faraday's discovery was followed up by numerous quantitative experiments carried out by Verdet between 1854 and 1858. These fundamental discoveries were regarded as of much importance by Maxwell, and were quoted by him in his celebrated paper in 1865 on the electromagnetic theory of light. Faraday attempted, but without success, to ascertain whether powerful electrostatic fields would cause rotation of plane-polarized light—there can be no doubt that he expected to observe some effect of this kind—and his reasoning was on correct lines, as was shown at a later date by Kerr. In 1875 Kerr showed that, when plane-polarized light is caused to pass through an isotropic medium in a powerful electrostatic field, the medium becomes doubly refracting to a high degree, and the light suffers elliptical polarization. A further interesting discovery was made by Kerr in 1877 in magneto-optics, namely, that when plane-polarized light is reflected from the polished pole of an electromagnet, it becomes elliptically polarized.

Broadly speaking, in the nineteenth century the various magneto-optical phenomena attracted very little attention from chemists, though physicists recognized their importance, particularly in connexion with the electromagnetic theory of light and physical optics generally. Nevertheless, their bearing upon subjects of chemical interest can be traced back to Faraday's distinction between diamagnetic and paramagnetic substances. Thus Verdet, in following up some earlier experiments of Edmond Becquerel, observed that when ferrous or ferric salts were dissolved in water, the magnetic rotatory power of the resulting solutions was less than that of pure water, but he was unable to correlate the magnetic properties of substances with their effects upon the magnetic rotation of polarized light. The first really important work dealing with the magnetic rotatory properties of substances and their chemical constitution was begun in 1882 by Sir William Perkin. Perkin determined the molecular magnetic rotatory power of numerous organic compounds keeping identical the necessary physical conditions, such as strength of the magnetic field and temperature, and using water as the reference substance. As the result of very numerous experiments extending for about a quarter of a century he found, as in the case of molecular refraction, that the property is both additive and constitutive. Furthermore, just as compounds having conjugated double bonds in the molecule exhibit optical exaltation, a corresponding exaltation was found to arise with similarly constituted compounds as regards magnetic rotation. As an example of the results obtained by Perkin, reference may be made once again to the constitution of benzene. In 1907 he determined the magnetic rotation of hexatriene and obtained a value of 12·196. His result for benzene, determined a few years previously, was 11·284; for hexane and for *cyclo*-hexane the values were 6·646 and 5·664 respectively. If benzene is considered as derived from hexatriene by the loss of two hydrogen atoms, and if *cyclo*-hexane is regarded as derived from hexane in the same way, the differences in the magnetic rotatory powers are somewhat similar, namely, 0·912 and 0·982 respectively. Perkin had established that, just as in the case of molecular refraction, ring formation makes practically no difference to the magnetic rotation, and the results were therefore regarded at the time as not inconsistent with the Kekulé formula for benzene.

Studies in magneto-optics have been extended in numerous other directions, some of which have become of importance to chemical science. A brief reference, on account of its historical interest, must be made to one of these, namely, to the Zeeman effect. As long ago as the year 1862, Faraday attempted to ascertain whether a powerful magnetic field would have any effect upon the sodium spectrum. He placed a sodium flame between the poles of a powerful electromagnet and examined the D lines with a spectroscope, but failed to observe any change in their appearance. A successful result was, however, realized in 1896 by Zeeman, who used a spectroscope having a much greater resolving power than the one used by Faraday, and observed a tripling of the lines. Zeeman's discovery will bear comparison with Kerr's discovery in electro-optics made some thirty years after Faraday's failure to observe any action of electrostatic fields upon plane-polarized light: the successful results realized by both subsequent experimentalists were directly due to improvements in the apparatus which they employed. Historically, the discovery of the Zeeman effect is of much interest as an outcome of the introduction of atomic conceptions into electrical science, an idea which can be traced back to Faraday's discovery of the law of electrochemical equivalence and which was very favourably considered by Maxwell in his *Treatise on Electricity*. At later dates—in 1892 and in 1895—more precise conceptions involving the definite existence of isolated electric units (for which the name of electrons had previously been used by Johnstone Stoney) were introduced by Lorentz. A similar approach towards the establishment of an electrical theory of matter but with a different theoretical treatment, was made by Larmor in his work *Aether and Matter*. The actual existence of discrete units of negative electricity was first demonstrated experimentally in 1897 by J. J. Thomson, who also determined the ratio of the charge to the mass of these particles (termed by him 'corpuscles') by measurements of the deviation of cathode rays by powerful magnetic and electrostatic fields. Very shortly afterwards, Lorentz showed how determinations of the ratio of the charge to the mass could be made from observations on the Zeeman effect, and good agreement was found with the results obtained from the cathode-ray experiments: the identity of Lorentz's electrons with Thomson's corpuscles was clearly established. It may be added that the best modern values for this ratio, which is always denoted by e/m, are of the order of $5\cdot3 \times 10^{17}$ electrostatic units per gramme.

Faraday's division of substances according to their behaviour in a magnetic field attracted the attention of Carnelley, who devoted much study to extending the scope of the periodic law. In 1879 he laid down the general principle that elements of the *even* series in the table, as then formulated by Mendeléeff, were diamagnetic, whereas paramagnetic properties were to be found in the *odd* series of the table. As some of the magnetic properties of certain elements were imperfectly known at that time, it would appear that some of Carnelley's conclusions were not quite accurate; but they received general acceptance from Lothar Meyer, who recognized the periodicity of diamagnetic and paramagnetic characteristics. In a further publication, in 1884, Carnelley pointed out that the production of coloured salts was also a periodic property, being in some manner associated with elements of low atomic volume. No serious attempt at any correlation of paramagnetism with the production of coloured salts was possible at that time.

In 1905 Langevin developed an electronic theory of induced magnetism according to which diamagnetism arises in consequence of compensation of the electronic orbits, whereas when compensation does not occur the resulting atom or molecule has a magnetic moment, and paramagnetism accordingly prevails. Modern theories of atomic structure, particularly those associated with Rutherford and Bohr, provide the means of explaining the paramagnetic properties of coloured elementary ions, and the absence of colour in such ions as are diamagnetic. When an element gives rise to a cation having an electronic configuration of the rare-gas type, it is diamagnetic and colourless because of the compensation of the electrons in the outermost shell; but when the cation has not the rare-gas electronic configuration, and is accordingly uncompensated, it is, in general, coloured and paramagnetic. Colour is usually, but not always, to be found associated with elements which can give rise to ions of more than one valency. This is well illustrated by the elements of atomic number 22–29, namely, titanium, vanadium, chromium, manganese, iron, cobalt, nickel and copper. Interesting examples of colour associated with paramagnetism are also to be found among many of the rare earths, the ions of which are fundamentally tervalent, though cerium also gives rise to quadrivalent salts. Silver salts are fundamentally univalent and colourless, but a few bivalent coloured compounds of this metal have been prepared. In 1932 Sugden determined the magnetic susceptibilities of certain silver and copper compounds, and found that in the case of both metals the univalent colourless compounds had zero magnetic moments, whereas with the coloured bivalent compounds there was definite paramagnetism.

The study of colour in organic compounds as related to constitution began in a manner altogether different from the problems of the colour of inorganic ions. In 1863 Baeyer discovered violuric (*iso*nitrosobarbituric) acid and noted the remarkable colours of its metallic derivatives, a subject which received elaborate investigation at the hands of Hantzsch and his collaborators at a much later date; but the first beginnings towards the establishment of relations between colour and constitution were made with aromatic compounds. It had been noted by Graebe and Liebermann that various coloured substances, such as indigo and triphenylmethane dyestuffs, could be converted into colourless derivatives by the action of reducing agents. In 1876 Witt pointed out that the presence of certain kinds of groupings in the molecule of an organic compound is necessary for the production of colour. Such groupings were termed *chromophores*, of which well-known examples are the azo group, —N=N—, the nitro group, $—NO_2$, and the carbonyl group, =CO. Thus although benzene itself and compounds containing the phenyl group without chromophores are colourless, compounds such as azobenzene, $C_6H_5—N=N—C_6H_5$, nitrobenzene $C_6H_5NO_2$, and benzil $C_6H_5.CO.CO.C_6H_5$ are coloured. Chromophores are unsaturated groupings which are capable of reduction to saturated derivatives with loss of colour. At a later date it became recognized that colour in aromatic compounds may be intensified by the presence of certain classes of groupings known as *auxochromes*, of which the hydroxyl, amino and dimethylamino groups may be quoted as examples. In 1888 Armstrong put forward his well-known quinonoid theory of colour, according to which all coloured organic compounds must possess a constitution similar to that ascribed to *p*-benzoquinone. This compound was first formulated by Graebe with a peroxide constitution but shortly afterwards as a diketone by Fittig, and the reversible process of reduction to the colourless hydroquinone and oxidation of the latter to the coloured quinone could be simply formulated as follows:

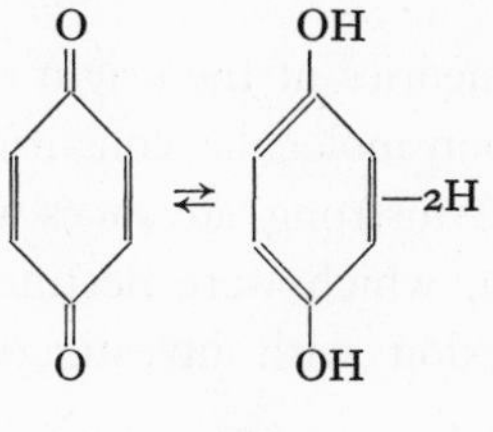

Armstrong made further developments of his theory of the origin of colour at various later dates, and it must be recognized that, apart from a few unimportant exceptions, it has been remarkably successful and consistent.

It must be admitted that theories of colour in organic compounds based on considerations such as those put forward by Witt and by Armstrong are subject to certain limitations, particularly in the case of compounds having unsaturated linkages in the molecules. A comprehensive theory of colour ought not to be subject to such restrictions. Thus it is most difficult to understand why a compound of simple molecular constitution such as iodoform should have a pronounced yellow colour according to those views; there can be no question regarding the mode of linking of the atoms in this compound—there is general agreement that the hydrogen atom and the three iodine atoms are attached to the carbon atom by covalent linkages. This difficulty was indeed recognized by Armstrong, whose views on this subject were summarized in his *Art and Principles of Chemistry* in 1927. He ventured the suggestion that the colour of iodoform might be identified with 'residual affinity' of the iodine, and even wrote a formula giving expression to this assumption. As the colour of iodoform persists in solution in many organic solvents in which polymerization is unlikely to arise, Armstrong's attempt to trace the origin of the colour to what he termed the formation of 'unsaturated centres' is scarcely convincing. It is erroneous to suppose that increase of molecular complexity *by itself* is necessarily favourable to the production of colour: the transformation of the colourless nitrogen tetroxide into the dark red nitric peroxide may be quoted as an illustration. In short it can but be recognized that the whole theory of the origin of colour is not yet sufficiently advanced for precise and consistent formulation.

Independently of theories of the origin of colour, and actually before those based upon molecular constitution had been formulated by Witt and by Armstrong, advances were made in the study of optical phenomena, which were destined later to become of importance in connexion with investigations on the relations between absorption spectra and molecular constitution. In 1852 Stokes published his celebrated paper entitled *On the change of refrangibility of light*. Stokes was attracted to his optical studies as a result of the work of Herschel on the properties of solutions of quinine sulphate, published in 1845, and by the experiments of Brewster on those of alcoholic solutions of 'the green colouring matter of leaves' and of the same investigator on fluorspar, which were published a few years previously. In his paper Stokes used the term *fluorescence* for the first time in connexion with fluorspar 'as the analogous term *opalescence* is derived from the name of a mineral'. The importance of Stokes's work for the study of natural organic colouring matters was soon recognized: thus Schunck in an investigation of the colouring matters of madder, published in 1860, concluded his paper with an appendix drawn up by Stokes on the optical properties of purpurine and alizarine. In his lecture delivered before the Chemical Society in 1864 entitled *On the application of the optical properties of bodies to the detection and discrimination of organic substances*, Stokes emphasized the importance of the choice of suitable solvents in studies of this kind.

The year 1860 is usually recognized as marking the foundation of spectrum analysis by Bunsen and Kirchhoff, since they discovered caesium then, and rubidium in the following year, by spectroscopic analysis of a mineral water from Dürkheim. In the preceding year Kirchhoff had published a paper on the Fraunhofer lines in which he concluded that the two dark D lines in the solar spectrum were coincident with the bright lines in the spectrum obtained by placing sodium chloride in a spirit flame. He concluded that the presence of the various dark lines in the solar spectrum was to be attributed to the existence of various elements in the sun's atmosphere. However, it was pointed out by Stokes in 1860, and also in correspondence with Kelvin at earlier dates, that Foucault, in a note published in 1849 entitled *Sur la lumière de l'arc voltaïque*, had obtained the double dark D line artificially by passing a strong ray of sunlight concentrated by a lens through an electric arc between carbon poles, which itself gave out the *bright* D lines. Although Foucault did not attribute his production of these lines, which he showed to be strictly coincident with the dark Fraunhofer lines in the solar spectrum, to the presence of sodium, Stokes regarded the observation as important and laid down the principle to Kelvin 'that a body may be at the same time a source of light giving out rays of a definite refrangibility, and an absorbing medium extinguishing rays of the same refrangibility which traverse it, seems readily to admit of a dynamical illustration borrowed from sound...'. It would thus appear that the principles of spectrum analysis received some theoretical prediction before they were established experimentally by Bunsen and Kirchhoff.

Since the time of Bunsen and Kirchhoff a great deal of work has been accomplished in spectroscopic chemistry, and much of this has resulted in consequence of improvements in experimental technique. Of these, two are of outstanding importance, namely, the use of diffraction gratings for the production of spectra, and the use of quartz prisms for work in the ultra-violet region and of rock salt and sylvine prisms for investigation in the infra-red parts of the spectrum. The production of spectra by diffraction had its beginnings early in the nineteenth century, but the most valuable advances from the point of view of their practical application are those due to Rowland since 1882, particularly his use of gratings ruled on concave spherical surfaces which enable spectra of great sharpness to be obtained. For some purposes, more especially in connexion with measurements of wave-lengths, diffraction spectra have been found preferable to spectra produced by prisms, since it is thus possible to obtain spectra in which the distances between the lines are proportional to the difference of their wave-lengths: with prism spectra this cannot be realized, as there is no simple relation between the degrees of deviation and dispersion. In the mapping of spectra, photography was introduced for investigation in the visible and ultra-violet regions at an early stage; its application for study of the infra-red region appears to have been first used by Abney in 1880, who sensitized plates for this purpose, but the extensive use of infra-red photography is of much more recent date.

The application of absorption spectra to the study of molecular constitution has been much advanced by extending the experimental work beyond the limits of the visible spectrum. In 1880 Hartley and Huntington published an important paper in which they pointed out that many organic compounds which show no selective absorption in the visible region may nevertheless be highly selective as regards light of shorter wave-length. They used photographic methods for investigating the ultra-violet absorption spectra of his compounds, which were examined in highly dilute solutions of definite molecular concentration, and the results were discussed in terms of the wave-lengths and of the thicknesses of the solutions. These researches were continued for many years partly in collaboration with others. The constitutive nature of the property of absorption of light was well established as the result of the numerous other workers in this field, of whom Dobbie, Baly, Desch, Lowry, Hantzsch and Kauffmann may be specially mentioned. In 1904 Baly and Desch made an important improvement on Hartley's original way of expressing the results, which has come into general use, namely, by plotting the logarithms of successive thicknesses of the solutions against the oscillation frequencies; this enables the curves to be more readily interpreted. The vast collection of results which has been accumulated through the work of the investigators already mentioned and of many others does not admit of any detailed discussion in the present chapter, but it may be interesting to advert in very brief outline to some of the problems which have been attacked by this method.

At an early stage of the work Dobbie urged that conclusions drawn from the study of absorption spectra should, whenever possible, be confirmed by purely chemical methods. This is not always practicable and doubtless accounts for the different interpretations which have been given of certain results. Broadly speaking, however, there is general agreement on the following points. When the concentration of a solution is altered without any change in the position of the absorption bands, but only in their intensity, the constitution of the solute is unaffected, change in constitution being indicated by the disappearance of certain bands or the appearance of new ones. If the character of the absorption spectrum is altered by a change of solvent, the constitution of the solute is regarded as having undergone some change. Thus if the nature of the absorption spectrum is varied according as the solution is made acid or alkaline, a change in constitution of the solute is definitely inferred. A brief reference to the bearing of this subject on the theory of indicators may be of interest. In the latter years of the nineteenth century there were two fundamentally different views on this subject. The Ostwald school of physical chemists discussed indicators as weak acids or bases, the molecules of which were regarded as differently coloured from the ions, in terms of ionic equilibria. Ostwald's ionization theory did not commend itself to many chemists, some of whom regarded it as an over-simplification, while others considered that changes in colour in acid or alkaline solution could be discussed more satisfactorily in terms of changes in constitution, e.g. from a benzenoid to a quinonoid structure and vice versa. Eventually it became recognized that both views are not inconsistent but complementary, and this has arisen very largely as a result of the investigations of Hantzsch and his pupils on the nitroparaffins and the nitrophenols. Both of these classes of compounds are pseudo-acids, that is, substances which are non-electrolytes but which are nevertheless capable of giving rise to metallic derivatives as the result of change into acidic isomerides. Hantzsch in 1906 showed that the nitrophenols could give rise to two classes of ethers, namely, the ordinary colourless compounds having the constitution such as $CH_3O-C_6H_4-NO_2$, in which the alkyl group replaces the hydrogen atom of the phenol oxygen, and highly coloured isomerides which could be formulated with a quinonoid constitution such as $O{=}C_6H_4{=}N(\rightarrow O)OCH_3$. Applying these considerations to *p*-nitrophenol, the indicator properties of which are well known, the colourless form in acid solution would have the true nitrophenol structure with a benzenoid nucleus, while the yellow colour in alkaline solution would correspond to the quinonoid anion. According to Hantzsch the colour changes of all indicators are to be regarded as a twofold process, namely, an ionic change together with a tautomeric change, the ion having a different constitution from that of the pseudo-acid or pseudo-base from which it is originally derived. It may be added that much modern investigation on the reversible transformation of colourless compounds into coloured ones has supported Armstrong's original idea that colour in organic compounds is associated with a quinonoid structure.

Hantzsch continued his work on pseudo-acids for many years, and employed other physico-chemical methods of investigation, such as electrical conductivity and catalytic activity, to supplement studies in absorption spectra. His original conceptions on this subject were considerably extended, but as he changed his views on more than one occasion, they were received with a certain amount of criticism. About the year 1909 he gave much attention to Baeyer's violuric acid and other compounds of the cyclic oximino-ketone type. This acid, which is colourless, can give rise to salts with colourless cations, such as those of the alkali metals, which according to the mode of preparation may be colourless, or partly yellow, red, blue or green. Hantzsch considered that this could be discussed from the standpoint of tautomerism, and regarded the colourless and yellow salts as derivatives of the oximino form $\mathrm{CO}\Big\langle\begin{array}{c}\mathrm{NH{-}CO}\\ \mathrm{NH{-}CO}\end{array}\Big\rangle\mathrm{C{=}NOMe}$, and the red and blue salts to be derived from the nitroso form of the acid (Me is a metal) $\mathrm{CO}\Big\langle\begin{array}{c}\mathrm{NH{-}C{-}OMe}\\ \mathrm{NH{-}CO}\end{array}\Big\rangle\mathrm{C{-}N{=}O}$. Hantzsch introduced the conception of what he called *chromoisomerism*, a term which would appear to be self-explanatory; but he seems also to have admitted the possibility of substances having relatively minor differences in colour without change of constitution, larger differences in colour being necessarily concerned with differences in constitution. Of Hantzsch's later work on pseudo-acids, much interest is centred around his publications on certain inorganic oxy-acids about the year 1923. Broadly speaking he regarded these acids as consisting of two types, namely, $H^+[OX^-]$, the true acid which gives rise to salts, and $HO[X]$, the pseudo-acid, which gives rise to esters.

Support was given to this view in the case of nitric acid: the concentrated acid has an absorption spectrum similar to that of the alkyl nitrates, and is therefore to be regarded as the pseudo-acid, whereas the acid in dilute aqueous solution has a spectrum closely similar to that of dilute solutions of the alkali nitrates, and altogether different from that of the esters. This latter absorption spectrum is accordingly a property of the nitrate ion which is present in solutions of the dilute acid. At a later date Hantzsch made further elaborations of his theories, but without adding much towards clarification of this somewhat difficult subject.

Phenomena due to the scattering of light by particles of the order of size of its wave-lengths are of much importance in chemistry. About the year 1868 Tyndall investigated the action of light in causing decomposition of certain alkyl iodides in the vaporous condition; the separation of iodine took place with formation of mists, which when viewed obliquely appeared blue. This production of 'artificial skies' was correctly interpreted in general terms by Tyndall as due to the scattering action of the ultramicroscopic particles. In 1871 Lord Rayleigh gave his well-known theory of the blue colour of the cloudless sky, according to which if the diameters of the suspended particles are small as compared with the wave-lengths, the proportions of scattered to incident light for different wave-lengths are inversely as the fourth powers of the wave-lengths. From this theory it follows that the proportion of scattered light to incident light is about seven times as great for the violet as for the red light of the visible spectrum, and the intensely blue colour of the clear sky is thus intelligible. Lord Rayleigh's calculations indicated that scattering of light may be produced not only by mists of minute droplets or solids but by gaseous molecules —a phenomenon which was demonstrated experimentally by Cabannes and by Lord Rayleigh (the younger) in 1918.

Ultramicroscopic methods of investigation have been much used in the study of colloidal solutions since their introduction by Siedentopf and Zsigmondy in 1903. It was generally accepted that whereas a solute in 'true' solution was incapable of scattering light, the existence of substances in colloidal solutions was demonstrable by the scattering action of the ultramicroscopic particles. This may, however, imply a more fundamental distinction between a 'true' solution and a colloidal solution than would appear to be altogether justified. The difference in optical behaviour may possibly be determined by other factors, such as the molecular weight of the solute independently of its actual condition in solution. An important observation on this subject was made by Lobry de Bruyn and Wolff in 1904. They showed that the Tyndall effect could be observed for certain substances of high molecular weight, such as cane sugar, raffinose and phosphomolybdic acid in aqueous solution, but not for substances of low molecular weight. Considerations of this kind thus emphasize the difficulty—indeed the impossibility—of drawing a strict distinction between the two classes of solutions.

The scattering action of light on gaseous molecules has assumed much importance in more recent years from the standpoint of molecular structure and of the shape of simple molecules. When gases and vapours are illuminated by polarized light the scattered light is, in general, only partially polarized, from which it follows that there must be some peculiarity in the molecules to account for this depolarizing action. Such molecules have been described as anisotropic, a term which had been applied long before to crystals the optical properties of which are different in different directions.* In 1920 Lord Rayleigh (the younger) showed that monatomic gases, such as helium and argon, exert an extremely slight depolarizing action, but larger effects were observed with diatomic gases and still larger effects with triatomic gases, such as carbon dioxide and nitrous oxide. These results were generally confirmed and greatly extended by Cabannes and others since 1920. It has become evident from the work of Cabannes, Stuart and others that the degree of depolarization is determined, not by the magnitude, but by the extent of departure from symmetry of the molecules.

* In the Baltimore Lectures, p. 122, Lord Kelvin suggested the term *aeolotropic* to denote substances which are variegated in any manner according to direction in contradistinction to Cauchy's term *isotropic* which indicates equality of properties in all directions. It may be regretted that this elegant word has not come into general usage rather than the awkward term *anisotropic*.

The molecules of the inert gases are regarded as spherical, which thus accounts for the extremely small depolarization shown by them. The stronger depolarizing action of more complex molecules is regarded as due to the existence of dipole moments, the effect of which is the more pronounced the greater the departure of the molecule from a spherical form. An extremely interesting example is to be found with methane and carbon tetrachloride; both show very slight depolarization, but definitely less with the halogenated compound. Stereochemically, both molecules are identical with the carbon atom within an imaginary tetrahedron and are accordingly spherically symmetrical. The explanation of the very slight depolarization shown by these two compounds has been ascribed to internal atomic vibrations, the lower value shown by carbon tetrachloride being presumably due to the effect of the heavy halogen atoms. The whole subject of dipole moments in compounds has been studied from several points of view, and methods involving determinations of dielectric constants, infra-red spectra, Raman spectra and diffraction of electrons have been introduced.

The nineteenth century is frequently quoted as the period in which the corpuscular theory of light was gradually abandoned in favour of some form of undulatory theory, first as expounded by Fresnel, and later in accordance with Maxwell's electromagnetic theory. It is true that certain aspects of purely geometrical optics could be discussed in terms of Newton's corpuscular ideas, but other phenomena—refraction, interference and diffraction, polarization, as well as magneto-optics and their related phenomena—could only receive satisfactory explanation in terms of Maxwell's theory. But even before the close of the century phenomena were discovered which could not be included within the framework of classical electromagnetic theory. In 1887 Hertz discovered that the passage of sparks between charged electrodes, separated just beyond the sparking distance, was facilitated by exposure to ultra-violet light. This discovery was confirmed and extended by Hallwachs in the following year and has been the subject of much experimental study since that time. Some ten years afterwards it was shown independently by Lenard and by J. J. Thomson that this photoelectric effect, as it is now termed, consists in the discharge of negative electrons from the metallic surfaces which are illuminated by ultra-violet light. The recognition of an atomic or discontinuous structure of electricity thus provided a possible means of embracing phenomena which could not be discussed in terms of Maxwell's theory. A further and most important step was taken in 1900 by Planck who introduced the conception of energy quanta for the discussion of radiation, certain aspects of which were inconsistent with classical thermodynamics.

In 1905 Einstein pointed out that certain photoelectric phenomena, and particularly a discovery by Lenard that the velocity of expulsion of an electron from a metal irradiated by ultra-violet light is determined by the frequency of the light and not by its intensity, would necessitate a partial return to some form of corpuscular theory of light interwoven with the undulatory theory. Briefly summarized, Einstein's important theoretical advance consisted in equating the energy of an electron ejected by light of frequency ν with the product $h\nu$, where h is Planck's constant. The quantum theory was invoked as far back as the year 1913 by Bohr in connexion with the development of his theory of atomic structure, and was applied by him to account for the production of spectra as determined by the displacement of electrons from their normal orbits or stationary states. Other optical phenomena, such as theories of dispersion, have been discussed on the basis of quantum theory. But an important later development, namely, that of wave mechanics, which was initiated in 1925 by Louis de Broglie, postulates a dual property for electrons by regarding them as having simultaneously the characteristics of waves as well as of particles. It is just possible to trace a similar dual conception of the nature of light expounded by Newton in the *Opticks*, in his use of the expressions *Fits of easy Reflexion* and *Fits of easy Transmission*. The numerous developments, theoretical and experimental, which have arisen in consequence of the new quantum mechanics do not admit of discussion in this chapter, but on account of its chemical interest, a single reference may be made to one of these, namely, to the Raman effect.

Briefly stated, the Raman effect consists in an alteration of the frequency of light as a result of the scattering action of matter. In 1923 Smekal predicted an effect of this kind on the basis of the quantum theory of dispersion, and his prediction received experimental verification by Raman in 1928. It may be noted that according to classical theory no alteration of the wave-length of monochromatic light should be expected to take place by scattering. In some respects the Raman effect bears a superficial resemblance to the phenomena of fluorescence and also to scattering, but there are certain distinctions between them. Thus Stokes had laid down the general principle that in fluorescence the emitted light is of greater wave-length than the incident light, whereas in a Raman spectrum lines of shorter as well as of longer wave-length are to be found. The most important aspect of Raman spectra is centred upon the differences in wave-length between those of the re-emitted lines and of the incident radiation. Definite relations between the Raman lines and the absorption bands of the infra-red spectra of substances have been found to exist. Since Raman's discovery was first made, a vast amount of work has been done on the subject, and its value as an instrument for the study of questions of constitution and of the shape of molecules has been repeatedly emphasized. Comprehensive accounts of the importance of the Raman phenomena for chemical studies have been published by Dadieu and Kohlrausch in a paper entitled *Raman Effekt und Chemie* in 1930, and also in a monograph by Hibben, *The Raman Effect and its Chemical Applications*, which appeared in 1939.

REFERENCES

SIR ISAAC NEWTON. *Opticks*. Reprinted from the fourth edition (1730) with a Foreword by A. Einstein and an Introduction by E. T. Whittaker. London, 1931.

ERNST MACH. *The Principles of Physical Optics*. Translated by J. S. Anderson and A. F. A. Young. London, 1926.

ROBERT W. WOOD. *Physical Optics*. Third edition. New York, 1934.

J. LARMOR. *Aether and Matter*. Cambridge, 1900.

A. FRESNEL. *De la Lumière*. Les Classiques de la Science. Paris, 1914.

LORD KELVIN. *Baltimore Lectures on Molecular Dynamics and the Wave Theory of Light*. Cambridge, 1904.

N. R. CAMPBELL. *Modern Electrical Theory*. Second edition. Cambridge, 1913.

LOTHAR MEYER. *Modern Theories of Chemistry*. Translated from the fifth German edition by P. Phillips Bedson and W. Carleton Williams. London, 1888.

S. SMILES. *The Relations between Chemical Constitution and some Physical Properties*. London, 1910.

FRITZ EISENLOHR. *Spektrochemie organischer Verbindungen*. Stuttgart, 1912.

H. KAUFFMANN. Über den Zusammenhang zwischen Farbe und Konstitution. *Ahrens Sammlung*, Band IX. 1904.

R. KREMANN. *Zusammenhänge zwischen physikalischen Eigenschaften und chemischer Konstitution*. Dresden und Leipzig, 1937.

SIR GEORGE STOKES. *Mathematical and Physical Papers*. Five volumes. Cambridge, 1880–1905.

LORD RAYLEIGH. *Scientific Papers*. Six volumes. Cambridge, 1899–1920.

J. CLERK MAXWELL. *A Treatise on Electricity*. Two volumes. Oxford, 1873. Third edition revised by J. J. Thomson, 1892.

E. VERDET. *Œuvres*. Paris, 1868–72.

LÉON FOUCAULT. *Recueil des travaux scientifiques de Paris*. 1878.

H. E. ARMSTRONG. The origin of colour and the constitution of colouring matters. *Proc. Chem. Soc.* 1888, p. 27.

W. HÜCKEL. *Theoretische Grundlagen der organischen Chemie*. Zwei Bänder. Leipzig, 1931.

J. CABANNES. *Diffusion moléculaire de la lumière*. Paris, 1929.

H. A. STUART. *Molekülstruktur*. Berlin, 1934.

C. P. SMYTH. *Dielectric Constants and Molecular Structure*. New York, 1931.

F. I. G. RAWLINS and A. M. TAYLOR. *Infra-red Analysis and Molecular Structure*. Cambridge, 1929.

W. G. PALMER. *Valency, Classical and Modern*. Cambridge, 1944.

T. S. MOORE. The Hantzsch Memorial Lecture. *J. Chem. Soc.* 1936, p. 1051.

LOUIS DE BROGLIE. *Matière et lumière*. English edition. Paris, 1937. Translated by W. H. Johnston. London, 1939.

J. W. BRÜHL. The optical influence of contiguity of unsaturated groups. *J. Chem. Soc.* 1907, p. 115.

SIR WILLIAM PERKIN. The magnetic rotation of hexatriene, $CH_2:CH.CH:CH.CH:CH_2$ and its relationship to benzene and other aromatic compounds; also its refractive power. *J. Chem. Soc.* 1907, p. 806.

A. DADIEU and K. W. F. KOHLRAUSCH. Raman Effekt und Chemie. *Ber. dtsch. Chem. Ges.* 1930, LXIII [B], p. 251.

N. V. SIDGWICK and E. J. BOWEN. The structure of simple molecules. *Annual Reports of the Chemical Society*, 1931, p. 367.

J. H. HIBBEN. *The Raman Effect and its Chemical Applications*. New York, 1939.

CHAPTER V

MOLECULAR MAGNITUDES

How much in common have the ideas regarding atoms and molecules, as understood in the nineteenth century, with those of certain early Greek philosophers and 'their majestic Roman poetic expositor, Lucretius', as he was designated by Lord Kelvin? This question has been frequently debated, and somewhat different answers have been given to it. There is, however, general agreement that a discontinuous structure had been assigned to matter long before it had received any very precise formulation. Definite atomic conceptions are to be found in the works of Newton, particularly in the *Opticks*; and in the eighteenth century, Father Boscovich had regarded atoms as mathematical points endowed with the property of mass. Coming to the nineteenth century, it is easy to see that the ultimate particles of matter were somewhat differently considered by the chemists, whose interests were concerned primarily with reactions between substances, and the physicists, whose studies lay in other directions. Broadly speaking the conceptions of the physicists were fundamentally mechanical; this was possibly a legacy from Newton's well-known principle of founding a system of natural philosophy on dynamical principles, as set forth in his Preface to the *Principia*: 'Deinde ex his viribus per propositiones etiam mathematicas, deducuntur motus planetarum, lunae et maris. Utinam caetera naturae phaenomena ex principiis mechanicis eodem argumentandi genere derivare liceret.' The further progress of ideas of this kind is clearly evident in the development of molecular dynamics in connexion with the kinetic theory of gases. The foundations of Dalton's atomic theory as expounded in the *New System of Chemical Philosophy* were very definitely laid upon considerations arising from studies of chemical changes. It may be added that Dalton's contemporaries and followers, such as Berzelius, Gay-Lussac, Gmelin, Gerhardt, Laurent and Cannizzaro, were very much concerned with the *relative* weights of atoms and molecules, but questions regarding the *absolute* values of the ultimate particles of matter made no appeal to them.

Having regard to this divergence of outlook it is by no means surprising that attempts to arrive at absolute determinations of molecular magnitudes should have been begun by the physicists. One of the most interesting of the early investigations on this subject is to be found in the work of Thomas Young on capillarity in 1805. Partly as the result of his own work and of that of Laplace, Young considered that 'the extent of the cohesive force must be limited to about the 250th millionth of an inch' (10^{-8} cm.), and continued: 'since the density of this vapour is about one sixty-thousandth of that of water, the distance of the particles must be forty times as great...and on the whole it appears tolerably safe to conclude that...the diameter or distance of the particles of water is between the two thousand and the ten thousand millionth of an inch' (between $0{\cdot}125 \times 10^{-8}$ and $0{\cdot}025 \times 10^{-8}$ cm.). In 1890 Lord Rayleigh made interesting determinations of the limiting thickness of oil required to stop the movements of camphor on water and obtained values between $8{\cdot}1 \times 10^{-8}$ and $10{\cdot}6 \times 10^{-8}$ cm. He commented favourably upon Young's experimental work. Röntgen, using a similar method to Rayleigh, obtained evidence of layers $5{\cdot}6 \times 10^{-8}$ cm. in thickness. Between 1862 and 1870 Lord Kelvin gave estimates of the order of 10^{-8} cm., based on studies on contact electricity and on the work done in stretching water films, and in the *Baltimore Lectures* he stated that Young would have obtained a more accurate estimate if he had been more familiar with the kinetic theory of gases: 'he [Young] thus arrives at a much finer-grainedness for liquid water than if he had given long enough free paths to molecules of the vapour to account for its approximate fulfilment of Boyle's law.'

The modern mathematical development of the kinetic theory of gases, the early beginnings of which are to be found in the works of Huygens and Bernoulli, is chiefly due, since 1857, to the labours of Clausius, Maxwell and Boltzmann. As Maxwell's calculations of the mean free paths were made some fifty years after Young's work, it is clear that Young was scarcely in a position to apply the kinetic theory to his own determinations. On the experimental side, the researches of Graham at various dates, particularly about the year 1846, on the effusion, diffusion and transpiration of gases, provided some of the strongest support for the development of the kinetic theory. Graham distinguished clearly between these three phenomena, but subsequent writers have not always been sufficiently careful to bear them in mind. Both diffusion (the intermingling of gases without the intervention of porous septa) and effusion (the passage of gases through a very minute hole in a flat plate) are governed by Graham's well-known law, according to which the rates of these processes are inversely proportional to the square roots of the densities of the gases. Transpiration consists in the passage of gases through long capillary tubes, and is determined not by the densities but by the viscosities of the gases: it is indeed a useful means of measuring such viscosities. In 1863 Graham carried out a few experiments on the velocities of diffusion of carbon dioxide upwards and of hydrogen downwards into air without using porous septa, and found that the relative rates of diffusion of hydrogen and of carbon dioxide to be in the ratio of 5:1. According to the square-root law the ratio should be 4·7:1, but, having regard to the difficulty of making accurate measurements, it was justifiable to conclude that the principle had been verified. Much more elaborate experiments on the inter-diffusivities of gases were carried out by Loschmidt in 1870, which have confirmed and extended Graham's results.

In 1865 Loschmidt published an important paper entitled *Zur Grosse der Luftmolecüle*, in which he demonstrated the possibility of calculating the number of molecules in a definite volume of a gas under specified physical conditions. The number of molecules in 1 cm.^{3} of a gas at normal temperature and pressure is thus very properly termed Loschmidt's number. Loschmidt based his estimate on the molecular free path and molecular diameters, assuming the molecules to be spherical, according to the considerations of Clausius and Maxwell, and he also took account of Kopp's studies on molecular volumes, which were begun as early as 1841 and continued for many years afterwards. The development of the kinetic theory of gases was based on the assumption that the molecules were minute spherical particles endowed with inertia—Boscovich atoms in fact—and in the year 1860 Maxwell calculated the mean velocities and molecular free paths on the assumption of a statistical distribution of velocities, an important improvement on a calculation made two years previously by Clausius in which equality in the molecular velocities was assumed.

Three properties of gases, namely, diffusivity, viscosity and thermal conductivity, have all been the subject of theoretical study and experimental investigation in connexion with the development of the kinetic theory of gases; in particular, the two first named are used for the evaluation of Loschmidt's number. In his theoretical writings at various dates from 1866, Maxwell derived two different formulae connecting the viscosity and density of a gas with its molecular diffusivity. His earlier formula gave $\mu/\rho = 0{\cdot}648\ D$, whereas in later papers he wrote $\mu/\rho = D$, ρ denoting the density, μ the viscosity and D the molecular diffusivity of any particular gas. Formulae of this kind postulate that the molecular mean free paths should be large, of the order of at least one hundred times, in comparison with the molecular diameters, a point on which there was general agreement. In 1873 Maxwell made an estimate of Loschmidt's number, which was derived from the diffusion experiments of Loschmidt himself, and obtained a value of $1{\cdot}9 \times 10^{19}$. As regards the two formulae which Maxwell gave relating the diffusivity of a gas to the ratio of the viscosity to the density, experimental study has given strong support to his earlier formula, making the ratio of the order of $0{\cdot}65\ D$. This was borne out by comparison made of Loschmidt's diffusion experiments with Graham's determinations of viscosity by the method of transpiration as calculated by O. E. Meyer, and with later experiments on viscosity such as those which Obermayer carried out about the year 1876. Support was given to the general correctness of Maxwell's theoretical ideas regarding the viscosities of gases by his own experiments in 1860, in which he employed oscillating vanes, a method which had been devised many years before by Coulomb for determining the viscosities of liquids. In particular, Maxwell showed that over a wide range of pressure the viscosity of a gas is independent of the pressure, unless the gas is in such a high state of rarefaction that the mean free paths of the molecules should be comparable with the actual dimensions of the apparatus. This departure of viscosity from independence of pressure at extreme rarefaction was demonstrated experimentally by Crookes in 1881, using an adaptation of Maxwell's experimental method. The same relations regarding thermal conductivity of gases as being independent of pressure, except the lowest pressures—a property for which the same principles of the kinetic theory of gases are valid—were predicted and have subsequently received experimental confirmation. More modern determinations of the viscosities of gases have usually been made by the method of transpiration. Thus Lord Rayleigh determined the viscosities of helium and argon by Graham's method in 1896; and his results were taken into consideration by Lord Kelvin, who reviewed the aid given by the kinetic theory of gases towards the estimation of molecular magnitudes over many years, and finally published them in the *Baltimore Lectures*, in 1904. Kelvin's estimate of Loschmidt's number, based on kinetic theory, gave a value of the order of 10^{20}, which is some five times as great as that obtained by Maxwell in 1873.

The celebrated equation of van der Waals, $(p+a/v^2)(v-b)=RT$, which was formulated by him in 1873 to explain the departure shown by actual gases from the simple gas laws, which are only strictly applicable to perfect gases, has been applied to the determination of Loschmidt's number. In the van der Waals equation, the constant b represents the sphere of influence of a molecule, and its value is four times the actual volume of the molecule. Van der Waals showed that the value of b for any particular gas can be determined from the critical constants, being equal to three times the critical volume, and also from the extent of its departure from Boyle's law, and actual values for b were calculated by him for several gases from the experimental results of Regnault and of Cailletet. These were employed by O. E. Meyer in his estimations of molecular diameters and mean free paths, and thus provided additional support to the information obtained from studies of experimental results on the viscosity and diffusivity of gases.

Another approach towards the determination of molecular magnitudes in gases is by measurements of refractivity and of dielectric constants; this is connected, though less obviously than the methods previously considered, with the kinetic theory. In 1872 it was shown by Stefan that the smaller the refractivity of a gas, the larger must be its molecular free path, or in other words, that the product of these two quantities must be constant. Now according to Maxwell's electromagnetic theory of light, the refractive index of a substance must be equal to the square root of its dielectric constant, and this important relation was verified experimentally by Boltzmann in 1875. In terms of the Clausius-Mossotti theory of dielectrics, the fraction $\frac{K-1}{K+2}$, where K denotes the dielectric constant, should represent the fraction of the total volume of a gas, which is actually occupied by the molecules, and accordingly be equal to $\frac{1}{4}b$. Determinations made in this way have given values of b for several gases, which are of the same order of magnitude as those obtained from their other properties; but it must be added that the agreement is by no means close.

The question how far it is possible to obtain *accurate* values of Loschmidt's number, as distinct from estimates of the order of magnitude of this constant, from considerations based on the kinetic theory of gases is complicated by the assumptions on which much of that theory rests. In particular, classical kinetic theory as developed by Clausius and Maxwell regarded the molecules of a gas as hard elastic spheres, and took little or no account of their specific properties. But in the latter years of the nineteenth century the necessity for a more 'chemical' outlook on the molecules began to be recognized. Thus in 1879 Lothar Meyer began a series of investigations on the viscosity of the vapours of a number of organic compounds by the transpiration method at temperatures considerably above their boiling-points, and was able to establish the principle that the coefficient of viscosity was independent of the temperature. In 1893 Sutherland devised a formula showing that the viscosity of a gas is proportional to $T^{\frac{3}{2}}$, where T is the absolute temperature. This formula, though not perfect, has met with considerable success when tested experimentally. Coming to more modern times, an important theoretical paper was published by Reinganum in 1909 in which he showed that an expression $L^3x^2 =$ a constant (L being the mean free path and x the volume actually occupied by the molecules), which had appeared in successive editions of Nernst's *Theoretische Chemie* and which had been used in 1908 for a calculation of Loschmidt's number by Sirk, required correction. Reinganum gave special attention to viscosity, and in 1910 Rappenecker, working under his direction, investigated anew the effect of temperature on the viscosity coefficients of vapours using the transpiration method. Rappenecker claimed that the improved formula which he introduced provided the means of calculating molecular volumes of 'Gase und Dämpfe von Stickstoff bis Benzol' accurately, and was able to show that a satisfactory value for Loschmidt's number followed accordingly. The value for this constant according to the considerations advanced by Reinganum and Rappenecker was $2{\cdot}77 \times 10^{19}$, a figure, which as will be seen in what follows, is remarkably close to determinations which have been derived from altogether different methods.

In 1899 Lord Rayleigh pointed out the possibility of estimating the number of molecules in a given volume of a gas by their scattering action on light. This was an outcome of his well-known theory of the blue colour of the sky, first published in 1871, according to which the proportion of scattered light to incident light is inversely proportional to the fourth power of the wave-length. If monochromatic light is diffracted, there is no difference in colour between the scattered light and the incident light; but, having regard to the difference in wave-length between the constituents of the visible spectrum, the fraction of scattered light for the violet waves must be about seven times as great as for the red waves. In his 1899 paper Lord Rayleigh pointed out that an inferior limit to the value of Loschmidt's number could be obtained in this way, on the assumption that the scattering was due *solely* to gaseous molecules; but he was careful to add that such a value would be vitiated by any scattering due to the presence of dust particles. This subject was analysed at length by Lord Kelvin in the *Baltimore Lectures*. He pointed out that a considerable fraction of the scattering of light must be due to dust particles, and this fraction was definitely greater than that due to the action of gaseous molecules. In elaborating his ideas, Kelvin took account of some observations made by Aitken in 1892 and 1893 on the number of dust particles in the lower regions of the atmosphere at various places, and particularly of observations made in 1901 by Majorana on Mount Etna, and by Sella on Monte Rosa, on the ratio of the brightness of the surface of the sun to the brightness of the sky. Kelvin recognized the difficulty which would arise from the comparison of two lights of different colours, but overcame this by giving consideration to some experiments carried out in 1900 and 1901 by Zettwuch, who made a comparison between prismatically analysed light from the sky and direct sunlight, reduced by passage through a narrow slit and also prismatically analysed. Taking the various factors into consideration Kelvin gave a value of $2{\cdot}47 \times 10^{19}$ for his estimate of Loschmidt's number.

An observation made in 1827 by the botanist Brown was destined some eighty years later to provide one of the most reliable methods for evaluating the Loschmidt number. Brown had observed that, when a drop of water containing minute solid particles in suspension was examined under a microscope, the particles were never stationary, but endowed with incessant motion. This phenomenon soon came to be known as the *Brownian movement*, but many years elapsed before it became the subject of serious study by physicists. Ideas of explaining the Brownian movement on the basis of some form of molecular agitation gradually began to be forthcoming, and in 1863 Wiener made a noteworthy approach towards a satisfactory explanation. In 1877 an important paper entitled *Thermodynamic origin of Brownian movement* was published by Father Delsaulx; he understood clearly that the Brownian movement is due to molecular heat agitation, and he seemed to grasp the significance of the statistical aspect of the second law of thermodynamics. The date of this paper is of interest, because there were references to the action of the Crookes radiometer, from which it was evident that the author had grasped the idea that molecular impact in highly rarefied gases would be made observable when the dimensions of the apparatus were comparable with those of the mean molecular free path. The origin of the radiometer is an interesting example of a research having an outcome altogether different from its original objective. In 1873 Crookes carried out a most elaborate investigation on the atomic weight of thallium, in which the weighings were made directly *in vacuo* with a special balance. Having observed that the behaviour of the balance was somewhat puzzling when operating in a high vacuum, Crookes directed his attention to phenomena in highly rarefied gases, and the radiometer was devised very shortly afterwards. Father Delsaulx's paper received less attention than it deserved, but an exposition due to Gouy in 1888 received general acceptance.

Little progress was made in the study of the Brownian movement until the early years of the twentieth century. In 1905 Einstein investigated the subject mathematically on the basis of the kinetic theory, and a similar theoretical study was made by Smoluchowski in the following year. The idea of applying studies on the Brownian movement with the object of evaluating Loschmidt's number was begun by Perrin in 1908. Before considering this work in detail, it should be noted that Perrin expressed his results in terms of a different unit, which he called Avogadro's number or constant. This unit, which soon came into general use, is defined as the number of molecules in one gramme-molecular volume (namely, 22·4 litres) of a gas at normal temperature and pressure. As the unit of volume of the Loschmidt number is 1 $cm.^3$, it is clear that the value of Avogadro's constant must be 22,400 times that of Loschmidt's number. In using the term 'Avogadro's number', it should be remembered that Avogadro formulated his well-known hypothesis in 1811; but beyond showing that it provided the means of establishing the molecular formulae of gases and showing that their molecular weights are proportional to their densities, he did not enter into any questions of actually *counting* molecules. As has been shown above, the first steps in this direction were taken by

Loschmidt in 1865. Apart, therefore, from the difference in actual numerical value between the two constants, there is a somewhat different historical significance associated with the names assigned to them.

Perrin's approach to the problems of the Brownian movement appears to have been directed primarily to the testing of the question whether the gas laws, which had been shown by van't Hoff in 1885 to be valid for dilute solutions, would still be applicable to emulsions of particles of very high molecular weight. Another object which he had in view was to obtain experimental verification of the laws of the Brownian movement. For this purpose the choice of a suitable colloid was of great importance. After unsuccessful experiments with colloidal solutions of inorganic substances, such as arsenious sulphide, Perrin found that emulsions prepared from certain resins, particularly gamboge, by dissolving the substance in alcohol and precipitating it by adding water yielded very suitable emulsions. By elaborate fractional centrifuging he was able to obtain emulsions containing grains of very nearly uniform size. His earlier experiments were concerned with the statistical distribution of the particles when sedimentation had reached equilibrium, brought about between the downward trend of the particles under the influence of gravity and the molecular agitation which gives rise to the Brownian movement. The idea was to ascertain whether the statistical distribution of the particles at different heights would follow the same law as that which governs the diminution of atmospheric pressure with height above the surface of the Earth. Halley in 1686 formulated the theorem that if the air is at a constant temperature the pressure diminished in geometrical progression as the height increases in arithmetical progression. It is obvious that the height which is necessary for the realization of a definite fractional diminution of the pressure of any particular gas will be inversely proportional to the density of the gas. By working with emulsions of gamboge, a substance of extremely high molecular weight, Perrin was able to make direct counts of the number of gamboge particles in a given volume of liquid at different small heights—of the order of a fraction of a millimetre—and succeeded in obtaining a very satisfactory confirmation of Halley's law. Having determined the densities of the particles and of the suspending liquid, he was enabled to calculate Avogadro's number. With the aid of his pupils, Perrin extended his experiments in several directions, such as varying the size and nature of the grains and the density of the suspending liquid, but it was found that the values of Avogadro's number remained constant within narrow limits, namely, between $6 \cdot 5 \times 10^{23}$ and $7 \cdot 2 \times 10^{23}$. If the values obtained for Loschmidt's number by Maxwell, which was based on the kinetic theory of gases, and by Lord Kelvin, which was obtained from the work of Lord Rayleigh and others on the scattering of light, are expressed in terms of Avogadro's unit, the figures are $4 \cdot 3 \times 10^{23}$ and $5 \cdot 5 \times 10^{23}$ respectively. The surprisingly close agreement of results obtained by such widely different considerations afford a remarkably convincing demonstration of what Perrin aptly described as *molecular reality* and of Avogadro's number as one of the constants of nature.

Perrin did not restrict his experimental studies on the Brownian movement to measurements of the statistical distribution of particles in emulsions. With the aid of his pupils, he investigated the translatory and rotatory movements of the colloidal particles, and also carried out measurements on their rates of diffusion. The work involved considerable experimental difficulties; nevertheless, satisfactory verification of some theoretical ideas due to Einstein was obtained, and the values of Avogadro's constant thus calculated varied between $6 \cdot 5 \times 10^{23}$ and $6 \cdot 9 \times 10^{23}$.

Subsequent to Perrin's original work, the study of the Brownian movement has been taken up by a number of other investigators. For the purpose of this book it is not necessary to consider these in detail, but a brief reference must be made to some experiments made by Westgren, working under the direction of Svedberg in 1915. Westgren employed hydrosols of selenium, gold and mercury, and measured the sedimentation equilibria and the rates of fall of the particles: Einstein's formula for the diffusion of colloidal particles was shown to be valid. Westgren's results for Avogadro's constant were somewhat lower than those obtained by Perrin, namely, $6{\cdot}05 \times 10^{23}$, with an uncertainty of the order of $\pm 0{\cdot}03 \times 10^{23}$, but are in much better agreement with other modern methods for determining this magnitude.

The Brownian movement has also been investigated in gases; but no serious quantitative work was done on the subject until 1908 when Maurice de Broglie began some experiments using the dust obtained from spark discharges between metallic electrodes, which he subjected to an electric field. His object was to determine the value of the charge on the particles. In the following year, but using tobacco smoke on which minute droplets of water were condensed instead of the metallic particles, he succeeded in measuring the rate of movement of the particles in an electric field, and was thus able to obtain values for the product Ne, N being Avogadro's constant and e the fundamental unit of electric charge. By taking Perrin's value for N, he was able to calculate e, for which he obtained a figure of $4{\cdot}5 \times 10^{-10}$ electrostatic unit. This constant had been previously determined by other methods: first, Townsend in 1897 showed that the charge on a gaseous ion is equal to the charge carried by a hydrogen atom in electrolysis, for which he obtained values for e averaging 3×10^{-10}; in the following year J. J. Thomson, using C. T. R. Wilson's method of causing condensation of moisture in air by ions generated by X-rays, obtained values for e approximating to 7×10^{-10}; in a later paper, published in 1903, using radium as the ionizing agency, Thomson gave a more accurate value for e, namely, $3{\cdot}4 \times 10^{-10}$.

In 1909 it was pointed out that the 'classical' determinations of the fundamental unit of electric charge by Townsend and by J. J. Thomson were limited as regards accuracy by two fundamental difficulties. One of these concerns the limitations of a law, derived theoretically by Stokes in 1850 concerning the rate of flow of a sphere moving slowly through a viscous fluid, as applicable to the rate of fall of water droplets through air under the influence of gravity. The other source of error arises in consequence of evaporation from the droplets during the fall of the cloud, and Millikan accordingly devised means for eliminating these two sources of error. The difficulty due to the possible failure of Stokes's law was overcome by holding the cloud in a stationary position by an electrical field sufficiently strong to prevent it from falling under the influence of gravity. This was termed the balanced drop method. The error due to evaporation from the aqueous mists was avoided by using oil droplets. These improvements enabled Millikan to investigate *single* drops, and thus not only to obtain an accurate value for the fundamental electric charge, but also to establish a proof that electrons, however produced, have all exactly the *same* charge, not the statistical mean of charges having divergent values. The value which Millikan assigned to this charge in 1913 was $4{\cdot}774 \times 10^{-10}$ electrostatic unit.

The development of the oil-drop method was extended in 1911 by Fletcher under Millikan's direction to investigate the Brownian movements of individual droplets in gases. As the displacements are considerably greater than in liquids, this improvement in experimental technique has provided the means for obtaining accurate values for Avogadro's constant. The Einstein equation for displacements was again verified, and, in later experiments, Fletcher in 1914 assigned a value of $6{\cdot}03 \times 10^{23}$ for that number. Other modern experimentalists have obtained similar figures, the differences between which have not gone beyond the second decimal place. Perrin's contention in regarding Avogadro's number as one of the constants of nature has thus been amply justified.

An altogether different approach towards solving the nature of individual atoms and thus a new step towards obtaining means of counting them was provided by studies on radioactive phenomena. As much of this work was carried out at the time that Perrin was making his experiments with gamboge emulsions, it is of great historical importance. In 1903 Crookes had obtained evidence of the discontinuous structure of α-rays by observing their scintillating effect on phosphorescent zinc sulphide, and he devised an instrument, which he termed a spinthariscope, consisting of a screen of this substance placed at a short distance from a speck of a radium compound and provided with a lens for viewing the effect. In 1908 Regener worked out the best conditions for counting the scintillations, using polonium as the source of radiation, as this element gives α-rays only. In the same year Rutherford and Geiger carried out their celebrated experiments to prove the identity of the α-particle and the helium atom. By an adaptation of a method, due to Townsend, of producing fresh ions by collision in a gas already ionized, they were able to follow the entry of individual α-particles from a radioactive source into an ionization chamber. Rutherford and Geiger found that the number of α-particles, counted by the scintillation method, was the same as the number of those particles incident on the screen as shown by the ionization method. The values of Avogadro's number derived from these considerations was $6{\cdot}2 \times 10^{23}$. An almost identical value for this constant was obtained in 1911 by Rutherford and Boltwood from considerations based on the rate of production of helium from radium. It will be noted that this value approaches more closely to those obtained by later studies on the Brownian movement than to the results obtained by Perrin.

The experiments on the spreading of oil on the surface of water, which were begun by Lord Rayleigh in 1890, have been extended in many directions by others. In 1891 Fräulein Pockels found that surface films could be handled by pushing them in front of strips or barriers, and in 1899 Rayleigh confirmed this work, and also showed that there was a fall in the surface tension when the film was of unimolecular thickness. Advances of outstanding importance were made in 1917 by Langmuir, who showed that the capacity for spreading was very much determined by the chemical nature of the substances concerned; in particular, he showed that the presence of polar groupings in the molecules, such as carboxyl groups, was of primary importance. The method consisted in dissolving a known weight of the substances in a volatile solvent such as benzene, placing a drop of the solution on water, and leaving the solvent to evaporate. The thickness of the monolayer was obtainable from the weight of the drop, the specific gravity of the substance, and the area of the film on the surface of the water. At an early stage of the work, Langmuir and others showed that the presence of unsaturated linkages in the middle of a fatty acid chain caused the films to expand more readily than films with saturated chains of similar length. He attributed this to the double bonds in the molecule exerting an attractive action on the water, since unsaturated hydrocarbons are more soluble in water than the corresponding saturated compounds. The carboxyl group of a fatty acid with a long chain, such as palmitic acid, may be regarded as the water-soluble constituent of the molecule, and is accordingly attracted by the water in a downward direction, the remainder of the molecule floating upwards and thus giving rise to a film on the surface. Hydrocarbon oils, such as paraffins, have very little spreading power; when placed on water, they tend to form isolated droplets. In this connexion it is interesting to note that it has long been known that the calming of waves by oil is effected much more efficiently by the use of fish oils than by mineral oils.

The properties of soap solutions—colloidal electrolytes, as they have frequently been termed—have been the subject of a great number of investigations. In 1924 Lecomte du Noüy carried out a very elaborate series of determinations of the surface tension of dilute solutions of sodium oleate,

$$CH_3.(CH_2)_7.CH:CH.(CH_2)_7.CO_2Na,$$

from which he obtained an accurate value for Avogadro's constant. Starting with a clear solution, having an initial concentration of 1 part per 1000, du Noüy found well-defined minima of surface tensions at dilutions of 1/750,000, 1/1,220,000 and 1/1,390,000. He attributed these minima to three different orientations of single molecules in the surface layer, the first being due to the vertical, the second to the horizontal orientation, and the third to a rotation of 90° of these molecules around the horizontal axis. It may be added that du Noüy remarked that this explanation was not in agreement with generally accepted adsorption theories. Nevertheless, he went on to calculate the thickness of the monolayers corresponding to the three critical dilutions. Regarding the molecule of sodium oleate as a rectangular parallelepiped he regarded its dimensions as 12×10^{-8}, $7{\cdot}56 \times 10^{-8}$ and $6{\cdot}64 \times 10^{-8}$ cm. By taking the product of these numbers and multiplying by 0·821 (the specific gravity of sodium oleate), the mass of the molecule of the compound is $506{\cdot}91 \times 10^{-24}$ gramme. The molecular weight of sodium oleate is 304·55, and if this number is divided by the mass of the molecule, the resulting quotient is du Noüy's value, namely $6{\cdot}004 \times 10^{23}$, for Avogadro's constant.

The importance of studies on capillarity as a means for obtaining information regarding the limits of material divisibility is of much historical interest. At the beginning of the nineteenth century this subject was approached from very different angles by Laplace and by Young, and it may be said that the researches of the latter laid the foundations of the modern studies on the subject. The classical investigations of Lord Rayleigh in 1890 on the spreading of oil films on water, followed by Langmuir's work, nearly thirty years later, on relations between spreading power and molecular constitution, enabled du Noüy in 1924 to elaborate a method by which he obtained a value for the Avogadro constant in remarkably close agreement with the best values derived from altogether different considerations.

REFERENCES

T. Young. On the cohesion of fluids. *Collected Works*, vol. I, p. 461.

Lord Kelvin. *Baltimore Lectures on Molecular Dynamics and the Wave Theory of Light*. Lecture XVII. Cambridge, 1904.

Lord Rayleigh. *Scientific Papers*. Six volumes. Cambridge, 1899–1920.

T. Graham. *Chemical and Physical Researches*. Edinburgh, 1876.

J. Loschmidt. Zur Grosse der Luftmolecüle. *Wiener Sitzungsberichte*, 1865, Band LII, 2, S. 395.

J. Delsaulx, S.J. Thermodynamic origin of Brownian Movement. *Trans. Roy. Micr. Soc.* (*Monthly Micr. J.*, July 1877).

O. E. Meyer. *Die Kinetische Theorie der Gase*. Zweite umgearbeitete Auflage, Breslau, 1899. English translation by R. E. Baynes.

J. Clerk Maxwell. *Scientific Papers*, vol. II. Cambridge.

J. Perrin. *Brownian Movement and Molecular Reality*. Translated by F. Soddy. London, 1910.

J. Perrin. *Atoms*. Translated by D. Ll. Hammick. London, 1920.

Arne Westgren. Untersuchungen über die brownsche Bewegung, besonders als Mittel zur Bestimmung der Avogadroschen Konstant. Dissertation, Uppsala, 1915.

K. Rappenecker. Über die Reibungskoeffizienten von Dämpfen und ihre Abhängigkeit von der Temperatur. *Z. Phys. Chem.* 1910, vol. LXXII, p. 695.

E. RUTHERFORD. *Radioactive Substances and their Radiations.* Cambridge, 1913.

M. REINGANUM. Molekulare Dimensionen auf Grund der kinetischen Gastheorie. *Ann. Phys., Lpz.*, 1909 (4), vol. XXVIII, p. 142.

R. A. MILLIKAN. *Electrons.* Cambridge, 1936.

P. LECOMTE DU NOÜY. *Surface Equilibria of Biological and Organic Colloids.* American Chemical Society Monograph Series, no. 27, 1926.

N. K. ADAM. *The Physics and Chemistry of Surfaces.* Oxford. First edition, 1930. Third edition, 1941.

S. VIRGO. Loschmidt's Number. *Science Progress*, 1933, vol. CVIII, p. 634.

J. R. PARTINGTON. *An Advanced Treatise on Physical Chemistry*, vol. I. *The Fundamental Properties of Gases.* London, 1949.

CHAPTER VI

ANALYTICAL CHEMISTRY

INORGANIC ANALYSIS

There is general agreement among historians that the early beginnings of chemistry were largely founded on a metallurgical basis, and that a certain amount of knowledge of a few metals, particularly of the precious metals gold and silver, existed in very early times. The story of the discovery by Archimedes (212 B.C.) of the fraud perpetrated by a goldsmith in partially substituting silver for gold in a crown ordered by King Hiero of Syracuse is well authenticated, and the principle of the method which he devised—the determination of specific gravity—has become of immense practical value in many directions. The processes of assaying precious metals by cupellation, and of testing their degree of fineness by examination of the streak left on a piece of rock, later known as a 'touchstone', when a fragment of the metal is drawn over the surface, are of very ancient date. Geber, described by more than one writer as the greatest of the Arabian alchemists, who lived in the eighth century A.D., knew that the precious metals resist oxidation when heated in air, whereas lead increases in weight when subjected to this treatment. Indeed, Geber has left descriptions of the method of obtaining gold and silver by cupellation which bear comparison with the dry methods of assaying these metals at the present time. The action of nitric acid in 'parting' alloys of gold and silver was also known to Geber, but, according to Roberts-Austen, the first official mention of its use in assaying was in 1343 in the work of the French Mint. The use of the balance in assaying has been practised for centuries; and again to quote Roberts-Austen 'the use of the balance in very early times, for the purpose of assay, absolutely demolishes the claim of quantitative chemistry to be considered of comparatively modern origin'.

As chemistry gradually evolved from alchemy, and as experimenters became familiar with an increasing number of substances, means for their recognition and classification were gradually evolved. In the eighteenth century, a period of great literary and scientific activity, some methods of considerable value in chemical analysis, both qualitative and quantitative, were devised. At the beginning of that century, Newton assumed the office of Master of the Mint, having occupied the office of Warden some three years previously.* At the outset he rapidly mastered the technique of assaying with the object of directing the work of his assistants, but he appears to have had no great regard for metallurgy as a science; indeed, he remarked that 'the assaymaster acts only as a manual artificer', and again, 'refining and assaying are manual trades'. Of greater interest are the researches of those who devoted their attention to experimental work in pure chemistry, and thereby devised analytical methods in the course of their investigations. Thus Black in his work on *magnesia alba*, which was published in 1755, worked out a gravimetric method for estimating the *fixed air* liberated from a carbonate by the action of heat or of an acid. Some eleven years later Cavendish determined the carbon dioxide displaced in reactions of this kind by the method of loss of weight. Qualitative analysis of minerals with the aid of the blowpipe appears to have originated with Cronstedt, and shortly afterwards was greatly extended by Bergman, who published a work entitled *De tubo ferruminatorio* in 1779. The value of the blowpipe as a means of obtaining information regarding the qualitative composition of minerals was thoroughly recognized by Berzelius, who published a book on the subject, an English translation of which appeared in 1822, entitled *The Use of the Blowpipe in Chemical Analysis and in the Examination of Minerals*. This work contains minute directions for carrying out experiments of this kind, together with clear descriptions of the behaviour of some thirty substances according as they are heated in the oxidizing flame or in the reducing flame in the presence of various fluxes, such as sodium carbonate, borax and microcosmic salt. The blowpipes in use at that time were usually operated in conjunction with candle flames or with the flame of an oil lamp; but spirit lamps were commonly used for

* *Newton at the Mint*, by Sir John Craig, Cambridge, 1946.

observing the effect of heat upon substances in glass tubes; indeed, in numerous chemical operations the spirit lamp was very generally employed as a source of heat until the invention of the well-known Bunsen burner about the year 1855.

Bunsen showed that most of the dry reactions of inorganic substances, which were effected with the aid of the blowpipe, could be carried out directly in the flame of his burner by careful attention to placing the substance under examination in the right zone of the flame according as an oxidizing or reducing action is required. Although analysis by dry methods was brought to a high degree of refinement by Bunsen, it is seldom employed in so elaborate a manner at the present time. Nevertheless, it is generally recognized by modern analysts that a preliminary examination of a substance by dry methods, particularly by the aid of borax bead tests and flame colorations, is of much value in modifying or even determining subsequent procedure.

The development of inorganic analysis, both qualitative and quantitative, was intimately connected with the study of minerals, and the influence of Berzelius and of some of his immediate followers—Rose, for example—extending from the very early years of the nineteenth century to much later times was far-reaching. The experimental work was difficult, often very difficult, but the skill shown in devising methods for the detection, separation and gravimetric determination of the elements, including some described by certain modern writers as 'rare' elements, had a profound influence on the whole subsequent development of inorganic chemistry. An important practical *Handbuch der analytischen Chemie* by Rose in two volumes, one qualitative and the other quantitative, first appeared in 1829, and by 1834 had reached a third edition. Even at that early date descriptions are to be found of operations which are still in use. These include the familiar division of the metals into analytical groups, the use of suspensions of barium carbonate for effecting the separation of the very weakly basic hydroxides from the less weakly basic ones, the use of succinic acid for effecting the separation of iron from manganese, and the use of tartaric acid for avoiding the precipitation of certain metals in alkaline solution. The *Handbuch* of Rose, after passing through several editions, appeared in an enlarged and revised form with the title of *Ausführliches Handbuch der analytischen Chemie* in 1851, and a number of references to the valuable methods there described are to be found in Mellor's *Treatise on Quantitative Inorganic Analysis*, which was first published in 1913. The standard work on *Applied Inorganic Analysis* by Hillebrand and Lundell, which appeared in 1929, contains a remarkable tribute to 'the great workers in chemistry of the earlier half of the nineteenth century, and for the painstaking care and accuracy of Berzelius, Wöhler and others, the mineralogists and geologists of to-day have reason to be thankful. Considering the limited facilities at their disposal in the way of laboratory equipment and quality of reagents, the general excellence of their work is little short of marvellous.'

As is well known, the analysis of minerals resulted in the discovery of some previously unknown elements, and this soon led to the determination of their atomic weights as well as to the revision of those of elements already known. Some of the values obtained by older workers will bear comparison with those obtained by more modern investigators, and a very interesting example is to be found in the case of boron. In 1822 Berzelius determined the water of crystallization in borax from which he obtained a value for the atomic weight of 11·08. Two years later he converted anhydrous borax into sodium sulphate, from which a figure of 11·0 was obtained. In 1893 Ramsay and Aston, using the original method of Berzelius, gave a value of 10·94. They also converted anhydrous borax into sodium chloride by repeated evaporation with hydrochloric acid and methyl alcohol, which was really an adaptation of a method used by Penny in 1839 by which he obtained results of great accuracy for several equivalent numbers, and thus obtained a figure of 10·96. Modern atomic weight determinations are nearly always made by the silver-halide methods elaborated chiefly by Stas and by Richards, and a redetermination of the atomic weight of boron by Briscoe and Robinson in 1925, in which the ratio of boron trichloride to silver was used on minerals containing the element obtained from widely different parts of the world, gave values of the atomic weight between 10·82 and 10·84.

A highly interesting example of the value of research in inorganic analysis is to be found in the chemistry of niobium and tantalum, the oxides of which are sometimes known as the earth-acids in order to contrast them with those of the rare earths which are strongly basic. Many compounds of niobium and tantalum are of ill-defined composition, and most of them show a marked tendency to undergo hydrolysis and to give rise to colloidal precipitates. In 1801 Hatchett analysed the mineral columbite and obtained evidence of the existence of a new element which was then termed columbium, and in the following year Eckeberg claimed to have discovered an element which he called tantalum. But, as Schoeller has pointed out, neither Hatchett nor Eckeberg was aware of the precise nature of the earth-acids, which were undoubtedly mixtures; it is therefore an error to ascribe the discovery of columbium, now usually termed niobium, to the former investigator, or of that of tantalum to the latter. Between 1809 and 1853 these earth-acids were the subject of investigation by Wollaston, Berzelius, Wöhler and Rose, and the results of their several labours appeared to indicate the existence of two distinct elements, though not one of them succeeded in separating the two earth-acids in a state of even approximate purity. No real progress was made until the year 1865 when Marignac was able to characterize niobium and tantalum as separate, though closely similar, elements. He also determined the composition of their alkali salts and complex fluorides and assigned correct formulae to them based on the quinquevalency of the two elements, which was established at about the same time by Sainte-Claire Deville and Troost from determinations of the vapour densities of the anhydrous chlorides. Marignac devised a method of separating the two earth-acids, which, though not perfect, was a marked advance on anything which had been accomplished hitherto. The process was based on the much greater solubility of potassium oxyfluoroniobate, K_2NbOF_5, as compared with that of potassium fluorotantalate, K_2TaF_7. Tantalum is more basic than niobium, and the resulting complex salt is not perceptibly hydrolysed under the working conditions. Determinations of the atomic weights of the two elements by Marignac, in which various ratios were used, yielded values of 94·0 for niobium and 182·0 for tantalum. Having regard to the dates at which these atomic weights were determined—1865 and 1866—the results are in reasonably good agreement with the modern values—92·91 and 180·88 respectively.

The analytical chemistry of niobium and tantalum was greatly advanced as a result of the researches of Schoeller and his collaborators since 1921. In 1925 they showed that tannin was a valuable precipitant for the earth-acids from their solutions in certain weak acids, or of their salts, particularly in tartrate and in oxalate solutions, the last named being used for separating niobium and tantalum from each other. Admittedly the chemistry of these operations is highly obscure. On this subject little can be said beyond recognizing—what had been known long before—that tartrates readily form complex ions with numerous metallic hydroxides which thereby prevent their precipitation by alkalis; but in what manner tannin can effect precipitation from complex niobo-oxalates and niobo-tartrates is much more difficult to follow. The precipitates have been described, no doubt correctly, as adsorption complexes, as opposed to compounds of definite stoichiometrical composition. The separation of the two earth-acids from each other by a method based on the differential stability of oxalotantalic and oxaloniobic acids in the presence of tannin in slightly acid solution was described in detail by Schoeller in 1930. Fractional precipitation was necessary, but could be followed by the difference in colour of the two adsorption products, that of tantalum being yellow, while the niobium complex is red. There can be no doubt that this series of investigations constitutes a major advance in modern analytical chemistry.

The progress in analysis since the time of Berzelius is to be attributed to more than one cause, but particularly to the discovery of new reactions and to the introduction of new reagents, especially organic compounds, many of which are highly sensitive. Microchemistry as such is no new subject. Not infrequently has it happened that some chemical change, such as the production of some visible effect such as a striking colour, has resulted first in its application as a qualitative test and sometimes afterwards in its elaboration into a colorimetric or gravimetric method for quantitative work. A few examples may be quoted by way of illustration.

The celebrated Marsh test for arsenic was devised by its discoverer in 1836, and has been the subject of numerous investigations since that time with the object of ascertaining its sensitiveness and of developing it quantitatively. In 1901 Wanklyn published a monograph on arsenic in which the value as well as the few limitations of this test were discussed in detail. Wanklyn had no hesitation in describing the Marsh test as superior to another test devised by Reinsch in 1842. The test is of great importance in forensic work; and for quantitative purposes, methods have been devised depending on comparison of the arsenical mirrors obtained when the arsine is decomposed by heat with those obtained under parallel conditions from a standard solution containing arsenic, and also depending on the reducing action of the gas upon silver nitrate.

It has long been known that curious complex compounds can be obtained by the action of ammonia on mercuric salts, and the well-known yellow product which is formed by the action of traces of ammonia on an alkaline solution of potassium mercuric iodide appears to have been discovered by Nessler in 1856. The compound which is formed is known as the iodide of Millon's base, and is now formulated as $[OHg_2NH_2]I$. For the purpose of determining traces of ammonia salts in water colorimetrically, the Nessler reagent has been found of the greatest value, but special directions are necessary for preparing the solution in order to obtain reliable quantitative results.

The production of an intense yellow colour when hydrogen peroxide is added to an acidified solution of a titanium salt appears to have been first observed by Schönn in 1869, and in 1882 Weller elaborated a colorimetric method for the determination of titanium based on this reaction. The value of the method for determining small quantities of titanium has since been fully recognized. The production of the colour was formerly attributed to oxidation of the titanium to the sexivalent condition, corresponding to the oxide TiO_3, since reducing agents destroy the colour, but of late it has been regarded as due to the formation of a complex acid to which the formula $H_2[TiO_2(SO_4)_2]$ has been assigned. In this, as in other colorimetric methods, attention has to be given to conditions, and especially to securing the absence of substances other than the one to be determined, which might give rise to similar colours. Now many substances which can exist in more than one stage of oxidation are liable to exhibit colours; thus vanadium gives rise to an orange-coloured peroxide derivative under similar conditions to the colour produced by titanium. An ingenious method for determining the two elements colorimetrically was devised by Mellor in 1912. Fenton in 1908 had shown that dihydroxymaleic acid produced a strong orange-yellow colour with titanium compounds, which he estimated to be 'some fifteen to twenty times as delicate as the hydrogen peroxide test' and 'it is not given by vanadium'. Mellor's method for estimating the two elements together consisted in dividing the very dilute acidified solution into two parts, treating one with hydrogen peroxide and the other with Fenton's acid, and making the necessary observations with the aid of a colorimeter.

The production of an intense scarlet colour or precipitate by adding an alcoholic solution of dimethylglyoxime to an ammoniacal solution of a nickel salt was observed by Tschugaeff in 1905. In the following year it was applied in qualitative analysis by Kraut, and one year later by Brunck in gravimetric analysis. A considerable literature on this subject has arisen since that time, and the method has been recognized generally as of great value—it is, indeed, regularly used for the determination of the element in nickel steels. The scarlet compound is regarded as a co-ordination compound of nickel to which the formula

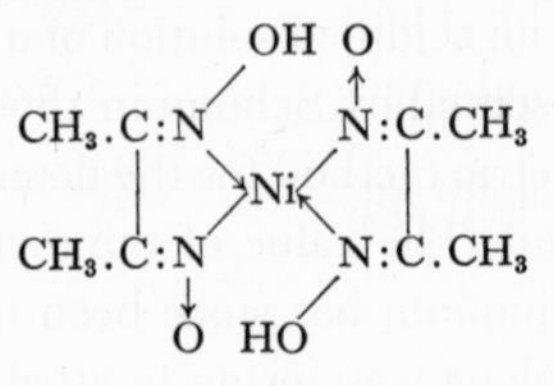

has been assigned.

In a number of directions a physico-chemical approach to various operations, which have long been practised in chemical analysis, has provided the means of obtaining a better understanding of their mode of action, and sometimes of effecting improvements on them. This has been particularly evident with regard to operations in which the degree of acidity is concerned. Reference to the directions for effecting certain separations, as set forth by the older experimenters, has disclosed what may fairly be described as real craftsmanship; and when these descriptions are considered in the light of modern views, it is frequently surprising how closely they correspond to what might have been expected from an approach directed from a more developed theoretical background. Thus the older methods for effecting the precipitation of certain metallic hydroxides while leaving others in solution, by various devices for limiting the precipitating powers of the basic substances which are added, are now discussed in terms of precipitating within the appropriate limits of hydrogen-ion concentration. The use of suspensions of carbonates or oxides in work of this kind, recommended by the older analysts, has received favourable notice by modern writers, of whom mention should be made of Hillebrand and Lundell. These authors have given careful attention to the pH values of a number of suspensions of carbonates and oxides and have correlated these values with the pH ranges between which certain hydroxides are and others are not precipitated, so as to indicate which are most suitable for effecting any particular separation. This subject has also been studied by a potentiometric titration method by Britton in 1925. Much assistance in this kind of work has also resulted from knowledge of the pH range of indicators, a subject to which much attention has been given in modern times.

VOLUMETRIC ANALYSIS

The earliest recorded example of the measurement of alkalinity is to be found in a work on bleaching by Home, published in 1756, in which the 'value' of pearl ashes (potassium carbonate) was estimated by counting the number of teaspoonfuls of dilute nitric acid which were required to be added until effervescence ceased. In 1806 Descroizilles estimated acids and alkalis by noting the volume of one liquid required to neutralize the other, neutrality being determined by using an infusion of violets to serve as an indicator. A few other examples of experiments of a similar kind are to be found in the works of others. The foundations of volumetric analysis, however, as generally understood, were undoubtedly laid between 1824 and 1832 by Gay-Lussac. His first experiments were concerned with the determination of the value of bleaching powder by employing its decolorizing action on a solution of indigo. He also worked on the quantitative neutralization of acid by alkalis. But his most important contribution to this branch of analysis was published in 1832 under the title *Instructions sur l'essai des matières d'argent par la voie humide*. Gay-Lussac's method of adding a solution of sodium chloride to a solution of silver dissolved in nitric acid, under strictly specified conditions of working, and ascertaining when precipitation no longer takes place, constitutes the 'wet' assay of silver; it has been regularly practised, with only minor modifications, in most mints ever since that time. Some twenty years after Gay-Lussac devised the method, Mulder investigated the conditions in the vicinity of the equivalence point, when the solution is saturated with silver chloride, the solubility of which though very small is nevertheless perceptible, and laid down the conditions for working the method to the best advantage.

Recognition of the value of volumetric methods was shown by the appearance of practical books on the subject. Mohr's *Lehrbuch der chemisch-analytischen Titriermethode* was published in 1855, and in 1863 was followed by the publication of Sutton's *Systematic Handbook of Volumetric Analysis*. Both works appeared at various later dates in subsequent editions. On the experimental side Mohr made a useful contribution by introducing potassium chromate as an indicator for titrating neutral chlorides by silver nitrate. The method is much more rapid than the original procedure of Gay-Lussac, but of an inferior degree of accuracy. In 1874 an important method for determining silver in acid solution by titration with ammonium or potassium thiocyanate was introduced by Volhard, in which the end-point is indicated by the use of ferric sulphate. The method has been very widely used since that time, not only for the determination of silver in alloys, but also for the estimation of halides by residual titration of the excess of silver by standardized thiocyanate. The determination of chlorides by this method was at first found to be inaccurate, until it was recognized that removal of the precipitated silver chloride was necessary before proceeding to the residual titration. The influence of studies on the solubilities of very sparingly soluble substances is very relevant in this connexion. By physico-chemical methods it has been shown that silver chloride is more soluble than the thiocyanate, the bromide is of nearly equal solubility, and the iodide is the least soluble of the three halides.

As ordinarily practised in mints the Gay-Lussac method for testing the purity of fine silver is capable of realizing a limit of accuracy of about 0·2–0·3 part per thousand. This is a considerably higher degree of accuracy than is possible by the Volhard method as ordinarily carried out. In 1900, however, T. K. Rose investigated the possibilities of the Volhard method, and found that when worked under certain specified conditions it could be made to yield results which surpassed the Gay-Lussac procedure in refinement, and he was able to realize a limit of 0·1 part per thousand; but the process was too slow to be of much practical value in routine assay work.

A new departure in argentometric work arose in 1923 by the introduction of adsorption indicators by Fajans. By using certain dyestuffs, such as fluorescein and its derivatives, the titration of halides by silver nitrate can be carried out with a degree of accuracy not inferior to what can be realized by the Mohr process or by the Volhard method. The use of the fluorescein class of indicators is limited to work in neutral solution. Extension of this work by Fajans and by others has led to the use of other dyestuffs which can enable such titrations to be carried out in acid solution, particularly tartrazine and phenosafranine. By taking advantage of the difference in solubility and of capacity for adsorption of silver chloride and silver iodide, it has been found possible to determine a soluble chloride and an iodide in the same solution by differential titration.

Gay-Lussac made some use of the reducing action of a solution of arsenious oxide to determine the value, or, as it is usually termed, the available chlorine, of bleaching powder. He expressed his results in what were termed Gay-Lussac degrees. These units indicate the number of litres of chlorine, reduced to 0° C. and 760 mm., obtainable from 1 kg. of the material; 100 of such degrees are equivalent to 31·8% of available chlorine. Gay-Lussac's arsenite method was improved by Penot in 1852, and is still in general use.

Several other volumetric methods of analysis were developed about the middle of the nineteenth century. Thus in 1846 Marguerite devised the well-known method of titrating acidified ferrous salts with potassium permanganate. This was followed in 1850 by Penny's potassium dichromate method for estimating iron. Mohr introduced ferrous ammonium sulphate—sometimes known as Mohr's salt—for standardizing these oxidizing agents. Iodometric methods were devised by Bunsen in 1853, and described in detail in a paper entitled *Ueber eine volumetrische Methode von sehr allgemeiner Anwendbarkeit*.

Bunsen's research on iodometry began with a thorough investigation of the reversibility of the reaction between iodine and sulphurous acid. It had previously been used as a means of determining iodine by titration with a dilute solution of the reducing agent by Dupasquier; but Bunsen was able to show that the oxidation to sulphuric acid, with simultaneous reduction of the iodine to hydriodic acid, is only quantitative if the concentration of the sulphur dioxide does not exceed 0·04% by weight. Bunsen developed methods for determining a number of oxidizing agents by quantitative liberation of iodine from acidified potassium iodide and for determining the iodine by titration under strictly specified conditions. Just after the publication of Bunsen's paper, Schwarz introduced sodium thiosulphate as a substitute for sulphurous acid in iodine titrations, and this reagent very soon came into general use on account of its much greater stability.

From the earliest beginnings of volumetric analysis, the determination of acids and alkalis by reciprocal titration has been a prominent feature of this kind of work. Among the various natural products which have been used as indicators in acidimetry and alkalimetry, litmus has long enjoyed an exceptional degree of popularity, and even at the present time its use has by no means been abandoned. But its limitations, particularly its sensitiveness to carbon dioxide, soon became recognized; and the introduction of methyl orange by Lunge in 1881 for titrating alkaline carbonates was an important practical advance. R. T. Thomson in 1883 made an exhaustive study of the various indicators in common use at that time, and pointed out the best practical conditions for applying them to any particular determination. In 1891 Ostwald published his well-known theory of indicators based on the principle of ionic equilibria. Although this theory is no longer accepted in the simple form presented by its author, and has been modified by the introduction of Hantzsch's views on pseudo-acids and pseudo-bases, Ostwald's ideas have been of very great value in obtaining a clear understanding of the mode of action of these substances and of making the right choice of the most suitable indicator for any particular titration. Since 1904 it has been shown by Salm, Thiel and others that the colour changes of indicators is determined by the actual concentration of hydrogen ions in solution, and this can be given numerical expression. In 1911 Tizard published a report on the sensitiveness of indicators, in which he drew attention to the effect of the amount of indicator on the end-point of a titration, according as a two-colour indicator, such as methyl orange, or a one-colour indicator, such as phenolphthalein, is used. A very important monograph entitled *Die Theorie der alkalimetrischen und azidimetrischen Titrierungen* was published by Bjerrum in 1914. In this work Bjerrum discussed some of the topics, to which reference was made in Tizard's report, in more elaborate detail, and dealt very thoroughly with problems such as the degree of hydrolysis of salts. He also adverted to the possibility of effecting further advances in this department of practical chemistry, in particular to titrating to any specified hydrogen-ion concentration. This has been realized experimentally in two ways, namely, by potentiometric titration and by using indicators having a colour change corresponding to the desired pH interval. The number of indicators, the pH range of which is accurately known, is now fairly large; and of these the sulphonephthalein series is of particular importance. This class of indicator has received much attention at the hands of Acree and his collaborators since 1916; and it may be noted, in passing, that certain sulphonephthaleins, such as thymol blue, have a double colour change, each corresponding to a definite pH interval. The existence of such a double colour change was explained by White and Acree in 1919 by regarding the sulphonephthaleins as dibasic acids, the primary salt being derived from the carboxylic acid resulting from the opening of the lactone ring and the secondary salt from one of the phenol groups.

Much progress in problems connected with the estimation of acids and alkalis has resulted from a correct understanding of the significance of the ionization constants of these classes of compounds including the physico-chemical properties of indicators. Two examples may be quoted by way of illustration. The accuracy attainable in the titration of mixtures of acids and bases, and the titration of polybasic acids, was discussed by Tizard and Boeree in 1921. They showed that dibasic acids can be titrated as monobasic if there is a wide difference between the values of the two ionization constants, but not when this difference is small; thus by using an indicator of the methyl orange type, maleic acid can, and succinic acid cannot, be titrated to the first stage. The estimation of ampholytes, particularly amino-acids, has been the subject of numerous investigations. In this kind of work the problem has been one of eliminating the effect of the basic constituent, and two methods for effecting this object have been devised and have come into general use. Sörensen in 1907 devised a displacement method which consisted in using formaldehyde to react with the amino-acid to form an extremely weakly basic derivative, which thus enables the acid to be titrated with alkali and phenolphthalein. The other method depends on the effect of alcohol in exerting a lowering effect on the strengths of amino-acids, but this effect is much more pronounced on the basic constituent. This method was introduced independently by Foreman in 1920 and by Willstätter and Waldschmidt-Leitz in 1921, and consists in titrating the amino-acids directly with alkali in a solution containing a very high concentration of alcohol and using a sensitive indicator such as phenolphthalein.

During the twentieth century several new volumetric methods depending on reactions involving oxidation and reduction came into existence. In 1903 Knecht introduced titanous chloride as a quantitative reducing agent for a number of determinations, particularly for estimations of certain classes of dyestuffs. On account of its very powerful reducing properties, titrations with titanous chloride require to be carried out in an atmosphere of hydrogen. Later it was found that the sulphate is more stable, and accordingly does not require such close protection from atmospheric oxidation. In 1903 Andrews showed that the reaction between an iodide and an iodate in acid solution can be made to take a wholly different course from the usual one in which one equivalent of the iodate reacts with five equivalents of iodide. He found that when a solution of potassium iodate is added to one of an iodide in presence of a very high concentration of hydrochloric acid, the iodine which is first liberated is oxidized to iodine monochloride, one equivalent of the iodate reacting quantitatively with two equivalents of iodide, and he elaborated a very valuable method depending on this principle. Andrews's method of direct titration with potassium iodate has been applied in a number of directions, for example, by Berry in 1926 for the determination of thallous salts. Another modern volumetric oxidizing agent, namely, ceric sulphate, was introduced in 1928 by Furman and independently by Willard and Young. Although the powerful oxidizing properties of this substance had long been known, and a few instances of its use in volumetric work had even been published, these authors demonstrated its great value and wide applicability. Broadly speaking, it can be used for all determinations which are commonly effected with acidified potassium permanganate, as well as for some for which that reagent is not altogether suitable.

The completion of the reaction of any volumetric method should, whenever possible, be indicated by some striking colour change within the liquid. The older oxidation methods, with the important exception of Penny's dichromate method which requires an external indicator, satisfy this requirement. But it has long been known that certain aromatic compounds can undergo reversible oxidation and reduction from the benzenoid to the quinonoid condition, the process taking place with well-marked colour changes, and in 1924 Knop utilized diphenylamine as an internal indicator for titrating ferrous salts with dichromate. The introduction of some of the newer volumetric oxidizing agents, especially ceric sulphate, has led to renewed studies directed with the object of discovering the most suitable substances to serve as internal indicators. In this connexion the oxidation potential of the indicator is of great importance. In 1931 Kolthoff and Sarver found the diphenylamine sulphonic acid was preferable to diphenylamine, and this derivative in the form of the barium salt has come into general use. Of the other substances which have been used as internal oxidation-reduction indicators, mention should be made of tri-*ortho*-phenanthroline-ferrous sulphate which was first employed in 1931 by Walden, Hammett and Chapman. They claimed that this substance fulfilled the requirements of an ideal indicator on account of its high oxidation potential, excellent reversibility of the colour change, and stability in solution.

GAS ANALYSIS

The subject of gas analysis should be dated from the latter years of the eighteenth century, and the name of Cavendish will always be associated with the first accurate measurements of the proportions of the two chief constituents of the atmosphere. In a paper entitled *An account of a new eudiometer* which appeared in 1783, Cavendish elaborated a method, founded on a discovery made by Priestley some eleven years previously, for estimating the proportion of dephlogisticated air (oxygen) in the atmosphere. This consisted in causing nitrous air (nitric oxide) to react with the oxygen, dissolving the soluble product of the reaction in water, and measuring the resulting contraction in volume. These experiments were attended with considerable difficulty in attaining reproducible results, because it was not at that time understood that nitric oxide can combine with oxygen in varying proportions. Cavendish, however, obtained consistent results by adding the air to the nitric oxide and measuring the volume which disappeared during contraction. According to Cavendish, 'the whole diminution in mixing is equal to the bulk of nitrous air, which is turned into acid, added to the diminution which the common air suffers by being phlogisticated'. In this statement the expression *being phlogisticated* meant what would in modern phraseology be termed *being deprived of oxygen*. Cavendish thus appreciated, what was later more clearly understood by Dalton and by Gay-Lussac, that oxygen can combine with twice or with four times its volume of nitric oxide; but, provided that the latter gas is in excess, the volume of oxygen withdrawn is constant. The accuracy which Cavendish attained by this method, long since abandoned, bears favourable comparison with that of modern experimentalists using more refined methods. The celebrated paper, entitled *Experiments on air*, which was published by Cavendish in 1784, contained an account of his determination of the combining ratios of hydrogen and oxygen by explosion, and may be regarded as marking the foundation of that method of analysis.

In 1790 Volta constructed a eudiometer for determining the composition of combustible gases by explosion with oxygen, and this apparatus was also used by others, notably by Dalton in 1804, who ascertained the volume composition of marsh gas (methane) and of olefiant gas (ethylene) by sparking and measuring the resulting contraction in volume. It will be appreciated that correct formulae could not at that time be assigned to these gases as Avogadro's hypothesis had not yet been formulated; but the results are of historic interest as having occupied Dalton's mind in connexion with his law of multiple proportions. Analysis by sparking has been widely used since that time, notably by Bunsen and by later experimentalists. Coming to more recent years, the method was used by Diels and Wolf in 1906 for determining the molecular composition of carbon suboxide, a compound discovered by them to which they assigned the formula C_3O_2.

Measurements in the analysis of gases are, broadly speaking, apart from noting contractions resulting from the condensation of steam after explosion, effected by the application of selected reagents, either liquid or solid, and observing the resulting diminution of volume, or, alternatively, by weighing. Analysis by absorption using solid reagents was brought to a high degree of refinement by Bunsen, and described in a work entitled *Gasometrische Methoden*, an English translation of which, by Roscoe, appeared in 1857. Greater rapidity of working, although of a somewhat inferior degree of accuracy, was secured by the introduction of liquid reagents a few years later and the invention of more convenient apparatus, especially the forms devised by Hempel in the latter years of the nineteenth century.

For the present purpose it is unnecessary to refer in detail to the various reagents which are commonly employed in the analysis of gases by absorption, but a few remarks may be added on the use of palladium for the estimation of hydrogen. The property possessed by this metal of occluding large volumes of hydrogen was discovered by Graham in 1866, and the nature of the material thus obtained—whether a true hydride or an adsorption product—has been the subject of numerous later investigations. It appears to have been first applied analytically by Keiser in 1887 in a determination of the atomic weights of hydrogen and oxygen, the hydrogen having been absorbed in palladium and weighed directly. This method was also employed in a more elaborate research on the same subject by Morley in 1895. Bone and Jerdan employed palladium in 1901 for absorbing hydrogen in ordinary gas analysis, but their method of working involved the use of a mercury pump. An important practical advance was made in 1910 by Paal and Hartmann, who introduced the use of colloidal palladium in conjunction with a Hempel gas pipette. Since Graham's time it has been recognized that the rate of absorption of hydrogen is very greatly affected by the physical condition of the metal, the greater the degree of subdivision the more efficient is the occlusive capacity. It is therefore not surprising that palladium in colloidal solution should be a very useful absorbent.

Many analytical processes are carried out by determining the volume of a gas generated in a reaction, and a brief reference to two examples of this kind of work may now be made. In 1847 Crum devised a method 'for the analysis of bodies containing nitric acid and its application to explosive cotton'. He showed that when nitrates are shaken with mercury in the presence of concentrated sulphuric acid, all the nitric acid is reduced quantitatively to nitric oxide, the volume of which is measured directly. In 1878 Lunge devised his well-known nitrometer for the analysis of nitrous vitriol by this means, and this apparatus, which at later dates was improved by him in various ways, has been of much practical value in various other directions. The determination of urea by oxidation with a solution of sodium hypochlorite to carbon dioxide and nitrogen, and measurement of the volume of the latter gas evolved, was apparently first suggested by E. Davy in 1854, and has been the subject of many subsequent investigations. It was soon found that more rapid decomposition was effected by using sodium hypobromite, and that the volume of nitrogen liberated was always lower than the calculated value, the deficiency being about 8%. In 1878 Fenton showed that when sodium hypochlorite was used in presence of excess of alkali, only about half of the calculated volume of nitrogen was obtained, whereas with hypobromite all the gas, with the exception of the defect of 8%, was evolved. Fenton traced the deficiency to the formation of cyanate which is not oxidized to nitrogen. These conclusions received general confirmation by E. A. Werner in 1922.

An interesting example of a problem which was finally solved by a specially devised method of analysis was that of the composition of the hydrosulphites, or, as they have also been termed, hyposulphites. In 1852 Schönbein had observed that solutions having remarkably powerful reducing properties could be obtained by the action of zinc on sulphurous acid, and in 1869 Schützenberger studied this subject at greater length, and obtained salts in an impure condition by causing zinc to react with aqueous solutions of the alkali bisulphites. Schützenberger regarded the acid in solution as having the formula H_2SO_2, but in 1881 Bernthsen suggested the formula $H_2S_2O_4$. On account of the unstable character of the compounds and the great difficulty of obtaining them in anything approaching a state of purity, it was for long difficult to decide between the two formulae. In 1902, however, the question was settled in a particularly elegant manner by Moissan. Having previously shown that the alkali metal hydrides were represented correctly by the formulae KH and NaH, Moissan demonstrated the formulae of the alkali hydrosulphites by passing sulphur dioxide over potassium hydride and measuring the volume of hydrogen generated. The reaction was found to take place in accordance with the equation:

$$2KH + 2SO_2 = K_2S_2O_4 + H_2,$$

and the formula suggested by Bernthsen was thus verified.

It is a matter of general agreement that great advances in chemical science have resulted from improvements in experimental technique, but in no branch of this subject is this more true than in gas analysis. Special mention may be made of the invention of Sprengel's mercury pump in 1865 for producing high vacua—an apparatus which was used by Graham in his investigations on the selective passage of gases through various materials. At a later date Töpler's mercury pump was in constant use in Ramsay's experiments on the inert gases. The introduction of charcoal cooled to very low temperatures by Dewar in 1904 provided a means of separating the rare gases more simply than was possible by the original method of fractional distillation of liquid air employed by Ramsay and Travers.

ORGANIC ANALYSIS

The determination of the two most abundant constituents of organic compounds, carbon and hydrogen, by complete combustion to carbon dioxide and water respectively, is really a special department of gas analysis. The first beginnings of this subject were made by Lavoisier between 1781 and 1784. His experiments were made by using oxygen for effecting the combustions and potash for absorbing the carbon dioxide, the water being determined by difference. In some unpublished notes which were found after his death, however, it is clear that Lavoisier had made some improvements in his method of working, particularly by using compounds such as mercuric oxide or manganese dioxide for carrying out the combustions and by weighing the water directly after absorption in a hygroscopic salt. It must be added that Lavoisier attained a very limited degree of success with these experiments. The subject was afterwards taken up by other chemists, notably by Gay-Lussac and Thenard and by Berzelius, who made various modifications in the method, notably by mixing potassium chlorate, together with an inert substance to moderate the action, with the organic compound and thus effecting the combustion. Some improvement was, no doubt, realized in this way, but it was not until the year 1831 that a really satisfactory procedure was devised by Liebig, which consisted in burning the substances in a stream of air or oxygen, and passing the products of combustion over heated copper oxide to ensure complete combustion before reaching the vessels for weighing them: a tube containing calcium chloride retained the water and bulbs charged with a solution of potash absorbed the carbon dioxide. It was soon found that irregular results were obtained when the combustible substance contained certain elements, notably nitrogen, which gave rise to oxides of nitrogen during combustion and consequently a fictitious increase in the weight of carbon dioxide; but these difficulties were overcome by using heated copper to decompose the nitrogen oxides. The process as devised by Liebig, except for the mode of heating the tube, has continued practically unchanged to the present time. For upwards of a quarter of a century until after the introduction of gas-fired furnaces, combustions were carried out by Liebig's original type of apparatus, a furnace heated by burning charcoal, and the operation required considerable manipulative skill.*

* An interesting remark on this subject is to be found in *The Life and Work of C. O'Sullivan, F.R.S.*, by H. D. O'Sullivan, Guernsey, 1934: 'You pampered votaries of chemistry, hark back to the time when a combustion required the artful building and preserving of a charcoal fire!'

The beginnings of a method for determining nitrogen are to be found in the works of Gay-Lussac and Thenard, but no real progress in this direction was made until Liebig had elaborated his method of determining carbon and hydrogen by combustion. In 1831 Dumas devised his well-known method for determining this element; and it may be said that this arose as a consequence of the irregularities which were observed when nitrogenous compounds were submitted to combustion. Dumas's method consisted in effecting combustion with heated copper oxide in an atmosphere of carbon dioxide, decomposing any oxides of nitrogen with hot copper, and finally collecting the resulting nitrogen by displacement with carbon dioxide over a concentrated solution of potash. Apart from the introduction of a useful form of nitrometer due to Schiff in 1868, the process as devised by Dumas is, with only minor modifications, still in general use.

As many organic compounds when heated with caustic alkalis evolve any nitrogen which they contain in the form of ammonia, methods of estimating this element by determining the ammonia by volumetric analysis received a certain amount of attention in the earlier years of the nineteenth century, but owing to their somewhat limited applicability, they were less popular than Dumas's method. But in 1883 Kjeldahl devised a valuable method, which consisted in decomposing the compound by heating it with concentrated sulphuric acid, and thus converting the nitrogen into ammonium sulphate. The resulting ammonium sulphate was then decomposed by sodium hydroxide and the ammonia determined volumetrically. The function of the sulphuric acid in the Kjeldahl method is partly one of dehydration and partly that of an oxidizing agent. Since the method was first devised, it has been the subject of many investigations directed with the object of extending its range of applicability. At the present time it may be said that the Kjeldahl method, as now practised, gives reliable results with widely different types of organic compounds, and for technical work it is in almost universal use; but for purely scientific investigations the Dumas method is still preferred.

From what has been stated it will be clear that the determination of the elements in organic compounds is a matter of destructive oxidation, whether by 'dry' or by 'wet' combustion, so as to render the element in question available in a form suitable for weighing or for volumetric estimation. These principles are to be seen in the method most commonly used for the determination of the halogens and sulphur, which was first devised by Carius in 1860, and improved by him at later dates. In Carius's method the destructive oxidation is effected by heating with fuming nitric acid in sealed tubes. For the determination of halogens the operation is carried out in the presence of silver nitrate, and the silver halide resulting from the reaction is collected and weighed. When sulphur is to be determined, the silver nitrate is omitted and the sulphuric acid is weighed as barium sulphate.

During the first half of the nineteenth century, many attempts were made to devise a method for determining oxygen directly in organic compounds. Such methods were foredoomed to failure, but the ingenuity which was expended in this direction showed clearly how much a direct method for determining this element was desired. Even as late as the year 1865 Ladenburg devoted attention to this subject, and described an ingenious method for elementary analysis in which the compound was decomposed by destructive oxidation with silver iodate and concentrated sulphuric acid. In this method the oxygen was estimated by an adaptation of Bunsen's iodometric procedure, but it is scarcely surprising that an elaborate method of this kind should never have come into general use. It soon came to be recognized that research of this sort was fruitless, and consequently oxygen is always determined by difference, after all the other elements in the compound have been detected and estimated. An oft-quoted example of the importance of a thorough search for elements other than those merely suspected is the substance taurine. This compound was first discovered by Gmelin in 1826 in the bile of oxen, and analysed twelve years later by Dumas and Pelouze, who assigned the formula $C_2H_7NO_5$ to it. But in 1846 Redtenbacher showed that the compound contains sulphur, and after a more thorough analysis he found the correct formula to be $C_2H_7NO_3S$, the atom of sulphur taking the place of the supposed two atoms of oxygen.

In consequence of the rapid development of organic chemistry it became necessary to supplement the methods of elementary analysis with means of determining the actual number of certain kinds of groupings in the molecules of the compounds, in order to deal with problems of establishing their constitution. The general principle of such methods has always consisted in preparing derivatives of such groupings in the form of compounds, which are themselves readily separable in fairly pure condition and analysable by gravimetric or volumetric methods. Thus compounds, such as carbohydrates which are rich in hydroxyl groups, are easily acetylated or benzoylated, and the resulting acetyl or benzoyl compounds analysed by quantitative hydrolysis. The investigation of many natural products which contain methoxy groups in the molecule has been greatly facilitated by a method devised in 1885 by Zeisel for determining such groups. This method consists in decomposing the compound by heating with concentrated hydriodic acid, which results in separating the methoxy group quantitatively as methyl iodide, and this latter compound is distilled into a solution of alcoholic silver nitrate. The resulting silver iodide is then weighed directly. The original procedure of Zeisel was somewhat elaborate, and has subsequently been improved and simplified, notably by W. H. Perkin (the younger) in 1903.

In every branch of analytical chemistry, much progress has resulted in consequence of the development of methods for dealing with successively smaller quantities of substances. Quantitative microchemistry has become of ever increasing importance, particularly during the last half-century. Much of this progress has arisen in consequence of improvements in the design and construction of balances capable of weighing quantities of material of the order of a few milligrammes with an accuracy corresponding to what was regularly obtainable in dealing with decigramme quantities. Apart from some highly sensitive balances which have been constructed at various times, usually in connexion with special researches, such as the quartz torsion microbalance devised by Nernst in 1903, the modern microbalances used in analysis are really an outcome of improvements of a type used in assaying precious metals. Roberts-Austen in his work on *The Metallurgy of Gold* stated that 'the balance must readily indicate differences of 0·5 per 1000 or 1/40th milligramme with a weight of $\frac{1}{2}$ gramme in each pan'. The practice of modern quantitative micro-analysis has resulted very largely in consequence of co-operation between the chemists and the scientific instrument-makers. Emich had shown that analytical determinations could be carried out with the aid of a Kuhlmann assay balance sensitive to $\frac{1}{100}$ mg.; and in 1910, as a result of the influence of Pregl, this type of balance was improved in two directions, namely, in respect of the maximum load and by a tenfold increase in sensitivity. As an example of the value of work on this scale the following figures obtained by Pregl may be quoted. A determination of the percentage of methoxyl in vanillin by Zeisel's method using 3·750 mg. of the substance gave a yield of 5·780 mg. of silver iodide, corresponding to 20·4% of methoxyl in the compound, in perfect agreement with the calculated value. It is no exaggeration to state that much of the modern development of organic chemistry, particularly on the biochemical side, is directly due to the introduction of these microchemical methods.

Adsorption phenomena are of great importance in several directions in analytical chemistry. In some kinds of preparative work the withdrawal of impurities by adsorption with charcoal has long been practised, and an interesting example of an adaptation of this principle arose in unexpected circumstances in 1853. It had been idly, or perhaps wickedly, rumoured in Paris that the bitter taste of ales brewed at Burton-on-Trent was produced by the use of strychnine, and considerable panic arose in consequence of this. Graham and Hofmann were invited to investigate this question. They found that when a known quantity of strychnine was *artificially* added to pale ale, the alkaloid could be completely removed by contact with animal charcoal; it was recovered by filtering and extracting the charcoal with alcohol. Having tested the method, Graham and Hofmann applied it to numerous samples of Burton and other ales, and not a single one was found to contain a trace of the poisonous alkaloid.

Another aspect of this subject must be mentioned briefly, namely, that of chromatographic analysis. The beginnings of this method, which depends upon fractional adsorption, are to be found in some experiments on the separation of the chlorophyll pigments by Tswett in 1906. It was shown that when a solution containing the plant pigments was allowed to flow through a vertical column of a suitable adsorbent, the various constituents are preferentially adsorbed at different levels. By repeatedly washing the adsorbent with the pure solvent, the separated zones become clearly visible. The method has been much elaborated in recent years, and great importance has been attached to making a suitable choice of the solvent and of the adsorbent; it should be added that specially prepared alumina has been found very satisfactory.

A great deal of experimental work in analysis has been directed with the object of effecting modifications and improvements in well-known processes. To quote a single example, the literature on the analytical chemistry of phosphorus probably exceeds that of any other element. Although work of this kind is admittedly less spectacular and interesting than investigations with more pretentious objectives, its importance should not be underrated because of the possibility of its ultimate influence on developments in pure and in applied chemistry.

REFERENCES

ROBERTS-AUSTEN. *A Record of his Work.* Compiled and edited by Sydney W. Smith. London, 1914.

J. J. BERZELIUS. *The Use of the Blowpipe in Chemical Analysis and in the Examination of Minerals.* Translated from the French of M. Fresnel by J. G. Children. London, 1822.

HON. HENRY CAVENDISH. *Scientific Papers.* Two volumes. Cambridge, 1921.

HEINRICH ROSE. *Handbuch der analytischen Chemie.* Bd. I, *Die Lehre von dem qualitativen chemisch-analytischen Untersuchungen.* Dritte Auflage. Berlin, 1833. Bd. II, *Die Lehre von den quantitativen chemisch-analytischen Untersuchungen.* Dritte Auflage. Berlin, 1834.

Ausführliches Handbuch der analytischen Chemie. Braunschweig, 1851. This work in two volumes was a revised and enlarged edition of the earlier *Handbuch.*

J. W. MELLOR. *A Treatise on Quantitative Inorganic Analysis.* London, 1913. Second edition by J. W. Mellor and H. V. Thompson. London, 1938.

W. F. HILLEBRAND and G. E. F. LUNDELL. *Applied Inorganic Chemistry.* New York, 1929.

J. A. WANKLYN. *Arsenic.* London, 1901.

H. BREARLEY and F. IBBOTSON. *The Analysis of Steel-works Materials.* London, 1902.

W. R. SCHOELLER. *The Analytical Chemistry of Niobium and Tantalum.* London, 1937.

F. MOHR. *Lehrbuch der chemisch-analytischen Titriermethode.* Braunschweig, 1855.

F. SUTTON. *A Systematic Handbook of Volumetric Analysis.* London, 1863. Twelfth edition revised by A. D. Mitchell. London, 1935.

I. M. KOLTHOFF. *Volumetric Analysis.* Translated by N. Howell Furman. Vol. I, *The Theoretical Principles of Volumetric Analysis.* New York, 1928. Vol. II, *Practical Volumetric Analysis.* New York, 1929.

ROBERT BUNSEN. *Gesammelte Abhandlungen.* Herausgegeben von Wilhelm Ostwald und Max Bodenstein. Drei Bänder. Leipzig, 1904.

E. BRENNECKE, K. FAJANS, N. H. FURMAN, R. LANG. *Neuere massanalytische Methoden.* Stuttgart, 1935.

NIELS BJERRUM. *Die Theorie der alkalimetrischen und azidimetrischen Titrierungen.* Stuttgart, 1914.

G. LUNGE. *Technical Gas Analysis.* Revised and rewritten by H. R. Ambler. London, 1934.

M. W. TRAVERS. *The Experimental Study of Gases.* London, 1901.

M. DENNSTEDT. Die Entwicklung der organischen Elementaranalyse. *Ahrens Sammlung*, Band IV. Stuttgart, 1899.

H. BEHRENS. *Anleitung der mikrochemischen Analyse.* Hamburg und Leipzig, 1895.

F. FEIGL. *Qualitative Analyse mit Hilfe von Tüpfelreaktionen.* Dritte Auflage. Leipzig, 1938.

F. EMICH. *Lehrbuch der Mikrochemie.* Zweite Auflage. München, 1926.

Annual Reports of the Chemical Society since 1904.

CHAPTER VII

CHEMICAL FORMULAE

The representation of the composition of substances by means of formulae is based ultimately on the results of quantitative analysis. But formulae cannot be derived *solely* from analytical results: the introduction of atomic conceptions is necessarily concerned with the interpretation of percentage composition. It has been pointed out by Kopp in the *Geschichte der Chemie* that although Proust had made accurate analyses of the two oxides of copper and tin several years before the appearance of Dalton's *New System of Chemical Philosophy*, the law of multiple proportions was discovered, not by Proust, but by Dalton, because Proust had not referred the quantities of oxygen to the *same weight* of the metal, whereas Dalton reasoned in terms of atoms. Similar considerations are valid in discussion of the composition of gases by volume. Cavendish had established the volumetric composition of water by sparking mixtures of hydrogen and oxygen, and, by varying the proportions of the two gases, he was able to determine the correct combining ratio; but he was in no position to assign a formula to it. The extension and generalization of Cavendish's work by Gay-Lussac in 1808, as formulated in his well-known law relating to the combination of gases by volume, and the explanation of that law by Avogadro's hypothesis three years later, were destined to lead to results of far-reaching importance in every direction in chemistry.

As is well known, Avogadro's hypothesis received by no means general recognition for many years. Although the first half of the nineteenth century was a period of much fruitful activity in chemical research and discoveries of outstanding importance were made, the symbolic language of the science was confused by the neglect of Avogadro's rule and the development of various rival 'systems' of chemistry.

The year 1858 is an important date in the history of chemical theory. In that year Cannizzaro published his celebrated paper in which he showed that a consistent system of atomic weights and chemical formulae could be founded upon the principles laid down by Avogadro. Nevertheless, it is worth while to consider briefly some of the conclusions (many of which are of permanent value) concerning the nature of substances, which were reached at a time when there was no common agreement regarding atomic weights. The system of formulae and atomic weights adopted by Berzelius in 1826 was seriously threatened by a rival one due to Gmelin, and expounded in his *Handbuch der Chemie* in 1843, an English translation of which appeared in 1848. At the outset it should be noted that although the atomic weights and formulae of Berzelius show a much greater similarity to those adopted after Cannizzaro's time—in a word, to modern formulae—than those of Gmelin, the system of the latter was preferred by many as being more logical. Gmelin's system was purely gravimetric—no account was taken of volume relations—and his atomic weights were really equivalents; thus the values of hydrogen, oxygen, carbon, chlorine and sulphur were 1, 8, 6, 35·4 and 16 respectively. Gerhardt, who paid much attention to volume relations and, implicitly at least, accepted Avogadro's principle in arriving at molecular weights, published a system of atomic weights which had much in common with that of Berzelius. Nevertheless, Gerhardt adopted Gmelin's system in the first three volumes of his *Traité de chimie organique*, doubtless with the object of getting the work more widely recognized; in the fourth volume, however, which was published in 1856, his own system was adopted.

The beginnings of studies on organic compounds, as regards their bearing on chemical theory, were chiefly laid down by Dumas and his immediate followers, the chemists of what has rightly been designated as the French school. An important consequence of the work of that school was the introduction, in various forms, of the type theory as a means of giving expression to the constitution of substances. The dualistic theory of Berzelius, which had been of great value in the study of inorganic compounds, was found to be altogether unsuited as a means of formulating organic compounds, and fell into disrepute as a result of the attacks made upon it by Dumas. Besides Gerhardt, who was the chief expositor of the unitary system, there were others whose works were of great importance in developing and extending the principles founded upon Dumas's discovery of substitution; special mention must be made of Laurent, Malaguti, Liebig and, at a slightly later date, Williamson. The researches of Williamson between 1850 and 1856 on etherification are of great theoretical importance. It had long been known that alcohol could be transformed into ether by the action of concentrated sulphuric acid, and it appears that the researches originated with the object of understanding the nature of the etherification process. At an early stage of his experiments, Williamson found that when ethyl iodide was made to react with ethyl alcohol, previously treated with potassium until the reaction had ceased, the products obtained were ether and potassium iodide, and without necessarily committing himself to definite molecular formulae, he expressed the result of the reaction by the equation:

$$\left.\begin{matrix} C_2H_5 \\ K \end{matrix}\right\} O + C_2H_5I = IK + \left.\begin{matrix} C_2H_5 \\ C_2H_5 \end{matrix}\right\} O.$$

He concluded that 'alcohol is therefore water in which half the hydrogen is replaced by carburetted hydrogen, and ether is water in which both atoms of hydrogen are replaced by carburetted hydrogen'. Williamson confirmed his conclusions by extending his experiments to the preparation of mixed ethers, such as methyl ethyl ether, which was obtained from sodium methylate and ethyl iodide and also from sodium ethylate and methyl iodide. The formation of these compounds, taken in conjunction with determinations of their vapour densities, led Williamson to declare 'the atomic weight of the alcohols to be half that of which they have of late been considered, so that their equivalent occupies in the state of vapour the same volume as that of ether, water, etc.' This sort of phraseology indicates the degree of uncertainty which was prevalent at that time regarding molecular and atomic weights. These experiments on the formation of mixed ethers were of much assistance to Williamson in obtaining a correct understanding of the continuous etherification process, which takes place, not by a direct withdrawal of the elements of water from alcohol, but through the intermediate formation of sulphovinic acid (ethylsulphuric acid).

The discovery by Gerhardt of acetic anhydride in 1853 was of great theoretical interest, as an example of what he termed 'les anhydrides ou acides anhydres'. Gerhardt regarded these acid anhydrides as related to their acids in the same way as the ethers are related to the corresponding alcohols, their formation from an acid chloride and the alkali salt of an organic acid being strictly comparable with the synthesis of an ether by Williamson's method. This classification of the acid anhydrides in Gerhardt's water type was immediately accepted by Williamson, and the formula of acetic anhydride was accordingly written as $\left.\begin{matrix} C_2H_3O \\ C_2H_3O \end{matrix}\right\}O$.

In considering the four types, namely, those of water, hydrochloric acid, ammonia and hydrogen, which constituted Gerhardt's system of classification, it is important to bear in mind that their gifted author never intended them to represent the actual constitutional formulae of compounds. On more than one occasion Gerhardt ventured the opinion that a compound might be given as many different formulae as might best give expression to its distinctive reactions—an idea for which there was a certain degree of justification. As an example of Gerhardt's way of expressing reactions, the formation of benzanilide from benzoyl chloride and aniline was written as follows:

$$ClC_7H_5O + N\left\{\begin{matrix} C_6H_5 \\ H \\ H \end{matrix}\right. = ClH + N\left\{\begin{matrix} C_6H_5 \\ C_7H_5O. \\ H \end{matrix}\right.$$

Benzoyl chloride was thus regarded as belonging to the hydrochloric acid type, and aniline (as a substituted ammonia) and its derivative, benzanilide, were properly assigned to the ammonia type. Gerhardt's hydrogen type is more fanciful, and many substances were brought into it which appear to be somewhat out of place.

In 1859 Kolbe published interesting views on structural formulae. His object was to demonstrate a natural connexion between organic and inorganic compounds, and he inclined to regard organic compounds as derivatives of carbon dioxide, which he formulated as C_2O_4. He disliked Gerhardt's theory of types as being much too artificial; and, in starting from carbon dioxide, he remarked that, since that compound was the source from which plants effect their marvellous syntheses, it would be fitting to build up a system of chemical theory in which some account was taken of the bearing of vegetable physiology on the subject. Kolbe's system of formulae was based throughout on Gmelin's equivalents; nevertheless, in the analogies which Kolbe demonstrated between organic and inorganic acids, it is possible to discern some of the doctrines of Berzelius. Kolbe had made important contributions to electrochemical studies between 1848 and 1850 in his investigations on the electrolysis of the alkali metal salts of some of the fatty acids, and the brilliant experimental work of Bunsen between 1837 and 1843 on the cacodyl compounds received his close attention. In the year 1760 Cadet had prepared a very remarkable liquid, having spontaneously inflammable properties, by distilling a mixture of dry arsenious oxide and potassium acetate. This dangerous substance appears to have received little further experimental study before Bunsen's time. Bunsen prepared large quantities of the compound, which he found to be extremely reactive, and as the result of an elaborate study of its derivatives, he was able to show that the cacodyl radical preserved its integrity throughout a great number of reactions. Having recognized that the original substance was cacodyl oxide, and by using Berzelius's system of atomic weights, he assigned the formula $C_4H_{12}As_2O$ to it. He succeeded eventually in preparing free cacodyl, $C_4H_{12}As_2$, and described it as 'ein wahres organisches element'. Although Bunsen established the correct molecular formula for the compound, his researches did not extend to the complete recognition of its constitution, namely, the presence of four methyl groups in the molecule. But Kolbe, using Gmelin's equivalents, regarded cacodyl as a methyl derivative of arsenic, and assigned the formulae $(C_2H_3)_2As$, $(C_2H_3)_2AsO$ and $(C_2H_3)_2AsO_3$ respectively to cacodyl, its oxide, and its acid—the remarkable non-poisonous compound discovered by Bunsen. It would appear that Kolbe really intended that formula to refer to cacodylic anhydride, because in the paper published in 1859 he remarked that when cacodyl oxide takes up two atoms of oxygen it is transformed, not, as might be expected, into a tribasic acid formulated as $3HO.(C_2H_3)_2As, O_3$, but into the monobasic cacodylic acid $HO.(C_2H_3)_2(AsO_2), O$. By writing the formula of carbonic acid as $2HO(C_2O_2)_2$, he derived the formulae of formic acid as $HO.H(C_2O_2)O$ and of acetic acid as $HO.(C_2H_3)(C_2O_2)O$. The similarity between Kolbe's formulae for formic and acetic acids and those which he assigned to arsenic acid, namely, $3HO.(AsO_2)O_3$, and to cacodylic acid, $HO.(C_2H_3)(AsO_2)O$, is obvious. Although such formulae may appear bizarre enough in comparison with our modern formulae, it cannot be denied that they have a logical basis. Undoubtedly the contribution of most permanent value to chemical theory made by Kolbe was his prediction of the existence of secondary and tertiary alcohols, of which dimethyl carbinol was discovered by Friedel in 1862 and trimethyl carbinol by Butleroff in 1864.

The beginnings of ideas on the subject of valency or, as it was for many years termed, atomicity, are traceable in the works of Hofmann, Williamson, Odling, Wurtz and others. In some respects the development of the conception of valency may be considered as an outcome of the theory of polybasic acids, associated with Graham and Liebig, and of the recognition of polyhydric alcohols some twenty years later by Berthelot and its extension by Wurtz. It was, however, in a paper entitled *On a new series of organic bodies containing metals* which Frankland published in 1852 that valency appears to have first been formulated as denoting the saturating capacity of elements or groups. In that paper, in which the subject was discussed in terms of Gmelin's equivalents, Frankland was emphatic in tracing similarities between the formulae of inorganic and organic compounds. He remarked upon the tendency of nitrogen, phosphorus, arsenic and antimony to form compounds containing three or five atoms of other elements, and stated: '*it is sufficiently evident, from the examples just given, that such a tendency or law prevails, and that, no matter what the character of the uniting atoms may be, the combining power of the attracting element...is always satisfied by the same number of these atoms.*' The use of Gmelin's equivalents by Frankland resulted in the formulae assigned to the hydrides and halides being identical with modern formulae, but with the oxides, sulphides and alkyl compounds the formulae were different. The influence of Kolbe's views is clearly traceable in Frankland's paper. Thus both chemists assigned the same formulae to cacodyl, cacodyl oxide and cacodylic anhydride, and Frankland regarded them as comparable with arsenious sulphide, arsenious oxide and arsenic oxide, which were formulated as AsS_2, AsO_3 and AsO_5 respectively. Frankland also wrote zinc methyl as $Zn(C_2H_3)$ and stannous ethide as $Sn(C_4H_5)$ to show similarities with zinc oxide, ZnO, and stannous oxide, SnO. By the year 1858, however, Frankland had abandoned Gmelin's equivalents, and incidentally Kolbe's notation, and expressed his formulae in the modern system.

Important steps towards the development of the conception of valency were made by Odling—a disciple of the Gerhardt-Williamson school—in 1854. In that year he published a paper dealing with the constitution of acids and salts in which clear ideas regarding what would now be termed the valencies of atoms and radicals were expressed by the use of dashes attached to the symbols thus: K', Sn'', Bi''', H', O'', NO_2', SO_2'', etc. Odling employed terms such as *equivalency* and *replaceable*, *representative* or *substitution* value to denote what Frankland understood by atomicity—the term 'valency' came into general use at a later time. Some ten years later Odling drew a distinction between elements of even and uneven valency, the former being termed *artiads* and the latter *perissads*; but the distinction was eventually found to be artificial and was accordingly abandoned. One of the most interesting contributions to chemical formulae associated with Odling was the formula $Ca\langle{}^{OCl}_{Cl}$ which he assigned to bleaching powder in 1861. The object of this formula was to give expression to the compound as a mixed salt, namely, a compound, not a mixture, of calcium chloride and hypochlorite. Although it may be doubtful whether it is justifiable to assign a formula to such a material, Odling's formula has nevertheless received favourable consideration from later generations of chemists, and it would be fair to say that no better formula has as yet been suggested.

The recognition by Berthelot in 1854 that glycerol can give rise to three different kinds of esters with acids, just as a polybasic acid can yield as many different salts as there are hydrogen atoms in the molecule replaceable by metals, was destined to lead to results of great importance. Glycerol was thus a tribasic, or, more correctly, a trihydric alcohol. Berthelot's discovery was extended immediately afterwards by Wurtz, who formulated the compound in terms of Gerhardt's theory of types, by regarding it as derived from three molecules of water by the substitution of the radical glyceryl for three atoms of hydrogen, one from each of the water molecules. Wurtz also noted that the glyceryl residue contained two atoms of hydrogen less than the propyl radical, and therefore that the difference in saturation capacity (or what would in modern phraseology be termed 'valency') between the two radicals was determined by the two hydrogen atoms, the glyceryl residue with five hydrogen atoms being tervalent and the propyl residue with seven being univalent. Following up this line of reasoning, Wurtz predicted the possibility of preparing dihydric alcohols, or, as he expressed it, diatomic alcohols, and by starting from ethylene he prepared the first example of this class of compounds. By causing ethylene dibromide to react with silver acetate and then hydrolysing the resulting glycol diacetate with alkali, the dihydric alcohol, glycol, was obtained. The equations representing these transformations were written thus:

$$2\left\{\begin{matrix}\text{€}_2H_3\text{ϴ}\\ Ag\end{matrix}\right\}\text{ϴ}+\text{€}_2H_4Br_2=\left\{\begin{matrix}\text{€}_2H_4\\ \text{€}_2H_3\text{ϴ}_2\end{matrix}\right\}\text{ϴ}_2+2AgBr,$$

$$\left\{\begin{matrix}\text{€}_2H_4\\ \text{€}_2H_3\text{ϴ}_2\end{matrix}\right\}\text{ϴ}_2+2KH\text{ϴ}=\left\{\begin{matrix}\text{€}_2H_4\\ H_2\end{matrix}\right\}\text{ϴ}_2+2\left\{\begin{matrix}\text{€}_2H_3\text{ϴ}\\ K\end{matrix}\right\}\text{ϴ}.$$

Wurtz confirmed the correctness of his ideas regarding the constitution of glycol by a careful study of its reactions, and in particular by showing that when oxidized it could yield the monobasic glycollic acid and the dibasic oxalic acid according to the experimental conditions.

It will be observed that Wurtz used crossed symbols, Ꞓ and Ɵ, in his formulae. Such symbols were first introduced by Berzelius to indicate a doubling of the atomic weight, the normal value of which was signified by the uncrossed symbols. As employed by Wurtz and by others they were doubtless intended to denote a doubling of the values of Gmelin's equivalents. In Gmelin's system $C=6$ and $O=8$, and accordingly Ꞓ $=12$ and Ɵ $=16$; but the practice was not always followed consistently and much confusion arose in consequence. The use of these crossed symbols was continued by some chemists after the publication of Cannizzaro's paper in 1858, and is to be seen in the first volume of Kekulé's *Lehrbuch der organischen Chemie* which appeared in 1861, and in some of Baeyer's earlier papers of about the same date. As Cannizzaro's system of atomic weights came to be generally adopted, the use of such crossed symbols gradually disappeared. A useful service was rendered by Frankland to modern readers of his *Experimental Researches* which was published in 1877: at the outset he explained that he had transcribed most of his formulae into modern notation 'except where theoretical discussions necessitated the employment of the formulae as they stand in the earlier original memoirs. In all such exceptional cases the formulae are printed in italics, thus $C_4H_5 = \mathrm{C_2H_5}$. The nomenclature and notation in some of my earlier writings have become obsolete, and are now almost unintelligible to younger chemists, who have not passed through the series of revolutions which have at last resulted in the use of tolerably consistent, though by no means uniform, names and formulae.'

During the years in which chemical theory was in a state of great confusion and there was no clear understanding of the distinction between equivalent, atomic and molecular weights, much attention was none the less given to the determination of what were regarded as molecular weights, since many chemists imagined that molecular weights could be arrived at by what have sometimes been described as 'purely chemical' methods. Thus in the course of his classical investigations on the substituted ammonias, Hofmann determined the equivalent weights of these amines by obtaining the ratio between the weight of the amine platinichloride and the weight of platinum resulting from the ignition of the salt. As the compounds with which Hofmann was concerned contained only one atom of nitrogen in the molecule, it is obvious that the values of the equivalent and the molecular weights were identical.

Much more important than these so-called 'purely chemical' methods are those which depend directly upon Avogadro's theorem, namely, vapour-density methods. Although it was not until after Cannizzaro's generalization of Avogadro's principle in 1858 that it was recognized that all molecular weights depend ultimately upon that principle, much attention was devoted to the study of vapour densities. Gay-Lussac in 1815 and Dumas in 1826 devised valuable methods for determining vapour densities. These methods are in a sense reciprocal: in Dumas's method the weight of a known volume of the vapour is measured, whereas in Gay-Lussac's method the determination is effected by measuring the volume which is occupied by a known weight of vapour. This latter method was improved in 1868 by Hofmann. Victor Meyer's well-known displacement method was devised in 1877. All three methods have been extensively used in the study of molecular weights in the vaporous state.

In the course of studies on vapour densities, some results were obtained which appeared to be inconsistent with Avogadro's hypothesis: the values which were calculated from such experiments led to impossible molecular formulae. Substances which behaved in this way were sometimes described as having 'abnormal' vapour densities, and were considered to be exceptions to Avogadro's rule. A great deal of work was done on this subject, particularly by certain chemists of the French school such as Cahours, Deville and Troost, and Wurtz. By carrying out the determinations at successively increasing temperatures, it was frequently found that apparently 'normal' values for the molecular weights were obtained at the lowest temperatures, but that as the temperature was raised they diminished and ultimately reached values corresponding to half the expected molecular weights. Results of this kind were obtained by Cahours for phosphorus pentachloride in 1867. Among other substances which were found to behave in this way mention may be made of nitrogen tetroxide studied by Playfair and Wanklyn in 1861, by Wurtz and by Deville and Troost at a slightly later date, and of amylene hydrobromide and chloral hydrate also studied by Wurtz. Some chemists, notably Deville, regarded such compounds as definite exceptions to Avogadro's rule; but the correct explanation of their peculiar behaviour—interpreted as due to thermal dissociation—was given by Wurtz in 1869 in the case of phosphorus pentachloride, by showing that the 'normal' value of the vapour density was obtained when the determinations were carried out in the presence of excess of one or other of the products of dissociation, chlorine or phosphorus trichloride. But phosphorus pentafluoride, which was first prepared by Thorpe in 1876 from arsenious fluoride and phosphorus pentachloride, does not undergo thermal dissociation and has thus a normal vapour density. This result was confirmed some ten years later by Moissan, who, however, showed that the compound can be dissociated into the trifluoride and fluorine under the influence of powerful sparks.

In 1858 Kekulé published his celebrated paper entitled *Über die Konstitution und die Metamorphosen der chemischen Verbindungen und über die chemische Natur des Kohlenstoffs*. In this paper, which exercised a great influence upon the subsequent development of organic chemistry, the constant quadrivalency of carbon was clearly asserted. It is not easy to ascertain how far Kekulé was influenced by other chemists in developing his ideas, but there can be no doubt that he must have derived considerable assistance from Gerhardt's theory of types. There was no mention of Frankland's work, indeed, it would appear that Kekulé considered himself the sole author of the classical doctrine of valency. Kekulé's later paper, in which he put forward his well-known formula for benzene, was published in 1865. From the outset Kekulé considered valency to be a constant property of an element as opposed to the idea of variable valency as understood by Frankland.

Kekulé regarded compounds such as phosphorus pentachloride, which undergo thermal dissociation, as additive compounds of phosphorus trichloride, in which phosphorus retains its tervalent character, and chlorine: such compounds were termed 'molecular' compounds. All subsequent work has shown that Kekulé's doctrine of constant valency, and the distinction which he drew between 'atomic' and 'molecular' compounds, cannot be maintained. It was pointed out by Brauner in 1882 that difficulties would arise at once with simple inorganic compounds in attempts to formulate them without recognizing the variable nature of valency. Thus Kekulé's arguments for writing the formula of phosphorus pentachloride as PCl_3, Cl_2 are obviously invalid for the more stable pentafluoride: there is no satisfactory reason for regarding phosphorus as other than quinquevalent in that compound. It is also thoroughly artificial to write formulae with lengthy chains to sustain the idea of constant valency for elements like sulphur and chlorine, by writing sulphuric acid as H—O—O—S—O—O—H, and potassium hypochlorite and chlorate as K—O—Cl and K—O—O—O—Cl respectively: the properties of the compounds are by no means consistent with such modes of expression. But the outstanding importance of Kekulé's contribution to chemical theory, namely, the quadrivalency of carbon and the linking property of carbon atoms, is very clearly reflected in the subsequent development of organic chemistry.

In 1858 an important paper which dealt with the quadrivalency of carbon and the linking of carbon atoms was published by Couper. His approach to the subject was on different lines from those adopted by Kekulé, and he preceded him in introducing dotted or continuous lines to indicate the linking of atoms. Unlike Kekulé, Couper raised strong objection to Gerhardt's theory of types, which he regarded as artificial, and considered a system of chemical theory deduced from such premises to be thoroughly unsound. There was a curious inconsistency apparent as regards the atomic weights adopted by Couper: he took the values of 12 for carbon and 8 for oxygen, and this led to his formulae containing twice as many atoms of oxygen in the molecule as are to be found in modern formulae. Couper distinguished between what he termed 'affinity of degree' and 'elective affinity', and applying this idea to carbon he represented its combining power in two degrees, by expressing the formulae of carbon monoxide and dioxide as CO_2 and CO_4 respectively. He added that 'it [carbon] enters into combination with itself', and claimed priority for this idea to which he was certainly entitled. Couper's theoretical ideas were entirely independent of those of Kekulé, but owing to an unfortunate circumstance resulting in delay in the publication of his paper, Kekulé's memoir was the first to appear.

In 1861—four years before the publication of Kekulé's paper dealing with the formulae of aromatic compounds—Loschmidt, who is better known for his calculation of the number of molecules in a given volume of a gas, published a monograph entitled *Konstitutions Formeln der organischen Chemie in graphischer Darstellung*, in which graphic formulae were introduced apparently for the first time. This monograph was published in a small brochure entitled *Chemische Studien*, and appears to have been entirely overlooked by contemporary chemists. It was not until the year 1912 that Anschutz edited the work as one of Ostwald's *Klassiker*. Not only was Loschmidt in advance of his time by introducing double and treble bonds to indicate unsaturation, but there is no doubt that he anticipated Kekulé in assigning a cyclic structure to benzene. The question whether Kekulé was aware of Loschmidt's work was considered by Anschütz, who concluded that he must have known about it as there was a reference to it in a footnote in Kekulé's paper, but that there were good reasons for thinking that Kekulé had never read it. Although Loschmidt's graphic formulae were clumsy, there can be no doubt that his theoretical ideas were fundamentally correct and the monograph contains many features of great interest: thus he represented cyanuric acid with a ring structure having the three carbon atoms alternately linked with three nitrogen atoms by single and double bonds.

Frankland's researches on the organo-metallic compounds were begun in 1849 and concluded in 1863, and in his introductory remarks to the series he made a generous acknowledgement of the work of others in the development of the conception of valency. 'In thus claiming the discovery of the law of atomicity in the study of the organometallic bodies, and, in conjunction with Kolbe, its application to the compounds of carbon, I do not forget how much, in its present developments, this law owes to the labours of other chemists, especially to those of Kekulé and Cannizzaro. Indeed until the latter had placed the atomic weights of the metallic elements upon their present consistent basis, the satisfactory development of the doctrine was impossible.' Frankland's ideas on the subject of valency were expounded in detail in his *Lecture Notes for Chemical Students* which appeared in 1866. In that work the distinction between the artiads and perissads as different kinds of elements is maintained, and the variable nature of valency was discussed in terms of his *law of even numbers: in every molecule of a chemical compound the sum of the bonds is always an even number*. Frankland defined the maximum number of bonds of an element as its *absolute atomicity*, the number of bonds united together as its *latent atomicity*, and the number of bonds actually engaged in linking it with the other elements of a compound as its *active atomicity*. Thus he regarded the absolute atomicity of phosphorus as five, which, in the case of phosphorus pentachloride, is identical with its active atomicity. In phosphorus trichloride the active atomicity is three and the latent atomicity has a value of two. It is true that in many cases Frankland's law of even numbers appears to be valid, but a closer scrutiny has shown it to be utterly unsound. His own defence of it in the case of ferrous and ferric compounds is worth noting. 'The apparent exceptions to this hypothesis disappear on investigation: thus iron is a dyad in ferrous compounds (as $FeCl_2$)...is apparently a triad in ferric chloride ($FeCl_3$); but the vapour density of ferric chloride shows that its formula must be doubled....' Hence Frankland wrote the formula of ferric chloride as $\begin{cases} FeCl_3 \\ FeCl_3 \end{cases}$ or $Cl_3Fe—FeCl_3$, regarding the active atomicity of iron as four. It is evident that Frankland considered the two atoms of iron in the molecule as linked together like the carbon atoms in ethane. It must be admitted that there was some justification for this point of view, because at that time determinations of the vapour density of the salt had all been conducted at temperatures below that at which any dissociation of the Fe_2Cl_6 molecule becomes apparent.

Frankland published two interesting papers on organo-boron compounds, the first in 1862 and the second in 1876. He distinguished between those in which the alkyl groups are directly attached to boron and those in which the linking is not direct, but with oxygen interposed between boron and the organic groups. 'The discovery of boric ethodiethylate and dihydrate definitely fixed the character of boron as a perissad, and severed it from the carbon group of artiad elements. Previously to the production of these bodies, it was held by some chemists that boric and carbonic anhydrides were constructed on the same type.' The two compounds upon which Frankland particularly relied to fix boron as a tervalent element have the formulae $C_2H_5B(OC_2H_5)_2$ and $C_2H_5B(OH)_2$ respectively, but he added that 'even now, however, the absolute atomicity of boron can scarcely be said to be clearly established; for although, in nearly all its compounds, boron functions as a triad, in ammonia boric methide and diboric ethopentethylate it appears to assume pentadic attributes'. Frankland formulated these two compounds as $NH_3,B(CH_3)_3$ and $C_2H_5B(OC_2H_5)_2,B(OC_2H_5)_3$ respectively, just as Kekulé might have done, thereby maintaining the constant tervalency of boron; but he also gave alternative formulae with quinquevalent boron, namely, $NH_3{=}B(CH_3)_3$ and $C_2H_5B(OC_2H_5)_2{=}B(OC_2H_5)_3$, with the boron atoms linked by double bonds. Presumably the use of double bonds was to give expression to his law of even numbers, because there did not appear to be any other means of justifying such a linkage. Subsequent work has shown that the valency of boron, a subject which was exhaustively studied some fifty years later by Stock in connexion with the hydrides of that element, has been a matter of considerable difficulty. It appears to be definitely established that boron is tervalent in its halides and in organic derivatives, but that there is no evidence for the existence of a stable molecule having the formula BH_3: the simplest boron hydride has the molecular formula B_2H_6, in which the element is apparently quadrivalent.

When Mendeléeff constructed his periodic table of the elements in 1869 he drew attention to the periodicity of valency. He remarked that 'the elements are capable of combining with a greater amount of oxygen, the less the amount of hydrogen they were able to retain', and pointed out that in many instances the sum of the 'hydrogen' and the 'oxygen' valencies is equal to eight. This conclusion was reaffirmed in electrochemical terms by Abegg some thirty years later, and was destined to lead to consequences of some importance in the later developments of the subject. But criticisms have at various times been raised against Mendeléeff's choice of what he regarded as the most characteristic oxides as his standards of reference. Thus when an element forms more than one oxide, Mendeléeff usually chose the highest oxide as his standard of valency, but in some instances a lower oxide was preferred. In any case it gradually became recognized that oxygen is an unsuitable element to serve as a standard of valency. Thus oxides of the type RO_2 can be formulated as $R\langle{}^{O}_{O}|$ or as $R\langle{}^{=O}_{=O}$, in which R is bivalent according to the first formula but quadrivalent in terms of the second. Dioxides, such as barium peroxide, which yield hydrogen peroxide by the action of acids, have long been formulated as $R\langle{}^{O}_{O}|$, whereas those, such as lead and manganese dioxides, which react with hydrochloric acid with the evolution of chlorine, are not regarded as peroxides but as containing the metal in the quadrivalent condition, and are therefore written as $R\langle{}^{=O}_{=O}$. It is true that in numerous instances conclusions regarding the valencies of elements which were derived from considerations of their oxides happen to have been correct, because subsequent work on other compounds, especially alkyl derivatives and fluorides, have provided the means of verification; but apart from such sources of information the valencies would necessarily have been uncertain. Thus Mendeléeff considered osmium to be octavalent from the formula of the tetroxide, OsO_4, but no means of checking this was forthcoming until the year 1913 when Ruff and Tschirsch prepared the octafluoride, OsF_8, the molecular formula of which was confirmed by a vapour density determination.

Until the year 1885 when van't Hoff laid the foundations of the theory of dilute solutions, followed very shortly afterwards by the classical theory of ionization propounded by Arrhenius, vapour-density methods were the only means of obtaining reliable information regarding molecular weights. But since that time the various methods derived from studies on osmotic effects and on the electrical conductivity of solutions have greatly extended our knowledge in this direction, and in particular regarding the valency of ions. The well-known empirical law (discovered by Ostwald and extended by Walden) governing the basicity of acids, derived from studies on the differences between the values of the electrical conductivity of the alkali metal salts at specified dilutions, has been found to be applicable in a similar way to the valency of the cations of salts derived from monobasic acids. Thus Muthmann in 1898 confirmed the tervalency of lanthanum from the differences between the equivalent conductivities of solutions of the chloride and the nitrate at dilutions of 32 and 1024 litres. This difference was found to be 27·5 units for the chloride and 29·5 units for the nitrate, the calculated value for solutions of a salt of a monobasic acid and a tervalent cation being about 30 units. Exact values are not to be expected in work of this kind, particularly on account of effects due to hydrolysis.

Much of the progress in chemistry, particularly in organic chemistry, is closely associated with the development of the classical conceptions of valency. Even at the present time many questions can be discussed in terms of the principles laid down by Frankland and Kekulé. This is especially evident in the rapid development of the chemistry of the aromatic compounds. Although the various modifications of Kekulé's original formula for benzene, such as the centric formula suggested by Armstrong in 1887 and shortly afterwards by Baeyer, are interesting and important, the great progress in the chemistry of the aromatic series which arose after the publication of Kekulé's paper in 1865 was, however, due primarily to Körner's investigations on position isomerism. Kekulé has assumed the inter-equivalence of the six hydrogen atoms of the molecule of benzene, but the verification of this idea was very largely effected as a result of Körner's work on orientation between 1867 and 1874. He reasoned that if a disubstitution compound $C_6H_4X_2$ is converted into a trisubstitution derivative $C_6H_3X_3$, the number of isomerides obtainable should be two from an *ortho*, three from a *meta*, and one from a *para* compound, and by skilful experimental work on the bromo-benzenes he verified the correctness of his argument. All subsequent work has confirmed the conclusions drawn by Körner.

A question of fundamental importance in connexion with the theory of valency as regards carbon—namely, the equivalence of the four bonds of the atom of that element—was studied by L. Henry in 1887. This date is of interest, as all the previous work in organic chemistry had provided evidence towards an affirmative answer to the question. Thus the symmetry of the molecule of benzene and the inter-equivalence of the six hydrogen atoms in the molecule—tacitly assumed by Kekulé—had been settled more than ten years previously as the result of the labours of various chemists, such as Hübner and Petermann and especially of Ladenburg. Henry attacked the problem by preparing four specimens of nitromethane in such a way as to secure that each preparation was derived, by the substitution of a different hydrogen atom, from the molecule of methane. Thus by writing the formula of methane as $CH_aH_bH_cH_d$, he prepared four nitromethanes, namely, $C(NO_2)_aH_bH_cH_d$, $CH_a(NO_2)_bH_cH_d$, $CH_aH_b(NO_2)_cH_d$ and $CH_aH_bH_c(NO_2)_d$, all of which were found to be identical. He also extended his experiments to the preparation of identical specimens of acetonitrile. As the reactions for the preparative work did not involve high temperatures, it was considered legitimate to conclude that no intramolecular changes had taken place, and that therefore the four bonds of the carbon atom were of equal value. It should be noted that the validity of this conclusion is strictly dependent on the absence of intramolecular changes—justified no doubt in this particular instance.

The good agreement between the number of isomerides actually realized experimentally and the number to be expected on theoretical grounds for many compounds of known molecular formulae was a highly convincing line of evidence for the soundness of the classical doctrine of valency. Nevertheless, some examples were forthcoming in which this agreement was not to be found: in some instances the number of existing isomerides exceeded the theoretically expected number, while in others the number of isomerides was apparently fewer. It was realized that some extensions of the current ideas on constitutional formulae were necessary to explain the isomerism of the tartaric and lactic acids, and suggestions of the necessity of introducing some kind of tridimensional formulae were made by Wislicenus. Victor Meyer also recognized that the non-existence of isomeric methylene chlorides could not be discussed in terms of plane formulae. The whole subject was clarified by van't Hoff and Le Bel in 1874 with their tetrahedral conception regarding the disposition of the valencies of a carbon atom in tridimensional space. The further development of this theory in a more generalized form, usually termed molecular dissymmetry, has become the cornerstone of the subject of modern stereochemistry. When it became known that some compounds could react in such a way that alternative constitutional formulae could be assigned to them—as in the classical example of ethyl acetoacetate, discovered in 1863 by Geuther and formulated by him as $CH_3C(OH):CH.COOC_2H_5$, and studied in detail by Frankland from 1865 to 1867, who regarded it as $CH_3.CO.CH_2.COOC_2H_5$—such cases were ultimately shown to be due to reversible isomeric change, usually termed tautomerism.

In 1869 an important book entitled *Die Chemie der Jetztzeit* was published by Blomstrand. The object which the author had in view was to revive the dualistic electrochemical theory of Berzelius—this purpose was expressed on the title-page—and to bring it into agreement with the current doctrine of valency. Blomstrand accepted the principle of variable valency, and many of his constitutional formulae are closely similar to those in use at the present time. Among the numerous subjects discussed in this work, the formulae which Blomstrand assigned to azo, diazoamino and diazonium compounds appear remarkably modern: he regarded both nitrogen atoms in the two first-named compounds as tervalent, but insisted that in diazonium salts one of the nitrogen atoms must be quinquevalent. Blomstrand even attempted to extend his theoretical ideas to the complicated subject of the cobaltammines, but the chemistry of these and other such-like compounds could not well be discussed without some extension of the classical conceptions of valency. The metallic ammines and other complex compounds were, however, brought under a satisfactory system of formulation as a result of the theoretical developments of the doctrine of valency introduced by Werner some twenty years later.

In reviewing the development of the conception of valency it is interesting to observe how much progress was made in various directions in chemistry before Cannizzaro's generalization, when there was no common agreement regarding formulae and atomic weights. Thus the nature of complex salts was successfully demonstrated by Hittorf, who used Gmelin's equivalents in connexion with his electrolytic experiments. Even after that time a few chemists continued to use these values in preference to Cannizzaro's atomic weights. Whereas this adherence to the older system was no serious impediment to progress in inorganic chemistry, as regards the study of organic compounds the situation was different. In the early stages of the development of organic chemistry a correct understanding of some important principles was doubtless obtained—Kolbe's prediction of the existence of secondary and tertiary alcohols might be quoted as an example—but a stage was soon reached when the discussion of isomerism became practically impossible. The classical researches of Berthelot and Péan de Saint-Gilles on esterification in 1862 and 1863 were discussed in terms of Gmelin's equivalents, and their work is difficult for a modern reader to follow because the words 'atomic weight', 'equivalent weight' and 'molecular weight' were used more or less synonymously. Berthelot's attitude to modern formulae appears to have been altogether exceptional, he evidently had no great regard for Avogadro's theorem, because he continued to the end of his life to use Gmelin's equivalents in preference to modern atomic weights.

REFERENCES

A. N. MELDRUM. *Avogadro and Dalton. The Standing in Chemistry of their Hypotheses.* Aberdeen University Studies, no. 10, 1904.

C. F. GERHARDT. *Traité de chimie organique*, especially tome IV. Paris, 1853–6.

A. W. WILLIAMSON. *Papers on Etherification and on the Constitution of Salts.* Alembic Club Reprints, no. 16.

R. W. BUNSEN. *Untersuchungen über die Kakodylreihe.* Ostwalds Klassiker der exakten Wissenschaften, no. 27.

A. WURTZ. *Abhandlung über die Glykole oder zweiatomige Alkohole und über Aethylenoxyd als Bindglied zwischen organischer und Mineralchemie.* Ostwalds Klassiker der exakten Wissenschaften, no. 170.

H. KOLBE. *Über den natürlichen Zusammenhang der organisch. mit den unorganisch. Verbindungen, die wissenschaftliche Grundlage zu einer naturgemassen Klassifikation der organ. chemischer Körper.* Ostwalds Klassiker der exakten Wissenschaften, no. 92.

A. WURTZ. *A History of Chemical Theory from the Age of Lavoisier to the Present Time.* Translated and edited by Henry Watts. London, 1869.

W. ODLING. *A Manual of Chemistry.* London, 1861.

A. KEKULÉ. *Lehrbuch der organischen Chemie*, Band I, Erlangen, 1861; Band II, Erlangen, 1866; Band III, Stuttgart, 1882.

E. FRANKLAND. *Experimental Researches in Pure, Applied, and Physical Chemistry.* London, 1877.

E. FRANKLAND. *Lecture Notes for Chemical Students.* London, 1866.

A. KEKULÉ. *Über die Konstitution u. die Metamorphosen der chem. Verbindungen u. über die chem. Natur d. Kohlenstoffs. Untersuch. über aromatische Verbindungen.* Ostwalds Klassiker der exakten Wissenschaften, no. 145.

J. LOSCHMIDT. *Konstitutions Formeln der organischen Chemie in graphischer Darstellung.* Ostwalds Klassiker der exakten Wissenschaften, no. 190.

A. S. COUPER. *On a New Chemical Theory and Researches on Salicylic Acid.* Alembic Club Reprints, no. 21.

S. CANNIZZARO. *Sketch of a Course of Chemical Philosophy.* Alembic Club Reprints, no. 18.

LOTHAR MEYER. *Modern Theories of Chemistry.* Translated from the fifth German edition by P. Phillips Bedson and W. Carleton Williams. London, 1888.

W. KORNER. *Über die Bestimmung des chemischen Ortes bei den aromatischen Substanzen.* Ostwalds Klassiker der exakten Wissenschaften, no. 174.

C. W. BLOMSTRAND. *Die Chemie der Jetztzeit von Standpunkte der electrochemischen Auffassung aus Berzelius Lehre entwickelt.* Heidelberg, 1869.

CHAPTER VIII

SOME PROBLEMS RELATING TO VALENCY, RADICALS AND CONSTITUTION

After the fundamental ideas regarding the classical conception of valency had been expounded by Frankland and Kekulé, various questions, some of which were of long-standing interest, still remained to be settled. Some of these problems presented considerable difficulties when regarded according to elementary theory, and hence arose various attempts, not indeed to set aside the classical conceptions, but rather to develop and extend them so that they might be brought to bear upon such questions. Among the more important problems to be considered, special mention should be made of questions regarding the nature of addition compounds such as salts containing water of crystallization, and of the ammine compounds of the salts of certain heavy metals, the question of the existence of radicals *as such* and the possibility of isolating them from the molecules of compounds, and the necessity of gaining information regarding the nature of valency, particularly with the object of discussing certain questions of constitution and of the mechanism of reactions.

At the outset it may not be irrelevant to remark that chemists have used the term 'valency' in more than one sense. Some have used the term in the purely numerical sense as a means of expressing saturating capacity, while others have applied it to indicate the bonds by which the atoms in a molecule are regarded as held together, and have even entered upon discussions regarding the nature of the forces by which this union is effected. This lack of uniformity of practice may be seen in the use of the terms *Valenz* and *Wertigkeit* by some writers. Ephraim in 1928 rightly remarked in his *Chemische Valenz- und Bindungslehre* that 'die Valenz eine Zahl und nicht etwa eine Kraft ist'. The numerical meaning is the correct one, and it is unfortunate to encounter expressions such as 'the four valencies of a carbon atom are directed towards the vertices of a regular tetrahedron', when strictly speaking the term *bond* should have been used in such a connexion.

The mode of combination of water with many salts, usually known as water of crystallization, has long been discussed by chemists. For many years it has been the practice to regard these hydrates in Kekulé's sense as molecular compounds, without going further; and for purely practical purposes this has been considered sufficient. But on theoretical grounds it cannot satisfy the mind, because it maintains the difficulty of attempting to draw a distinction between 'atomic' and 'molecular' compounds. Some extension of the classical conception of valency is clearly necessary for a satisfactory formulation of these and other such-like addition compounds.

Long before Kekulé's time, actually in 1836, Graham published an interesting paper entitled *On water as a constituent of salts*, in which he showed that, when certain hydrated salts, which crystallize with several molecular proportions of water, are heated, dissociation proceeds by more than one stage—usually one molecular proportion of water resists dissociation much more strongly than the remainder. Thus he stated that 'the common blue rhomboidal crystals of sulphate of copper contain five atoms of water, four of which are readily expelled by drying the salt in air at 212° F.... At a temperature between 430° and 470°, the sulphate of copper loses its fifth, or saline, atom of water, and is found in the state of a powder, which is white without any shade of colour....' Graham's use of the expression *saline* water was founded upon his discovery, three years previously, of the three well-known modifications of phosphoric acid, which he regarded as hydrates of phosphorus pentoxide. 'That the water is basic in these different hydrates, follows from the fact that, on treating them with an alkali, the water is constantly replaced by a quantity of alkali chemically equivalent to the water.' He continued: 'I have subsequently found water to exist in a different state in certain salts, not possessed of a true basic function, being replaceable by a *salt*, and not by an alkaline base'; and he gave a number of examples in support of this idea. Thus he found that zinc sulphate heptahydrate readily parts with six molecular proportions of water on heating gently, the last molecule—the saline water—being more firmly held. But when a solution of zinc sulphate was allowed to crystallize with one of potassium sulphate, a double salt having six molecules of water of crystallization was obtained. According to Graham the molecule of saline water was replaced by an equivalent of potassium sulphate. All Graham's formulae were expressed in the dualistic Berzelian system, but his meaning is none the less perfectly clear. Adopting modern formulae the molecules of zinc sulphate heptahydrate and of the double zinc potassium sulphate hexahydrate would have been written by Graham as $ZnSO_4(H_2O),6H_2O$ and $ZnSO_4(K_2SO_4),6H_2O$ respectively, to give expression to the equivalency of the saline water with the potassium sulphate.

The results obtained by Graham on the thermal dehydration of salt hydrates have been confirmed and extended by measurements of the vapour pressures accompanying *isothermal* dehydration of this class of compounds. According to the doctrine of the phase rule, a univariant system consisting of two solid phases and a gas should have a constant vapour pressure, the value of which depends solely upon the temperature. This was shown in 1886 by Lescoeur for copper sulphate pentahydrate: he found that when this salt was subjected to isothermal dehydration, there were two abrupt falls in the vapour pressure corresponding to three univariant systems, namely, those consisting of pentahydrate, trihydrate vapour; trihydrate, monohydrate vapour; and lastly monohydrate, anhydrous salt vapour; the vapour pressure of the last named was extremely small, thus confirming Graham's discovery of the considerable stability of the monohydrate. The conclusions reached by Lescoeur have been verified by others; in particular, the non-existence of a tetrahydrate or of a dihydrate has been established.

The numerous compounds which are formed by the addition of ammonia to salts resemble hydrated salts in many respects, and present similar problems in the way of assigning constitutional formulae to them. Such compounds have long been known, and are a prominent feature of the chemistry of some of the heavy metals, particularly cobalt, chromium and platinum. Apparently the first of such ammine salts was discovered by Gmelin in 1822; he obtained a crystalline oxalate from an ammoniacal solution of a cobalt salt, subsequently known as luteo-cobaltic oxalate. Some thirty years later other coloured ammoniacal derivatives of cobalt salts became known, notably the compound purpureocobaltic chloride, which was studied in 1851 by Frémy. He showed that when this salt is treated with silver nitrate, the precipitation of silver chloride is incomplete under ordinary conditions, and only becomes quantitative after prolonged boiling. As the result of a number of investigations by various experimentalists, especially Wolcott Gibbs, during the next twenty-five years, it became recognized that these ammoniacal compounds of cobalt could be grouped into apparently distinct series, and were derived from the sesquioxide of the metal. From 1878 onwards, Jörgensen made an elaborate study of these substances, which enabled him to trace important relations between them and to give expression to their constitution according to the classical theory of valency as applied by Blomstrand. One of his earliest experiments was a continuation of Frémy's work on the reactivity of the chlorine in the purpureo salt. He showed that, when purpureocobaltic chloride is treated with concentrated sulphuric acid in the cold, the product of the reaction is a chlorosulphate of which the chlorine is not precipitated by silver nitrate in the cold. In 1884 Jörgensen showed that ammonia in the luteo (hexammine) salts could be partially replaced by water, thereby giving rise to the roseo (aquopentammine) salts. For a number of years there was much uncertainty regarding the number of cobalt atoms in the molecules of these compounds, and it was a fairly common practice to write formulae with two atoms of cobalt in the molecule; but in 1892 Petersen showed clearly by experiments on the freezing points and the electrical conductivity of the solutions that the compounds were monatomic as regards cobalt.

In 1895 Jörgensen published a valuable summary on the chemistry of the cobaltammines, and showed how differences in the reactivity of the chlorine (or other electronegative constituent) in many of these compounds could be expressed in terms of the constitutional formulae suggested by Blomstrand. In these formulae a readily reactive chlorine atom was regarded as being attached to one bond of a nitrogen atom of one of the molecules of ammonia, whereas an inert chlorine atom was represented as being directly attached to the metallic atom. Thus the formulae of luteo (hexammine), roseo (aquopentammine) and purpureo (chloropentammine) cobaltic chlorides were written as

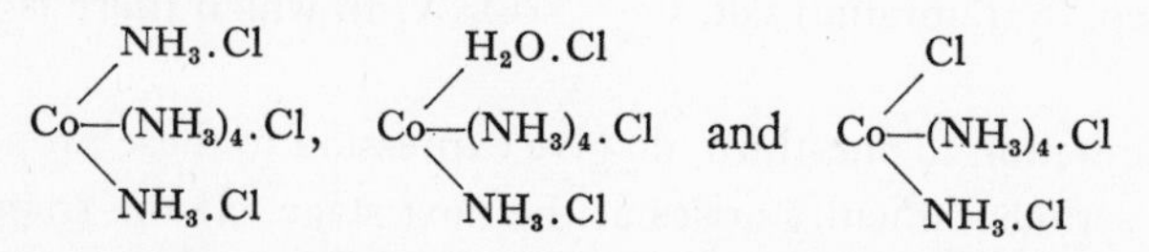

thereby giving expression to the reactivity of the chlorine being complete in the luteo and the roseo salts, but limited to the extent of two-thirds in the purpureo salts. It may be remarked that there does not appear to be any particular reason for regarding one of the reactive chlorine atoms as having a chain of four molecules of ammonia interpolated between it and the cobalt atom, and the other to be separated from the metallic atom by a single molecule of ammonia, the distinctive features of the compounds could have been expressed with equal clarity by a less uneven distribution of the ammonia molecules in the formulae. It should also be noted that where a molecule of ammonia is replaced by one of water, as it is in the roseo salts, the oxygen of the water was regarded as quadrivalent, just as the nitrogen of the ammonia was considered to be quinquevalent. This means of giving expression to differences in the reactivity of a halogen atom according to the mode of linking may be compared with what was at one time accepted for organic compounds, as in the case of ethyl chloride and methylammonium chloride.

In 1893 Werner discussed the constitution of complex salts, particularly the cobaltammines and the ammine salts of other metals, such as those of chromium and platinum, and pointed out that many of these compounds exhibit reactions which are inconsistent with the system of formulation adopted by Blomstrand

and Jörgensen. Admittedly the formulae assigned by them to a luteo salt, $\mathrm{Co}\begin{matrix}\diagup \mathrm{NH_3}.X \\ -(\mathrm{NH_3})_4.X \\ \diagdown \mathrm{NH_3}.X\end{matrix}$, in which the reactivity of the electronegative constituent is complete, a purpureo salt, $\mathrm{Co}\begin{matrix}\diagup X \\ -(\mathrm{NH_3})_4.X \\ \diagdown \mathrm{NH_3}.X\end{matrix}$, in which this reactivity is limited to the extent of two-thirds, and a praseo, (tetrammine) salt, $\mathrm{Co}\begin{matrix}\diagup X \\ -(\mathrm{NH_3})_4.X \\ \diagdown X\end{matrix}$, in which there is a further limitation to one-third, do give expression to these properties. But a serious difficulty arises at the next stage. If the triammine compounds, which are derived from the praseo salts, are written as $\mathrm{Co}\begin{matrix}\diagup X \\ -(\mathrm{NH_3})_3.X \\ \diagdown X\end{matrix}$, such a formula would seem to imply that there is still some reactivity associated with the electronegative constituent attached to the ammonia chain, whereas in this series it is altogether inert. Werner's system of formulation, to be presently discussed, was based very largely on determinations of the electrical conductivities of the solutions of these complex salts, which he carried out in collaboration with Miolati in 1893, and continued during the next few years. They found that the values for the molecular conductivities at infinite dilution had well-defined values for the several types of salts; the conductivities were highest for the luteo and roseo salts, lower for the purpureo salts, and still lower for the praseo salts, the differences between the series being well marked. Of particular importance was their discovery that the triammine compounds such as the nitrite, $(\mathrm{NO_2})_3\mathrm{Co}(\mathrm{NH_3})_3$, are non-electrolytes, and should therefore not be described as salts. Going still further, Werner found that, when the ammine constituent is replaced by more nitro groups, the complex cobalt ion now becomes *electronegative*, and can thus form salts with metallic cations, this replacement being complete in sodium cobaltinitrite, $\mathrm{Na_3Co(NO_2)_6}$, the well-known analytical reagent for potassium.

Werner's approach towards a theoretical understanding of the constitution of the cobaltammines and other complex salts appears to have begun on numerical lines. Having observed that a large number of metallic chlorides crystallize with six molecular proportions of water, and that in the cobaltammines, the luteo salts contain six, the purpureo salts five, the praseo salts four, and the triammine salts three molecular proportions of ammonia, and at the same time the number of *inert* electronegative constituents, such as chlorine atoms, is such that the total (ammonia molecules *plus* inactive halogen atoms) is equal to six, he introduced a new conception, termed 'co-ordination', to discuss questions of constitution. At a very early stage of his work he defined two kinds of valency, namely, principal or primary valency (*Hauptvalenz*) and subsidiary or secondary valency (*Nebenvalenz*). The object of this classificatory principle was to introduce some sort of order into what had at various times been discussed in an ill-defined way as 'residual affinity'. Werner regarded principal valencies as concerned with ions, namely, with those parts of a molecule which separate in electrolytic dissociation. Subsidiary valencies were defined with somewhat less precision, but, broadly speaking, they were intended to be applicable, not only to atoms, but to the attachment of molecules which can have an independent existence, such as those of water or ammonia. The formulae for the luteo, roseo, purpureo, and praseo cobaltic chlorides were written by Werner as

$$[Co(NH_3)_6]^{3+}Cl_3^{3-},$$

$$[(H_2O)\,Co(NH_3)_5]^{3+}Cl_3^{3-},$$

$$[ClCo(NH_3)_5]^{2+}Cl_2^{2-}, \text{ and}$$

$$[Cl^2\,Co(NH_3)_4]^{+}Cl^{-}$$

respectively. The co-ordination number of six, to which Werner attached great importance, is clearly shown by the total number of units (ammonia or water molecules or chlorine atoms) enclosed together with the cobalt atom within the square brackets, and the valencies of the cations were in full accord with the results of the conductivity measurements. It will be noted that the valencies of the hexammine and of the aquopentammine ions are equal to that of the fundamental valency of cobalt in these compounds, each being balanced with three chlorine ions. The subsidiary valencies by which the ammonia and water molecules are co-ordinated around the cobalt atoms in these two cations have no influence upon their tervalent character. With the purpureo and the praseo salts the case is different. The replacement of each molecule (of water or ammonia), which is held by a subsidiary valency, by a chlorine atom, has the effect of diminishing the valency of the complex cation by one unit—the chloropentammine ion thereby being bivalent, and the dichlorotetrammine ion univalent. The triammine compounds were formulated as $[Co(NH)_3X_3]$, which indicates clearly their non-electrolytic properties.

The significance of the co-ordination number was considered in great detail by Werner, whose investigations on this subject continued for upwards of twenty years. The most common value of this number is six, but values of four, as in ammonium salts, are by no means infrequent, and values higher than six, though somewhat rare, are occasionally to be found. Werner soon discerned the possibility of discussing questions of isomerism among co-ordination compounds in stereochemical terms, and indicated the types of structure in which isomerism—geometrical and optical—should be expected to arise. His ideas have been extraordinarily fruitful, and many instances of stereoisomerism have been realized experimentally by Werner himself, and by others who have followed up the chemistry of the co-ordination compounds of numerous metals. Indeed, the theoretical conceptions introduced by Werner have exerted an influence upon the study of inorganic compounds which bears comparison with the effects on the development of organic chemistry which resulted from the ideas of Le Bel and van't Hoff.

Compounds having the co-ordination number of six were regarded by Werner as having an octahedral configuration. Thus in the cobaltammines, the metallic atom was regarded as situated centrally within a regular octahedron, and having the co-ordinated units (whether molecules or electronegative elements or groups) attached to the corners. Assuming an octahedral configuration, it will be evident that stereoisomerism should not be expected in hexammine or in acidopentammine ions. But *cis-trans* isomerism should be possible with a cobalti-tetrammine ion $[Co(NH_3)_4X_2]^+$, according as the X's, each occupying two corners of the octahedron, are separated by an axis or by an edge. This kind of isomerism was first observed in 1890 by Jörgensen, who prepared cobaltic salts in which four molecules of ammonia were replaced by two of ethylenediamine. These isomerides are closely similar in chemical properties, but differ markedly in colour, one series (the praseo salts) being green, and the other (the violeo salts) being violet. Jörgensen regarded the difference in colour to be a consequence of structural isomerism, possibly connected in some way with the presence of the ethylenediamine molecules. But at a later stage Werner was able to show that the isomerism is not structural but geometrical, because he was able to realize it with the simple tetrammine salts. The history of the discovery by Jörgensen in 1893 of dinitrotetrammine cobaltic salts (flaveocobaltammines) isomeric with, but differing in colour from, the croceocobaltammines first described by Gibbs in 1875, followed a similar course. The stereochemical nature of the isomerism was shown conclusively by Werner.

The year 1911 is an important date in the history of the stereochemistry of inorganic compounds. In that year Werner, having recognized that *cis*-2-acido-4-tetrammine salts should, and the corresponding *trans* salts should not, be resolvable into optical isomers, succeeded in resolving several ethylenediamine derivatives, including compounds such as salts having the *cis* $\left[\begin{matrix}\text{en} & & X \\ & \text{Co} & \\ \text{en} & & X\end{matrix}\right]^+$ cation, where X was a chlorine atom or a nitro group. As was to be expected, the corresponding *trans* compounds were found to be incapable of resolution.

The chemistry of the chromiammines, which began with Frémy in 1859, has followed a course very similar to that of the cobaltammines, and the influence of Jörgensen's work on these compounds and afterwards that of Pfeiffer is clearly evident in the later developments. In 1911 Werner succeeded in effecting the resolution of the *cis*-dichlorodiethylenediaminechromic salts into their optical isomerides, and also of the chromioxalates, in which the optical activity is due to an asymmetric anion $[Cr(C_2O_4)_3]^{3-}$. All these results were of great value in confirming Werner's views that co-ordination compounds with the number six had an octahedral configuration.

The constitution of ammonium salts has been very widely discussed. The idea of regarding them as molecular compounds in terms of Kekulé's doctrine of constant valency soon gave way to the views adopted by van't Hoff, Blomstrand and others, according to which the tervalent nitrogen atom of ammonia became quinquevalent in ammonium salts. Werner in 1902 rejected the simple theory of quinquevalent nitrogen, and showed how expression could be given to the properties of ammonium salts —as good electrolytes—in terms of his theory of principal and subsidiary valencies, the ammonium cation being regarded as a unit with four hydrogen atoms co-ordinated around the nitrogen atom. Ammonium chloride was thus formulated as $[NH_4]^+Cl^-$. At about this time much attention was being given, especially by Pope and his collaborators, by Jones and by Wedekind, to the study of optical isomerism in substituted ammonium halides of the general formula NabcdX, where a, b, c, d are different alkyl or aryl groups and X is a halogen; and configuration was mostly discussed in terms of a suggestion due to Bischoff, according to which the nitrogen atom was regarded as within a square pyramid having the four organic groups at the corners and the halogen at the apex. But von Braun, in his article 'Stickstoff' in Abegg's *Handbuch der anorganischen Chemie*, supported Werner's co-ordination formula: 'Mit der Wernerschen Ammoniumvorstellung ist die Tatsache des Auftretens optischer Modifikationen im besten Einklang, ja sie folgt aus ihr, wenn man eine räumlich symmetrische Anordnung der vier Alkylreste um das N-atom annimmt, mit derselben Konsequenz, wie sich die Erscheinungen der optischen Isomerie bei Kohlenstoffverbindungen aus der van't Hoffschen Tetraedervorstellung ableiten lassen.' Von Braun's article on nitrogen was published in 1907, but it was not until 1925 that an elegant proof of the correctness of Werner's views regarding the configuration of the ammonium ion was given by Mills and Warren. They prepared some compounds having a spirocyclic ammonium ion showing optical activity, due to molecular asymmetry, in which the pyramidal configuration was definitely excluded. It necessarily followed that in the quaternary ammonium ion the four radicals are disposed tetrahedrally around the nitrogen atom, and incidentally that the ammonium ion and the methane molecule have similar configurations.

Besides the ammonium salts, numerous others are known which have a co-ordination number of four, but it does not follow that they have a tetrahedral configuration. The platinammines derived from bivalent platinum are of interest in this connexion. This metal gives rise to derivatives of the bivalent platinous salts and of the quadrivalent platinic salts, and may be present in either anion or cation as a complex. For the present purpose the compounds in which the fundamental valency of the platinum has a value of two are the more interesting. The first of such compounds, known as Magnus's green salt, was obtained by its discoverer in 1828 by the action of ammonia on a solution of platinous chloride. Its empirical composition corresponds to the formula $Pt(NH_3)_2Cl_2$, but was later shown to be more correctly formulated as

$$[Pt(NH_3)_4]\ [PtCl_4].$$

Some twelve years later Magnus's green salt was studied in greater detail by Reiset and by Peyrone who prepared several derivatives. Further progress in the direction of making some sort of classification of the various ammoniacal platinum compounds known at the time was made by Gerhardt in 1850, but it was not until about the year 1869 that Blomstrand was able to deal with them theoretically, according to the same principles which he applied to the cobaltammines and chromiammines. In elaborating his theoretical ideas, Blomstrand derived much assistance from the experimental work of others, notably that of Cleve and of Drechsel. Both Blomstrand and Jörgensen recognized the existence of two series of compounds, namely, those of bivalent and those of quadrivalent platinum, but their mode of formulation did not admit of satisfactory discussion of various questions of isomerism; in short, the same sort of difficulties were encountered which arose with the cobaltammines.

From 1893 onwards Werner was able to formulate both series in terms of his co-ordination theory: those derived from bivalent platinum were regarded as having a co-ordination number of four, and, for reasons to be discussed immediately, were considered to have a planar configuration, while an octahedral configuration was assigned to the derivatives of quadrivalent platinum, as in the case of the cobaltammines and chromiammines.

Werner's reason for choosing a planar configuration for the compounds of the general formula $Pt(NH_3)_2X_2$ was briefly as follows. According to the tetrahedral doctrine of Le Bel and van't Hoff, isomerism should only arise if all four groups around the platinum atom were different, but actually two series of isomeric compounds corresponding to the above formula were known. Werner accordingly regarded the isomerism as geometrical, the compounds

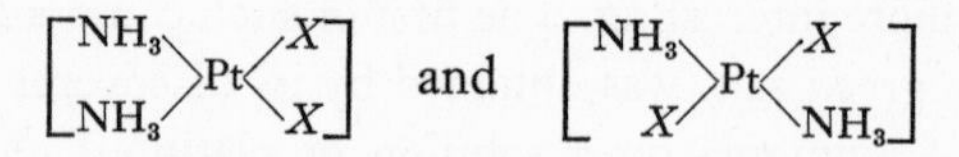

having the *cis* and *trans* configurations respectively, and he was able to bring forward much experimental evidence in support of his views. In 1935 a rigid proof of the correctness of Werner's theory of a planar configuration for these types of compounds was given by Mills and Quibell. They prepared a compound having a complex platinum cation, with the groups around the platinum atom such that optical activity should arise in consequence of molecular dissymmetry if the configuration were planar, but not if it were tetrahedral—a tetrahedral configuration would have a plane of symmetry, and therefore would not be resolvable. Mills and Quibell succeeded in resolving the compound, thereby confirming the correctness of Werner's theoretical ideas.

The chemistry of co-ordination compounds of numerous heavy metals has been greatly extended in more recent years, and much of the progress in this department of study has resulted from the introduction of reagents capable of forming *chelated* compounds, a term first introduced by Morgan and Drew in 1920. Reference has already been made to the use of ethylenediamine—one molecule of this base taking the place of two molecules of ammonia in co-ordination compounds—which figured largely in Werner's researches. In 1925 and 1926 Mann and Pope introduced $\alpha\beta\gamma$-triaminopropane, $H_2N.CH_2.CH(NH_2)CH_2.NH_2$, a tri-acid base equivalent to three molecular proportions of ammonia. Of the numerous compounds which they prepared mention may be made of *bis*-triaminocobaltic chloride

$$[(NH_2CH_2.CH(NH_2).CH_2NH_2)_2Co]^{3+}Cl_3^{3-},$$

which is the analogue of the well-known luteo compound, hexammine cobaltic chloride. A number of investigators have developed the study of co-ordination compounds with these newer chelating reagents, and some of the results have given rise to questions which involve theoretical difficulties. Thus Mann in 1929, continuing his researches with $\alpha\beta\gamma$-triaminopropane, discussed the stability of complex salts, and pointed out that certain examples of salts of considerable stability were difficult to reconcile with the generally accepted electronic theory of co-ordination compounds, first suggested in 1923 independently, and with different terminology, by Lowry and by Sidgwick. It will be seen in what follows that while the whole subject of valency, and Werner's doctrine of co-ordination in particular, has been very greatly illuminated by the introduction of electronic theories, some questions still remain which appear to require further consideration.

The stability of hydrates is a subject of much interest. Broadly speaking when a salt is found to crystallize with a number of molecular proportions of water equal to a well-defined co-ordination number, such as six, the salt may be expected to prove fairly stable. Many examples of such relatively stable hexahydrates are known. But the problem is actually more complicated: a most interesting example is that of the isomeric chromic chlorides, $CrCl_3,6H_2O$. Two modifications, one violet and the other dark green, were studied by Werner and Gubser between 1901 and 1906, and afterwards in 1906 and 1907 by Bjerrum. The violet salt was found to have all the chlorine in the ionic condition and the six molecular proportions of water to be firmly held, while in the dark green salt only one-third of the chlorine is in the ionic condition, and two of the six molecular proportions of water are more easily removed than the remaining four. In terms of Werner's co-ordination theory Bjerrum assigned the formulae $[Cr(H_2O)_6]^{3+}Cl_3^{3-}$ and $[Cr(H_2O)_4Cl_2]^+Cl^-,2H_2O$ to the violet and to the dark green isomerides respectively. In the course of studies on the kinetics of the transformation of these salts in solution, Bjerrum was led to predict, and also to prepare, a third isomeride, a light green salt intermediate in properties to the others, which he formulated as $[Cr(H_2O)_5Cl]^{2+}Cl_2{}^{2-},H_2O$. All the distinctive features of these compounds thus received satisfactory expression in terms of the formulae assigned to them, and in particular the representation of those molecules of water actually co-ordinated around the chromium atom, as being the more firmly held, was in full agreement with the results of experiment. But other cases are known which are much less straightforward. Reference has already been made to the great stability of copper sulphate monohydrate, which was first demonstrated by Graham. There is general agreement in regarding the blue hydrated cupric salts as having a co-ordination number of four, the pentahydrated sulphate being accordingly formulated as $[Cu(H_2O)_4]^{2+}SO_4^{2-}$, H_2O; and similar considerations are applicable in writing the formula of copper tetrammine sulphate as $[Cu(NH_3)_4]^{2+}SO_4^{2-},H_2O$. In what manner the unco-ordinated molecule of water is held in these compounds is not easy to determine, and in any case the experimental results on the isothermal dehydration of copper sulphate are at variance with the idea that molecules of water which are actually co-ordinated are more firmly held than those which are attached in some other way.

The early history of organic chemistry was very much concerned with radicals—groups of atoms which could participate in a number of reactions without losing their individuality—such as the radical cyanogen discovered by Gay-Lussac in 1815 and the benzoyl radical discovered by Liebig and Wöhler in 1832. The question regarding the possibility of the existence of these and other radicals in the free state became a burning one towards the middle of the nineteenth century, when much attention was being given to the development of the classical theory of valency, and at that time the idea of free radicals was not seriously entertained. But long before that time—actually in 1808—Seebeck had observed that when a solution of ammonium carbonate was electrolysed using a mercury cathode, the metal swelled considerably with evolution of gas. This phenomenon was also studied by Berzelius, by Davy, and by Gay-Lussac and Thenard, who varied the experimental procedure in several ways, such as using sodium amalgam upon solutions of ammonium salts instead of direct electrolytic preparation. As the ammonium salts were known to resemble those of the alkali metals in many respects, the theory that this 'ammonium amalgam' actually contained the radical ammonium united in some manner with mercury received a certain amount of support. Against this view was set the instability of the product. But for upwards of a century researches were instituted with the object of discovering the nature of the ammonium amalgam, and particularly with the purpose of ascertaining if the radical had even a transitory existence. Thus in 1901 Moissan conducted experiments on the electrolysis of ammonium salts dissolved in liquid ammonia at low temperatures, but he failed to isolate the radical. Moissan noted that in the decomposition of the material the volumes of ammonia and hydrogen were in the ratio of two to one, but he did not regard this as sufficiently convincing evidence of the existence of the ammonium radical as such in combination with mercury, and suggested an alternative explanation. On the other hand, experiments by Coehn in 1900 and afterwards provided evidence of a contrary nature. Coehn found that the amalgam had an exceptional capacity for precipitating metals from solutions of their salts, and could therefore scarcely be regarded as a mixture of the gases occluded in mercury. In 1920 and 1921 Schlubach, working on lines similar to those employed by Moissan, but using more dilute solutions, isolated the radical tetraethylammonium and afterwards the still more unstable ammonium in what he claimed to be a yield of the order of 50%.

The discovery of cyanogen by Gay-Lussac was not an example of the isolation of a free radical, but the preparation of its polymer, C_2N_2, and the same considerations apply to Kolbe's experiments on the electrolysis of the alkali-metal salts of the fatty acids. The gas which was obtained in this way by the electrolysis of a solution of potassium acetate was not methyl but ethane. In the light of the Frankland-Kekulé doctrine of valency, a group of atoms having a free bond, such as $—CH_3$ or —CN, could not possibly exist as a stable molecule, but if the molecules were doubled the free bonds would of course disappear, and stability would therefore follow. The subsequent course of chemistry throughout the nineteenth century was wholly in accordance with this view. But the possibility of radicals having a *transitory* existence was considered by a few chemists, chiefly as a means of understanding the mechanism of some reactions. Between 1892 and 1904 Nef published a series of papers in which he abandoned the doctrine of the universal quadrivalency of carbon, and suggested that in some compounds, such as isonitriles, the element must be bivalent. In developing these views Nef regarded the radical methylene as having a very brief existence, but he was unable to support his ideas with any direct experimental evidence. As will be seen in what follows, work carried out at a much later date has supplied confirmation of many of Nef's ideas.

In 1900 the first example of the isolation of a free radical having a certain degree of stability was accomplished by Gomberg. In attempting to prepare hexaphenylethane, $(C_6H_5)_3C.C(C_6H_5)_3$, by the action of metals on triphenylmethyl chloride, he obtained a product having properties altogether different from what might be expected in a saturated hydrocarbon of this molecular formula. The substance was found to be highly unsaturated and to give strongly coloured solutions. Molecular weight determinations appeared to support the hexaphenylethane formula, but Gomberg attributed this to polymerization of the triphenylmethyl radical, $(C_6H_5)_3C—$, and later work has certainly supported this view. In 1922 Gomberg and Sullivan showed that the absorption spectrum of the compound in ionizing solvents, such as sulphur dioxide or hydrogen cyanide, is totally different from that in non-ionizing solvents like benzene. In the ionizing solvents there is definite electrical conductivity, so that the existence of positive and negative triphenylmethyl ions must be recognized. In addition to these ions, non-electrolytic radicals—actual free radicals—undoubtedly exist in non-ionizing solvents. Hexaphenylethane can thus dissociate in two different ways according to the nature of the solvent. It may be noted that the term *free* as applied to radicals is usually restricted to uncharged groups of atoms as opposed to ions; and thus its use in connexion with the ions of triphenylmethyl is to some extent a departure from established custom. As triphenylmethyl forms compounds with halogens in which it functions as a cation, and with alkali metals where it acts as an anion, studies on the properties of the two ions were accordingly made in suitable solutions of these two kinds of compounds. Experiments on solutions of the chloride in liquid sulphur dioxide showed that the cation had a fair degree of stability, but investigations on the anion did not result in much progress until 1925, when Kraus and Rosen, in following up a suggestion due to Ingold, confirmed the existence of the less stable anion in solutions of potassium triphenylmethide in liquid ammonia. A great deal of work has been carried out with various substituted triphenylmethyls, much of which was concerned with the effect of various substituents on the stability of the free radicals. A very interesting result of this kind was realized by Ziegler and Boye in 1927. They found that a trinitrotriphenylmethyl having the formula

$$\begin{matrix} NO_2C_6H_4 \diagdown & \\ NO_2C_6H_4 - & C \\ NO_2C_6H_4 \diagup & \end{matrix}$$

, with the three nitro groups in the *para* position, was sufficiently stable to be obtainable in crystalline condition. In terms of classical theory, this would amount to a demonstration of a fairly stable compound having a tervalent carbon atom in the molecule.

Carbon is not the only element capable of giving rise to compounds in which questions of valency present difficulties according to classical theory. A conspicuous example is to be found in nitric oxide. Lothar Meyer (*Modern Theories of Chemistry*, English edition, 1888) remarked that 'nitric oxide, NO, is undoubtedly an unsaturated compound, as is also nitric peroxide, NO_2, at temperatures above 150° C. These compounds are unsaturated whether we regard nitrogen as tri- or pentavalent, and in both cases the number of free combining units is an uneven one. Hence the subterfuge, that the affinities of one and the same atom are able to combine with one another, used to explain the free combining units in carbon monoxide, cannot avail in such cases.' Coming to more modern times Wieland and Lecher in 1911 showed that the tetra-arylhydrazines, such as tetraphenylhydrazine,

$$(C_6H_5)_2N—N(C_6H_5)_2,$$

dissociate reversibly in solvents such as boiling toluene, giving dark green solutions of the simpler molecule $(C_6H_5)_2N$—, which may be regarded as a compound of bivalent nitrogen. Free radicals of this kind, as might be expected, were found to be highly unsaturated. The chemistry of these and of other closely relative compounds has been studied extensively by Wieland and his collaborators and, since 1922, by S. Goldschmidt.

The aromatic free radicals are characterized by a fair degree of stability. In this respect they differ greatly from the aliphatic free radicals, the existence of which was first predicted in 1897 by Nef. But it was not until the year 1929 that the existence of free methyl was first clearly demonstrated by Paneth and Hofeditz; other free aliphatic radicals were discovered in the course of the next few years. It may be noted that the recognition of these extremely reactive residues owed their discovery to the development of great improvements in experimental methods. In 1908 Bone and Coward in the course of their work on the thermal decomposition of hydrocarbons had postulated the transitory existence of such radicals as methylene, $>CH_2$, thereby reviving a conjecture made by Nef some years previously. The methods developed by Paneth, Rice and others were based on the principle of effecting rapid removal of the products of a pyrolytic or of a photochemical reaction so as to avoid recombination of the radicals to form stable molecules. Their methods were indeed modern adaptations of a technique first employed by Deville in the course of his studies on thermal dissociation about the year 1864. Free methylene was actually recognized by Rice and Glasebrook in 1933 in the thermal decomposition of diazomethane.

The question of the much greater stability of aromatic, as compared with aliphatic, free radicals has been discussed in terms of the theory of resonance by Ingold in 1928 and by Pauling and Wheland in 1933. It was considered that the explanation must be sought in the aromatic nuclei providing centres of resonance. This is an outcome of the modern view that it is impossible to assign a *single* formula to the molecule of benzene: the true formula is to be found as a mean of all the theoretically possible structures among which resonance takes place.

In the course of the last century there was a vast accumulation of substances—many of highly complex structure—the constitution of which was established, with a steady gain of precision, upon the foundations of classical theory. Similar considerations are applicable to questions of configuration: thus the establishment of the configuration of the sugars by Emil Fischer was a direct outcome of the principles laid down by Le Bel and van't Hoff. At the same time it should be noted that in some instances it had apparently become possible to assign alternative constitutional formulae to certain compounds, each capable of representing the characteristic behaviour with a sufficient degree of accuracy. Various refinements in the classical conceptions of valency were sometimes introduced for particular requirements; for example, Thiele suggested his theory of partial valencies in 1899 to discuss the peculiarities of compounds having conjugated double bonds in the molecule, especially their behaviour in reactions involving addition. A much more interesting departure was made by Bjerrum in 1923 regarding the constitution of amino-acids. These compounds have well-defined amphoteric properties: thus glycine, $CH_2(NH_2)CO_2H$, when treated with alcoholic hydrogen chloride forms glycine ester hydrochloride, $CH_2\langle\begin{smallmatrix}NH_2, HCl\\CO_2C_2H_5\end{smallmatrix}$, in which the amphoteric character of amino-acetic acid is clearly expressed in terms of classical theory. Bjerrum, however, considered this mode of formulation deficient, as being inconsistent with the physico-chemical properties of these classes of compound. Thus the aliphatic amino-acids have high melting-points and the electrochemical properties of their solutions are in some respects not unlike those of ammonium salts. This subject had received attention at the hands of several investigators many years previously; thus J. Walker published an important paper in 1904 on the conductivity of various amphoteric electrolytes, in which he showed that Ostwald's dilution formula is not applicable to these classes of substance. But Bjerrum made an important departure from current ideas regarding the nature of the ions. Instead of regarding a solution of an amino-acid as consisting chiefly of molecules of the type $NH_2.R.CO_2H$, together with cations, $NH_3^+.R.CO_2H$, and anions, $NH_2.R.CO_2^-$ the relative amounts of the three constituents being determined by the values of the basic and acidic ionization constants, Bjerrum regarded the neutral molecules of aliphatic amino-acids as consisting almost wholly of doublet ions, $NH_3^+.R.CO_2^-$. The apparent acidic and basic ionization constants are not to be regarded as such, but as hydrolysis constants which are related to the constants of the older theory by the equations

$$K_{acid}=k_{water}/k_{base} \quad \text{and} \quad K_{base}=k_{water}/k_{acid}.$$

The case of the aromatic amino-acids is somewhat different. The values of the hydrolysis constants indicated that the solutions contained both non-ionized molecules and doublet ions and that the proportions of the former varied over a wide range depending on the nature of the particular compound.

At various times problems concerned with chemical bonds have been discussed in mechanistic terms. Thus Baeyer's theory of strain in cyclic compounds, put forward by him in 1885, according to which the angle between the bonds of a carbon atom, when unstrained, has a value of $109^\circ 28'$, was a direct outcome of van't Hoff's tetrahedral conception. This theory has been remarkably successful in the way of explaining the instability of ethylenic linkages, and questions connected with the relative stability of cyclic compounds as determined by the number of atoms in a ring. It has been extended in certain directions, notably by Sachse in

1890, to the problems of strainless rings, and has thus been the means of tackling questions of stereochemical importance on a mechanical basis. In a very real sense, discussion of questions of constitution and configuration according to classical theory may be regarded as fundamentally mechanical.

Questions concerning the location of double bonds in cyclic compounds have long been a source of great interest. The principles according to which the well-known formula for benzene was established by Kekulé were applied shortly afterwards by Dewar and by Körner in assigning a precisely similar formula to pyridine. As Kekulé assumed the double bonds in his formula to be mobile, similar considerations were applicable to the Dewar-Körner formula for pyridine. In 1922 Mills and Smith, in a paper on the reactivity of methyl groups in heterocyclic bases, brought forward reasons for considering that a methyl-pyridine (CH_3, N) should be much more reactive than (CH_3, N), the increase in reactivity being determined by the double bonds in the vicinity of the methyl group. At the outset they realized that it would be a practical impossibility to demonstrate the existence of two such isomeric methyl pyridines, unless means could be found for 'locking', or at least impeding the mobility of, the double bonds. This they succeeded in doing in two ways, one of which consisted in fusing a benzene nucleus with the pyridine ring so as to produce an *iso*quinoline nucleus. Two isomeric methyl*iso*quinolines were prepared having the formulae:

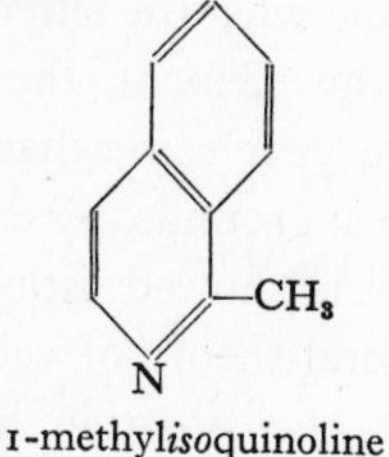

1-methyl*iso*quinoline

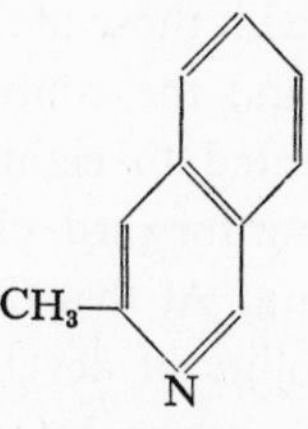

3-methyl*iso*quinoline

It is obvious that the difference between the two compounds lies in the position of the double bonds with respect to the methyl group; and it was assumed that the fusion of the benzenoid with the pyridine nucleus gave rise to the *iso*quinoline derivatives having the double bonds fixed in a manner precisely similar to what obtains in Erlenmeyer's formula for naphthalene.

Mills and Smith considered that the methyl group in 1-methyl-*iso*quinoline should be much more reactive than that of the 3-methyl compound, and such was found to be the case. Thus when each compound was heated with benzaldehyde and zinc chloride, the 1-methyl compound condensed readily giving 1-styryl*iso*quinoline, but no condensation occurred with the 3-methyl compound; even after prolonged heating, the base and the benzaldehyde were recovered unchanged. A number of other means of testing the marked difference in reactivity between the two isomerides were applied, and the results fully justified the assumptions made by the authors that the reactivity of methyl groups in these classes of compound is influenced by the contiguity of the double linkages.

Electrical theories of chemical union began with the dualistic conceptions of Berzelius, but soon fell into disrepute chiefly as a consequence of the rapid progress in organic chemistry. The discovery of electrons as universal constituents of matter by J. J. Thomson in 1897, and the great developments in the studies of radioactive phenomena in the course of the following years, gradually attracted attention towards the possibility of discussing chemical combination and the nature of valency in terms of electrons. In 1908 Ramsay devoted his presidential address to the Chemical Society to this subject, and some of his ideas were comparable with those of Abegg concerning what the latter termed the normal and the contra-valencies of an element, the sum of which amounted to eight. In the same year somewhat similar views were put forward, chiefly on physical grounds, by Stark and by Kauffmann. At that time most chemists showed little interest in the possibility of developing any general theory of valency on an electronic basis; by 1913, however, the situation began to change. In that year a number of discoveries, notably Rutherford's experiments on the scattering of α-rays by matter, resulted in the abandonment of J. J. Thomson's original conception of atoms consisting of electrons within a uniform sphere of positive electricity, in favour of regarding them as having the positive electricity concentrated in a small sphere at the centre of the atom with the electrons revolving in spherical or elliptic orbits around it. This was the Rutherford-Bohr model atom. The chemical properties of this atom were regarded as determined by the peripheral electrons, the nucleus being concerned with the mass of the atom and with radioactive phenomena. In consequence of evidence from various lines of inquiry, notably the radioactive displacement law of Soddy, Fajans and Russell, the recognition of isotopes, and Moseley's work on X-ray spectra, a correct understanding of the significance of the periodic law was gained, in particular that the atomic number of an element is a more fundamental characteristic than its atomic weight. It should be added that Moseley assumed in 1913 that the atomic number of an element represents not only its ordinal number in the periodic table, but also the magnitude of its nuclear charge. The correctness of this latter assumption was verified in 1920 by Chadwick as the result of experiments on the scattering of α-particles by metals.

In 1916 electronic theories of valency were propounded independently by Kossel and by Lewis. Their approach to the subject was on somewhat different lines. Kossel avoided the use of any kind of model atom, but elaborated his theory chiefly from Abegg's rule of eight, and from a suggestion made by van den Broek according to which the atomic number of an element in the periodic table is numerically equal to the number of electrons in the atom. It was noted that in the periodic table an inert gas is always preceded by a halogen and followed by an alkali metal, and great importance was attached to the atomic structure of the inert gases. With the exception of helium, the atom of which contains two electrons, all the other inert gases were considered to have an outer ring of eight electrons. Thus neon with an atomic number of 10 and argon with one of 18 were regarded as having the electronic structures of 2, 8, and 2, 8, 8 respectively. The formation of ions was explained in terms of the loss or gain of electrons taking place in such a manner as to produce a stable system with eight electrons in the outer ring—an inert gas configuration. Thus the cation derived from sodium and the anion derived from chlorine were considered to be due to a loss of an electron by the atom of sodium and the gain of an electron by the chlorine atom. The ionizable valency of sodium chloride was thus explained in terms of a simple transference of electrons, and precisely similar considerations were applicable to electrolytes generally.

While Kossel's theory was concerned primarily with ionizable or, as they are sometimes termed, polar compounds, Lewis devoted his attention chiefly to non-polar compounds. The importance of the distinction between the two classes had been stressed by J. J. Thomson in 1914, and was again emphasized by Lewis. At the outset Lewis made use of a cubical atomic model in which the electrons actively concerned with chemical combination were regarded as situated at the corners of this cube. Thus the lithium atom had one corner of the cube occupied by an electron, the beryllium atom had two, and so on until neon was reached with the eight corners each holding an electron. The stable system of an inert gas structure consisting of eight electrons was thus realized. Non-polar bonds were regarded as consisting of shared electrons, and were represented by two dots to indicate the electrons constituting the bond between the atoms. Lewis's ideas were further elaborated by Langmuir in 1919 and 1920, who emphasized the fundamental distinction between electrovalency in which the union is effected by a transference of electrons, and covalency in which the electrons are shared.

The Lewis-Langmuir theory of chemical combination with the cubical model atom as the fundamental unit met with a very fair degree of success in the early years of the development of electronic theories of valency. Nevertheless, the more elaborate Rutherford-Bohr model atom, although at that time less popular with most chemists, was greatly preferred by physicists. The cubical model atom was strongly condemned by Millikan in the

Faraday Lecture which he delivered before the Chemical Society in 1924 in the following picturesque terms: 'The chemist in America has in general been content with what I have called a loafer electron theory. He has imagined the electrons sitting around on dry goods boxes at every corner, ready to shake hands with, or hold on to, similar loafer electrons in other atoms.' In pointing out the argument advanced by chemists for a static electron theory, namely, the existence of localized valencies in chemistry, Millikan continued: 'but it is simply due to a misunderstanding that this argument was ever used against the orbit theory. *For no physicist—and I wish to emphasize this fact—has ever advanced the theory that the electrons all rotate in coplanar orbits.* Localized valencies are probably just as compatible with the orbit theory when the orbits are properly distributed in space, as with the conception of stationary electrons....'

From 1922 onwards the theory of valency discussed in terms of electrons was the subject of numerous publications. In that year the theory of induced polarity in atoms, including such conceptions as Thiele's theory of partial valencies, was discussed at length in two papers, one by Lapworth, and the other by Kermack and Robinson. The idea of polarity in atoms was no new subject. In 1850 Brodie published an interesting paper entitled *On the condition of certain elements at the moment of chemical change*, in which he assumed that a molecule of an element may divide into two atoms, each carrying electric charges of opposite sign. Brodie's ideas received favourable consideration by Schönbein in developing his theory of autoxidation, and in any case the idea of polarity in atoms was clearly expressed. Lapworth's approach to the subject was begun by considerations based on the conception of Faraday's tubes of force, but extended in terms of electronic theory. Kermack and Robinson made free use of the Lewis-Langmuir cubical atom, and applied electronic theory to a number of problems, including the formula of benzene. In 1923 several important papers on electronic theories of valency appeared, including the first of a series by Lowry entitled *Studies in electrovalency*. In this paper Lowry discussed the polarity of double bonds from a somewhat novel point of view: thus the peculiarities of butadiene, $CH_2{=}CH{-}CH{=}CH_2$, which when brominated yields the dibromide, $CH_2Br{-}CH{=}CH{-}CH_2Br$, had been formulated by Thiele in terms of his theory of partial valencies to indicate the migration of the double bond, were explained by Lowry by assuming the superposition of an electrovalency on a covalency. He wrote the formula of butadiene as $CH_2^+{-}CH^-{-}CH^+{-}CH_2^-$, and insisted that in a conjugated system the distinction between double and single bonds disappears altogether. Among the numerous topics discussed in this paper, Lowry with magnificent boldness described the halogens, $Cl_2 \rightleftarrows Cl^+ + Cl^-$, as behaving 'like amphoteric electrolytes' in connexion with the relative positions which they take up by substitution in an aromatic nucleus. Lowry's idea of mixed or, as they were sometimes termed, semi-polar double bonds, received a certain amount of support on physical grounds, notably from studies by Sugden and others on parachors, which are molecular volumes determined under conditions of equality of internal pressure. Admitting the possibility of some form of mixed bonding, such as Lowry assumed, it would appear necessary to recognize a third type of valency.

Up to about the year 1923 some chemists discussed their electronic conceptions of valency without introducing any particular model atom, while others committed themselves definitely to the Lewis-Langmuir cubical atom; but in that year an important departure was made by Sidgwick. In a paper entitled *Co-ordination compounds and the Bohr atom*, Sidgwick showed how the conceptions of classical organic chemistry could be unified with Werner's theory of co-ordination compounds, and emphasized that this could not be done without using the Bohr atom as a basis. It should be added that the problem of the actual distribution of the electrons in atomic shells and the characterization of the electronic orbits had been solved by Bohr in 1921; and in that year an important advance on Langmuir's ideas was made on strictly chemical considerations by Bury which resulted in assigning the same electronic structures to the inert gases as had been done by Bohr. Sidgwick gave precision to the nature of co-ordinate linkages, as consisting of two electrons donated by one atom and received by another, and thus differing from an ordinary bond in which the electrons are shared equally between the two atoms. He was able to give a precise significance to Werner's co-ordination numbers, and particularly to the behaviour of numerous types of compounds as regards ionization. Sidgwick elaborated his ideas in further detail in two books, namely, *The Electronic Theory of Valency*, which appeared in 1927, and *Some Physical Properties of the Covalent Link in Chemistry*, which embodied the substance of a course of lectures which he delivered in Cornell University in 1931.

The recognition of three main types of union is now a well-established feature of modern chemical theory, and it must be stated that much of the progress in the development of this branch of the subject has resulted from the greatly increased attention which has been given to physical methods of investigation. In the forefront of these methods mention must be made of spectroscopic studies, and particularly of X-ray methods of analysis. Since the nature of X-rays was first clearly demonstrated in 1912 by Laue, Friedrich and Knipping, practically valuable methods were developed by the Braggs, and later by Debye and Scherrer, and applied by numerous investigators to the study of crystalline substances. By these means the constitution of many compounds which had been arrived at by purely chemical methods received ample confirmation; but, in addition to this, direct information regarding the distances between atoms was obtained. Thus it has been shown that the carbon to carbon distances in singly, doubly and trebly linked aliphatic compounds are 1·54, 1·33 and 1·20 Ångstrom units respectively. The distances between the carbon atoms in a benzenoid nucleus were all found to be approximately 1·4 Ångstrom units; and whereas this value is a distinctive feature of these compounds, it has been concluded that no single constitutional formula can give an accurate representation of the molecule of benzene. At the present time the formula is best discussed in terms of the conception of resonance.

The methods of X-ray analysis have been amplified, if not to some extent superseded, in more recent years by those of electron diffraction. This subject arose out of theoretical considerations on wave mechanics—a subject largely founded by Prince Louis de Broglie since the year 1922. Some two years later de Broglie showed that electrons must be considered as having a dual character, namely, as behaving in such a manner as to indicate properties of both waves and particles connected by the equation $\lambda = h/mv$, where λ is the wave-length and mv the momentum of the electron. Experimental confirmation of this idea was given in 1928 by G. P. Thomson and by others, and methods for investigating the structure of molecules by electron diffraction have been worked out, notably by Wierl, since 1930. Thus practically identical values for the distances between the chlorine atoms in carbon tetrachloride were obtained by Wierl and by Debye, the former by the method of electron interference, and the latter by the X-ray method. The degree of accuracy attainable by the two methods is much the same, but the electron diffraction method is the more practically valuable, especially for work on gases and vapours. A single illustration may be given in connexion with a subject of long-standing difficulty.

Diazomethane, CH_2N_2, the simplest aliphatic diazo compound, was first obtained by von Pechmann in 1894, and has since been widely used in organic work as a methylating agent. The formula $H_2C\left<\begin{array}{c}N\\ \| \\ N\end{array}\right.$ was assigned to it at an early stage, and as all its reactions are consistent with such a formula, it received general acceptance. Nevertheless, the possibility of an open-chain formula was considered seriously by Angeli and Thiele in 1911, who preferred to express its constitution as $H_2C{=}N{\equiv}N$. It will be noted that this formula represents one of the nitrogen atoms as quinquecovalent—an idea which would be repugnant to modern chemists, but was widely accepted at the time. In 1935 Boersch investigated the question by the method of electron diffraction. His results were regarded as definitely against the cyclic formula; the distance between the carbon and the nitrogen atom adjacent to it, and that between the two nitrogen atoms were 1·34 and 1·13 Ångstrom units respectively. The open-chain formula was accordingly rewritten as $H_2C\overset{\leftarrow}{=}N{\equiv}N$ and $H_2C{=}N\overset{\rightarrow}{\equiv}N$, with a co-ordinate link. Diazomethane, according to this view, is considered to be a resonance hybrid, namely, a compound the constitution of which cannot be strictly expressed by any *single* formula.

The subject of resonance is an outcome of studies on quantum mechanics, especially those of Heisenberg about 1925, and has been eagerly pursued by chemists, particularly by Pauling. The term mesomerism was suggested by Ingold as being more appropriate, but has not come into general favour. It is to be noted that resonance is concerned with the movement of electrons, not of atoms, and is thus to be carefully distinguished from tautomerism. The distinction between the two phenomena is doubtless perfectly clear in well-defined cases, but Pauling in his important work, *The Nature of the Chemical Bond*, which was published in 1939, has admitted that it is not always possible to maintain it. Pauling expressed this distinction in general terms by stating that 'whereas a tautomeric substance is a mixture of two types of molecule, differing in configuration, in general the molecules of a substance showing electronic resonance are all alike in configuration and structure'. To this statement may be added a further remark, namely, that the molecules of a resonance hybrid possess not only all the properties represented by the alternative electronic formulae, but certain additional properties, particularly an increase of stability, which is a direct consequence of the resonance energy.

REFERENCES

F. Ephraim. *Chemische Valenz und Bildungslehre*. Leipzig, 1928.

T. Graham. *Chemical and Physical Researches*. Edinburgh, 1876.

J. H. van't Hoff. *The Arrangement of Atoms in Space*. With a Preface by Joannes Wislicenus and an Appendix 'Stereochemistry among Inorganic Substances' by A. Werner. Translated by A. Eiloart. London, 1898.

A. Werner. *New Ideas on Inorganic Chemistry*. Translated from the second German edition by E. P. Hedley. London, 1911.

N. V. Sidgwick. *The Electronic Theory of Valency*. Oxford, 1927.

N. V. Sidgwick. *Some Physical Properties of the Covalent Link in Chemistry*. Cornell University Press, New York, 1933.

N. Bohr. *The Theory of Spectra and Atomic Constitution*. Second edition. Cambridge, 1924.

M. GOMBERG. *Radicals in Chemistry, Past and Present.* The Chandler Lecture, Columbia University Press. New York, 1928.

F. O. and K. K. RICE. *The Aliphatic Free Radicals.* Baltimore, 1935.

R. A. MILLIKAN. Atomism in modern physics. The Faraday lecture. *J. Chem. Soc.* 1924, p. 1405.

R. WEINLAND. *Einführung in die Chemie der Komplex-Verbindungen.* Zweite neubearbeitete Auflage. Stuttgart, 1924.

B. C. BRODIE. On the condition of certain elements at the moment of chemical change. *Phil. Trans.* 1850, vol. CXLI, p. 759.

T. M. LOWRY. Studies in electrovalency. Part I. *J. Chem. Soc.* 1923, p. 822.

N. V. SIDGWICK. Co-ordination compounds and the Bohr atom. *J. Chem. Soc.* 1923, p. 725.

A. LAPWORTH. A theoretical derivation of the principle of induced alternate polarities. *J. Chem. Soc.* 1922, p. 416.

W. O. KERMACK and R. ROBINSON. An explanation of the property of induced polarity of atoms and an interpretation of the theory of partial valencies on an electronic basis. *J. Chem. Soc.* 1922, p. 427.

Transactions of the Faraday Society. Vol. XIX, 1923–4. The electronic theory of valency. A general discussion held by the Faraday Society in the Department of Physical Chemistry, Cambridge.

Annual Reports on the Progress of Chemistry. Issued by the Chemical Society since 1904.

L. PAULING. *The Nature of the Chemical Bond.* New York, 1939.

W. G. PALMER. *Valency, Classical and Modern.* Cambridge, 1944.

CHAPTER IX

SOME CONSIDERATIONS ON KINETIC CHEMISTRY

The title of this chapter is intended to embrace some remarks on the subject of chemical change in its widely diversified aspects. Throughout the history of chemistry its devotees have been very much concerned with reactions for preparative purposes, both on the laboratory and the industrial scale. The objective in preparative work is thus primarily a practical one; nevertheless, many long-known reactions have at various times been the subject of close experimental study, and work of this kind has not infrequently been rewarded with improved yields and purer products. Questions of much theoretical interest have sometimes arisen in this way, and the application of physico-chemical methods of investigation has frequently illuminated much that would otherwise have remained obscure.

Progress in preparative work has been very closely concerned with effecting improvements in the means of separating substances, and thereby obtaining the desired product in the purest possible condition. It is obvious that closely similar substances necessarily present greater difficulties of separation than substances having greater diversity of chemical or physical properties. The separation of the rare earths has largely been a matter of effecting prolonged fractional crystallizations of substances differing little in solubility. On the other hand, the preparation of pure gases by the removal of impurities by absorption with reagents has usually been a matter of no great difficulty. An example of historical interest is to be found in Dumas's work on the combining ratios of hydrogen and oxygen in 1842. In that year Dumas effected a marked improvement in a method first used in 1819 by Berzelius and Dulong, namely, that of passing hydrogen over heated copper oxide and determining the weight of water formed and the loss in weight suffered by the copper oxide. Dumas's success with this method was primarily due to the care with which he removed impurities from the hydrogen before causing it to react with the copper oxide. His result was noteworthy in showing that the combining ratio is not exactly a matter of whole numbers; the departure which he observed, though not its precise magnitude, has received ample confirmation by later work. Progress in atomic weight research has been brought about far more as the result of success in preparing highly pure substances than by improvements in the construction of sensitive balances, the importance of which is of course without question. On this subject the remarks of Hillebrand and Lundell in the Preface to their *Applied Inorganic Analysis* are of interest. 'The most elaborate precautions in weighing and measuring and in the final determination of the element go for naught if the analyst has failed to prepare quantitatively the compound on which the calculation is based, and to free it quantitatively from all other compounds that would affect the calculation.' After a remark on the relevance of this to atomic weight determinations the authors continued as follows: 'For example, in 1921 the accepted atomic weights of aluminium, silicon, and antimony were 27·1, 28·3, and 120·2, respectively. In 1925 these were changed to 26·97, 28·06, and 121·77, the differences in parts per thousand being 4·8, 8·6, and 12·9.'

As might be expected, the more reactive or, what comes to the same thing, the less stable a substance may be, the greater is the difficulty in obtaining it in pure condition. The history of preparative chemistry is very much a collection of records of improvements in experimental technique which have resulted in surmounting previously existing practical difficulties. Frequently it has happened that the substance in view has given rise to fairly stable derivatives, but the last stage—the isolation of the substance itself—has presented the most serious obstacles, and sometimes it has been a matter of prolonged experimental work to bring it to a successful conclusion. Thus hydroxylamine, which was discovered by Lossen in 1865, and hydrazine, which was discovered by Curtius in 1887, were for many years well known in solutions and their reactions had become part of the common stock of chemical knowledge before the bases had been isolated in anhydrous condition. Anhydrous hydroxylamine was first isolated in 1891 by

Crismer, and by Lobry de Bruyn. Crismer obtained it by heating the additive compound with zinc chloride, $(NH_2OH)_2,ZnCl_2$. The method employed by Lobry de Bruyn consisted in dissolving the hydrochloride in methyl alcohol, decomposing this compound with sodium methylate, and after separating the resulting sodium chloride, subjecting the liquid to distillation under reduced pressure. Four years later anhydrous hydrazine was isolated from the hydrochloride by Lobry de Bruyn using the same method. By way of contrast it is of interest to note that Berzelius first prepared pyruvic acid in 1834 by distilling a mixture of tartaric acid and potassium bisulphate, and no improvement on that method has since been discovered.

Success in preparative work directed towards the synthesis of some compound of definite constitution has sometimes been frustrated by the occurrence of unexpected developments, such as intramolecular transformations. An example of historical interest arose in connexion with the first synthesis of an alkaloid, namely that of coniine, the alkaloid of the spotted hemlock (*Conium maculatum*). Hofmann in a long series of experiments between 1881 and 1885 showed the compound to be *dextro*-α-propyl piperidine,

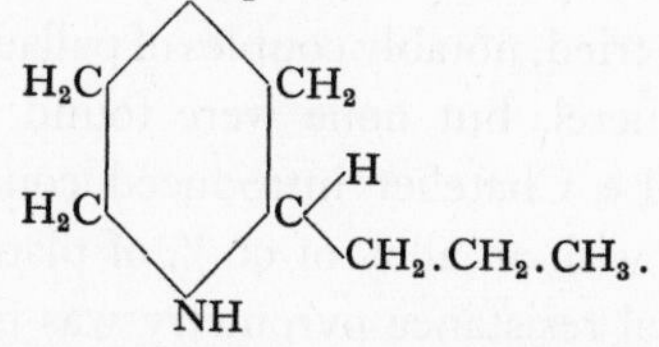

In 1886 Ladenburg attempted to prepare α-propyl pyridine by heating pyridine with *n*-propyl iodide, since it was known that α-methyl pyridine could be prepared in a similar manner. But because of intramolecular change, the method resulted in failure—the product being α-*iso*propyl pyridine—and was accordingly abandoned. Ladenburg, however, succeeded in preparing α-allyl

pyridine, N $CH:CH.CH_3$, by condensing α-picoline with acetaldehyde and this compound on reduction yielded *dl*-α-propyl piperidine. By fractional crystallization of the tartrates of the externally compensated base thus obtained, he prepared the *dextro* constituent, which was found to be completely identical with the natural product.

Black, in his lectures, which were published in 1803 four years after his death, had attempted to define chemistry as 'the study of the effects of heat and mixture'; and even at the present time his definition is not without some value, because so much progress in practical chemistry has resulted from careful attention to temperature. Success in the study of reactions at high temperatures, such as metallurgical processes, has been much associated with developments in pyrometry. It may be noted that temperature, strictly speaking, is not a measurable quantity, but it may be made so by reference to the thermodynamic scale. For practical purposes the reference scale is that of the gas thermometer, and the various methods, electric, calorimetric and optical, which have been devised for work at high temperatures, require to be standardized in terms of the gas scale. Thermocouples were first suggested by Antoine Becquerel in 1830, and shortly afterwards Pouillet made some experiments with couples of iron with platinum. Various other combinations were tried, notably couples of palladium and platinum by Edmond Becquerel, but none were found to be satisfactory until 1887 when Le Chatelier introduced couples consisting of platinum together with an alloy of 90% of platinum and 10% of rhodium. Electrical resistance pyrometry was first introduced by Siemens in 1871, but was not at first altogether satisfactory. However, between 1886 and 1892 Callendar and Griffiths developed the method with great success, and it was employed by Heycock and Neville in the course of a long series of researches on alloys. In 1863 Edmond Becquerel used the radiation from incandescent solids as an index of their temperature, and the method was developed later by Violle, Le Chatelier and others. Calorimetric methods have been used by several experimenters, notably by Violle in 1895 who estimated the temperature of the arc as 3600° C. by determinations of the specific heat of carbon, and values not differing very greatly from this figure have been obtained by various optical methods.

For experimental work at temperatures above those attainable in fuel furnaces, the chief sources of heat have been the electric arc, the oxy-hydrogen blowpipe, and Goldschmidt's aluminothermic process. Of these the arc, first discovered by Davy, was used by Despretz in 1849 in some experiments on the fusion and volatilization of certain highly refractory substances; but it was not until 1892 that Moissan, in an important series of researches requiring the use of furnaces, was able to separate the heating effect of the arc from the electrolytic action which it exerts. These investigations, which were continued for upwards of twenty years, embraced experiments on the preparation of crystalline carbon, and of various elements, such as chromium, manganese, molybdenum, tungsten, uranium, vanadium, titanium and zirconium, which had hitherto only been obtained by methods involving very great difficulty, and also studies on some new compounds, the metallic borides, carbides, and silicides. The temperatures in the flame of the oxy-hydrogen blowpipe, a source of heat first discovered by Drummond in 1826, are much lower than those which are reached in the arc: according to Moissan temperatures of the order of 2000° C. are obtainable by means of this apparatus. Nevertheless the oxy-hydrogen blowpipe was found to be a valuable instrument in the hands of experimentalists in the nineteenth century, among whom mention must be made of Debray and Deville. The intense heat obtainable from mixtures of finely divided aluminium and metallic oxides, sometimes known as thermite, was discovered by H. Goldschmidt in 1898, and the temperature thus realized in this way has been estimated at about 3000° C. The thermite process has been employed not only as a means of reducing certain metallic oxides, but is also of importance in work where intense heat is required locally, and is thus commonly employed in welding steel rails. Still higher temperatures can be realized by substituting *mischmetall* (an alloy of rare-earth metals of variable composition) for aluminium. Thus in 1904 Weiss and Aichel were able to prepare vanadium and niobium from the pentoxides by using mischmetall, whereas aluminium did not give satisfactory results.

For such operations as cutting steel plates the oxy-hydrogen blowpipe has been superseded by a similar apparatus in which the hydrogen is replaced by acetylene. The temperatures obtainable in this way are much higher, and exceed 3000° C., because acetylene is a highly endothermic compound, and its heat of combustion therefore is considerably greater than that of its constituent elements. According to the equation for complete combustion, one volume of acetylene should require two and one half volumes of oxygen, but in practice it has been found more advantageous to use less oxygen—about one half of the above-mentioned proportion—and thus deliberately to avoid complete combustion.

In 1912 Langmuir began a series of experiments on heating hydrogen at low pressures by glowing tungsten or platinum wires, and obtained direct evidence of dissociation of the gas into atomic hydrogen. In later work he devised a blowpipe in which a jet of hydrogen was directed upon an arc between tungsten electrodes. The temperature realized in this way was of the order of 3300° C., as it was sufficient to melt tungsten. It is to be noted that the extremely high temperature attained in the Langmuir blowpipe is due, not to the heat of combustion of hydrogen, but to the intensely exothermic reaction of the transformation of atomic into molecular hydrogen.

The cause of the luminosity of flames has long been a subject of discussion. In 1816 Davy ventured the opinion that the luminosity of a flame, such as that of a candle, was due to the presence of incandescent particles of solid carbon. This question was regarded very differently by Frankland. In an ascent of Mont Blanc in 1859 Frankland observed that stearin candles burnt at the same rate at Chamonix as at the summit, but there was a very marked diminution of illuminating power at the higher altitude. In some experiments carried out between 1861 and 1868 he was able to show with the aid of a Bunsen grease spot photometer that the decrease of illuminating power is directly proportional to the diminution of atmospheric pressure. Candles were found to be unsuitable for these experiments, so he employed coal gas and sometimes a lamp fed with amyl alcohol as the source of light. Analysis of the products of combustion of candles showed no perceptible difference with variation of the external pressure. Frankland also conducted some experiments on the combustion of hydrogen and of carbon monoxide in oxygen under pressures up to 20 atmospheres, and obtained luminous flames showing continuous spectra; he finally concluded that Davy's theory must be erroneous. In arriving at this conclusion, Frankland pointed out that brilliant light is produced when substances such as arsenic, phosphorus, and carbon disulphide are burnt in oxygen, and that the temperatures thus produced would preclude the presence of solids; all the products would be gaseous under those conditions. He considered that the cause of the luminosity of gas or candle flames was to be sought in radiation emitted from dense but transparent hydrocarbon vapours. The subject is admittedly complicated and difficult, but it appears now to be recognized that the presence of white hot particles of carbon cannot altogether be abandoned in seeking for an explanation of the luminosity of hydrocarbon flames.

Although the combustion of carbonaceous materials has been used as a source of heat from very early times, the scientific study of the subject had its beginnings in the nineteenth century, and was approached from various directions. The investigations of Sainte-Claire Deville into thermal dissociation, which were carried out with the aid of his hot-cold tube, have been of particular value in the subsequent development of the subject. By his method Deville, in 1864 and 1865, was able to demonstrate the dissociation of carbon dioxide into carbon monoxide and oxygen and also of carbon monoxide into carbon and carbon dioxide. This latter reaction was also followed up by Lowthian Bell and taken into consideration with numerous other experiments on the chemical reactions in blast furnaces. In this connexion it is worthy of note that although the smelting of iron in this country can be dated from the middle of the eighteenth century, the chemistry of the process was not properly understood until Bell had concluded his investigations which were published in 1872 in a work entitled *Chemical Phenomena of Iron Smelting*. Another subject of great importance is the chemistry of water gas. The beginnings of acquiring a correct understanding of the water gas reaction were made by Bunsen in 1853 who conducted experiments on the combustion of mixtures of hydrogen and carbon monoxide with insufficient oxygen for complete oxidation, and determined by analysis how the oxygen was divided between the two combustible gases. Bunsen's experimental results were studied theoretically by Horstmann in 1877. He showed that at every temperature an equilibrium was set up as represented by the equation

$$\frac{C_{H_2O} \times C_{CO}}{C_{CO_2} \times C_{H_2}} = K.$$

The water gas equilibrium has been the subject of numerous later experimental studies. One single example may be quoted. The well-known Bunsen burner was invented in 1855, and about the year 1892 Smithells and Teclu, independently constructed a simple apparatus for separating the two chief cones of the flame for purposes of analysis. A further step was taken by Haber in 1904. He showed that it is incorrect to suppose that coal gas burns *as such* in the flame: on the contrary, as he was able to demonstrate in the inner green zone, carbon monoxide, steam, hydrogen, and carbon dioxide (diluted of course with nitrogen) are all present together in the proportions which are set up in the water gas equilibrium. Combustion of the hydrogen and carbon monoxide takes place in the outer zone by contact with the external oxygen of the air.

The study of thermal dissociation of gases such as carbon dioxide by the Deville hot-cold tube method was continued by Le Chatelier about 1888. Improved forms of apparatus depending upon the principles of this method, namely intense heating of the gas followed by removal of the products of the reaction, were devised by Nernst and von Wartenberg in 1906, and by Langmuir in the same year. The discovery of atomic hydrogen by Langmuir was a direct outcome of the hot-wire method.

That chemical change may be facilitated, or, it may be, actually brought about, by the presence of substances which apparently undergo no visible change has long been known, and the term *catalysis* was first applied by Berzelius to describe the phenomenon. Very widely different types of chemical change are affected by catalysts, but it is significant that Berzelius included catalytic action in the section on electricity in the German edition of his *Lehrbuch der Chemie*, which was published in 1843. Döbereiner in 1823 observed the property of spongy platinum of causing hydrogen and oxygen to combine. This effect was shortly afterwards studied at greater length by Dulong and Thenard, and in very elaborate detail by Faraday in 1833 in the course of his electrochemical experiments. Dobereiner regarded the effect as purely electrical, but Dulong and Thenard and also Faraday were much more reserved in venturing upon explanations. As the catalytic efficiency of platinum was found to be greatly influenced by its physical condition, Faraday became convinced that the explanation was to be sought in the property of the metal condensing or absorbing the gases, and thereby bringing them into a condition such that reaction could readily take place. This theory of surface action has received much, though by no means universal, support from later investigators.

As catalytic phenomena are so extremely common and of such varied types, attempts have not been wanting to introduce some sort of classification. Broadly speaking there have been two schools of thought on the theory of the subject. Ostwald and his followers have regarded catalysts as in the nature of accelerators—substances which greatly increase the velocity of reaction but without actually *causing* chemical change to take place. Armstrong viewed the subject very differently: he regarded completely pure substances as chemically inert, the presence of what he called a *determinant* being necessary for any reaction to proceed. In 1885 he stated, and on numerous later occasions repeated, his idea that chemical combination consists in reversed electrolysis, but, it must be added, without giving any very precise indication of what was to be understood by this process. For long Armstrong was careful to draw a distinction between a determinant and a catalyst. The determinant was regarded as a trace of a substance having electrolytic properties which is active in solution, while the catalyst was supposed to function in a state of suspension, and was intended to include contact substances and enzymes. Armstrong gave renewed expression to these views in the First Messel Memorial Lecture which he delivered before the Society of Chemical Industry in 1922. It may be remarked that Armstrong's ideas on chemical change, though interesting, have not secured any very general acceptance, and in one notable instance have given rise to serious misunderstanding.

The effect of moisture on chemical change was studied by Dixon, chiefly in connexion with the reaction between carbon monoxide and oxygen since 1880, and afterwards in very elaborate detail with other gaseous mixtures such as hydrogen and oxygen by Baker. In one of Baker's experiments carried out in 1902, a silver wire was heated in a well-dried mixture of hydrogen and oxygen up to the point of fusion of the metal. The gases combined rapidly at the surface of the wire with formation of drops of water, but without any explosion taking place. This phenomenon was interpreted in terms of Armstrong's ideas of reversed electrolysis as being due to the great purity of the water, in short to the absence of an electrolytic determinant. The fallacy in this explanation of the absence of any explosion was pointed out by Dixon in his presidential address to the Chemical Society in 1910. The correct explanation, which was given by Dixon, is that by the time that drops of liquid water have formed, the wire is surrounded by steam and there is scarcely any electrolytic gas left to explode. Attention was directed to this subject by Hinshelwood in a Report on Chemical Kinetics, published in 1927, because the erroneous interpretation of Baker's experiment had persisted for many years notwithstanding the true explanation of it by Dixon.

Reactions between gases which are effected or facilitated by the aid of solid catalysts are very numerous; evidence has accumulated from various sources, for example, the very exhaustive investigations of Sabatier and Senderens of which they published a summary in 1905, were concerned with the hydrogenation of numerous organic compounds under the catalytic action of certain finely divided metals, such as nickel, and the evidence appears to indicate that any explanation based upon occlusion of gases on the surface of the metal, as considered by Faraday, must be regarded as an over-simplification. Contact substances have been found to be highly specific in respect of their catalytic properties: thus if primary alcohols are passed over heated copper they are resolved into the corresponding aldehydes and hydrogen, whereas if alumina is used the products are olefines or ethers together with steam. Phenomena of this kind have given rise to explanations which take into account the formation of intermediate compounds which are alternately formed and decomposed.

Numerous chemical reactions are known to take place in consequence of the formation of intermediate compounds, and theories concerning catalysis in such reactions have constantly been formulated. But difficulties have very frequently arisen regarding the actual composition of these real or supposed intermediate compounds. A very striking example is to be seen in the chemistry of the lead chamber process in the manufacture of sulphuric acid. In passing it may be noted that it was at one time thought that the success with which the contact process was worked since the beginning of the present century would result in the gradual abandonment of the older lead chamber process. This prediction has been completely falsified: the lead chamber process continues to be an important source of sulphuric acid. The nature of the reactions by which the sulphur dioxide is oxidized to sulphuric acid under the influence of oxides of nitrogen in presence of steam has at various times been debated since the early years of the nineteenth century. It was clearly understood by chemists such as Davy that the higher oxides of nitrogen, for instance nitrogen dioxide (or its polymer, dinitrogen tetroxide), can part with oxygen to sulphur dioxide and become reoxidized by contact with the air; the cyclic nature of the process was evident. It was also well known that, when the supply of steam was deficient, a crystalline substance, usually termed 'chamber crystals' having the empirical formula $HSNO_5$, separated out, but was immediately hydrolysed by water to sulphuric acid and nitrous acid. The formula of this intermediate product was written by some as $SO_2\langle^{OH}_{ONO}$ (nitroso-sulphuric acid) and by others as $SO_2\langle^{OH}_{NO_2}$ (nitrosulphonic acid); the substance may well be tautomeric. In the early years of the present century much of the controversy regarding the chemistry of the lead chamber process was centred around views put forward by Lunge and by Raschig, both very closely connected with the sulphuric acid industry. One aspect of this subject concerned the formation of an intermediate product to which Raschig in 1905 assigned the formula H_2SNO_5, having the probable constitution $HO.SO_2.NO.OH$. This acid was regarded by him as identical with an acid obtained in solution by Sabatier in 1896 by the action of reducing agents upon solutions of nitrous acid in sulphuric acid. The solution of the acid has a deep blue colour. Lunge in 1879 had observed the production of deep blue or violet solutions in the course of experiments on the reduction of nitrous vitriol by mercury to nitric oxide in connexion with the invention of his well-known nitrometer. There is every reason to suppose that the same product was formed in both sets of experiments. It will be noted that Raschig's formula for this acid, usually known as nitrosi-sulphonic acid, represents the nitrogen atom as quadrivalent—an unusual valency for this element. Nevertheless Raschig in 1911 stated definitely that the blue colour of the compound was to be attributed to quadrivalent nitrogen. Raschig's explanation of the various reactions in the lead chamber process was somewhat more elaborate than that of Lunge—the latter had more in common with the simpler schemes current during the nineteenth century. In any case it must be recognized that, having regard to the complexity of the chemistry of nitrogen and sulphur compounds and their numerous oxy-acids, it must be practically impossible to decide which of the various possible reactions is the predominant one in the lead chamber process. It may be remarked that Raschig's ideas have been the subject of much criticism, and that there has been a certain tendency to return to the simpler theories of the process; but there is no general agreement on the subject.

The direct formation of sulphur trioxide from sulphur dioxide and oxygen under the influence of platinum appears to have been first discovered by Davy between 1817 and 1820, and the first attempts to manufacture sulphuric acid by the contact process were made by Peregrine Phillips in 1831. Practical difficulties arose in consequence of the poisoning of the catalyst, and the process was accordingly abandoned. When the various practical difficulties were finally overcome, nearly seventy years later, the contact process became more important than the lead chamber process as the source of concentrated and of fuming sulphuric acid. Platinum has been found to be the most efficient catalyst for this reaction, but good results have also been obtained with much less costly materials such as ferric oxide and vanadium pentoxide. The catalytic action of metallic oxides has been attributed to alternate oxidation and reduction. Thus Lunge in 1902 regarded ferric oxide as alternately reduced to ferroso-ferric oxide by sulphur dioxide and the latter oxidized back to ferric oxide. Similar considerations are applicable to vanadium pentoxide, V_2O_5, which is reduced to the blue vanadyl oxide V_2O_4 with formation of sulphur trioxide; the vanadyl oxide is then re-oxidized to the pentoxide by the free atmospheric oxygen: indeed the function of the vanadium oxides is similar in some respects to that of the oxides of nitrogen in the lead chamber process. But a satisfactory explanation of the exceptionally high catalytic properties of platinum still remains to be discovered. In this connexion experiments carried out by Mond, Ramsay and Shields in 1898 on the catalytic action of platinum black in effecting the union of hydrogen and oxygen are of some importance, since they found that platinum in a very finely divided condition always contained oxygen, whether simply occluded or actually in chemical combination was not clear. And in 1912 Wieland, as the result of extensive investigations on oxidation, emphasized the importance of regarding the removal of hydrogen, much more than the addition of oxygen, as the means of obtaining an understanding of the reaction mechanisms. In particular

Wieland showed that, when moist sulphur dioxide was passed over palladium black in the absence of oxygen, sulphuric acid was formed with considerable evolution of heat, presumably as follows:

$$H_2SO_3 \rightarrow SO_3 + H_2 \quad \text{and} \quad SO_3 + H_2O \rightarrow H_2SO_4.$$

It is possible to regard the contact process from this point of view, according to which the function of the oxygen is concerned with the removal of hydrogen resulting from the dehydrogenation of the sulphurous acid, and not as *directly* effecting the oxidation of sulphur dioxide. Support for Wieland's views is forthcoming as regards the necessity for the presence of moisture, thoroughly dried sulphur dioxide and oxygen being remarkably inert.

The slow oxidation of white phosphorus at ordinary temperatures has been the subject of a large number of investigations. The luminosity which is observed when a stick of the element is exposed to moist air at ordinary temperatures and pressures is a well-known feature of the absorption of the oxygen. There are, however, certain curious phenomena, some of which have long been known and for which no simple explanation was forthcoming, but which have later become subjects of minute experimental study. A collection of the literature on the subject up to the year 1898 was made by Centnerszwer. One of the early valuable series of quantitative experiments on the subject was carried out by Graham in 1829. At that time it was known that pure oxygen does not react with phosphorus at ordinary temperatures and pressures, but does so if the pressure of the gas is reduced, either directly, or by dilution with other gases. It was also known that certain gases, notably ethylene, possess the remarkable property of preventing the action of oxygen on phosphorus altogether at ordinary temperatures. Graham's investigation was concerned with determinations of the minimum quantities of substances such as ethylene, ether, and the vapours of certain essential oils, capable of quenching the luminescence of phosphorus in air. In one of his numerous experiments he remarked that 'a stick of phosphorus was repeatedly left for upwards of 24 hours over water in air containing only one four-hundredth part of its bulk of pure olefiant gas during the hot weather of July and August 1828, thermometer frequently above 70°, without diminishing the bulk of the air in contact'. These observations were of much importance in connexion with developments in the study of autoxidation in general.

Graham's remarks in the concluding paragraph of his paper are of much interest in connexion with later work, particularly with an extended series of experiments carried out by Moureu and Dufraisse nearly a century later. He stated that 'the interference of those gases in preventing the oxidation of phosphorus, etc., is probably allied to the influence of the same and several other gases in preventing the accension of the explosive mixture of oxygen and hydrogen by the electric spark, first observed by Sir H. Davy (Essay on Flame), and since confirmed and investigated by Dr Henry (*Phil. Trans.* 1824), and Dr Turner (*Edin. Phil. J.* vol. XI). Olefiant gas was found to act most powerfully, half a volume preventing the combustion of the explosive mixture, that is, defending the hydrogen from oxidation; and here, as in the case of phosphorus, the olefiant gas seemed to suspend the usual action between the supporter and combustible, without undergoing any change itself. If the nature of this *influence* of olefiant gas is the same in both cases, it forms a singular and interesting subject of inquiry, readily accessible in its most minute details in the case of phosphorus.'

In 1917 Moreu and Dufraisse began a lengthy course of investigations on the influence of various substances in stopping the autoxidation of certain classes of organic compounds, especially aldehydic substances, and they found that many phenols, such as hydroquinone and pyrogallol, were extremely efficient in this respect. In 1925 they published an interesting paper entitled *The so-called poisoning of oxidizing catalysts*, in which reference was made to the early work of Davy, Henry and Turner, and they formulated a theory of what they termed *antioxygenic properties* of substances, an important feature of which was that all substances which possess the property of impeding the autoxidation of readily oxidizable substances must themselves be readily oxidizable. The 'antioxygenes' were considered to act by decomposing catalytically the peroxides which are formed by the union of the autoxidizable substances with free oxygen.

Schönbein's well-known investigations on the production of ozone during the autoxidation of phosphorus were begun about the year 1840. At that time the nature of ozone was not understood, but Schönbein succeeded in showing that the properties of the gas generated in this way were identical with those of the gas produced in the vicinity of a frictional electric machine, and sometimes in the oxygen generated in the electrolysis of dilute sulphuric acid. Schönbein and later investigators conducted quantitative experiments on the manner in which oxygen is divided between an oxidizable substance and itself becoming activated. The experiments of van't Hoff and his pupils, notably those of Ewan in 1894 and 1895, were of much importance in this connexion. Ewan found that the rate of oxidation of phosphorus in moist oxygen was proportional to the pressure up to a certain critical value, it then fell abruptly, and finally became zero as the pressure approached one atmosphere. In dried oxygen the results were different, the rate under those conditions being proportional to the square root of the pressure. The conversion of some of the oxygen into ozone was regarded by van't Hoff as a secondary reaction, because the luminosity of phosphorus is impeded by a sufficient pressure of oxygen; but experiments made by Chappuis in 1881 showed that the presence of ozone favours such luminescence.

It has become evident that many apparently simple reactions proceed less directly than might at first sight have been supposed. The contrast between the rate of oxidation of phosphorus with the effect of variation of pressure, according as the gas is moist or dried, is by no means exceptional. Reference has already been made to the experiments of Dixon and of Baker on this subject, and it may be added that Baker was able to distil phosphorus in oxygen which had been dried with extreme care without inflammation taking place. Even before that time, actually in 1869, Wanklyn showed that thoroughly dried chlorine is without any action upon sodium, and this observation was confirmed by Cowper a few years afterwards. It must, however, be added that since Baker's time the centre of interest in gaseous reaction has been much more concerned with the effect of the walls of the containing vessels. The importance of taking account of disturbances which may arise in consequence of wall effects was first pointed out by van't Hoff in connexion with reactions such as the polymerization of cyanic acid to cyamelide, and the effects were studied by conducting the experiments in vessels of identical volume but of widely different areas. This subject was discussed at length in the *Études de dynamique chimique*. It was found by van't Hoff that in many reactions between gases the walls of the containing vessels exert a marked effect, and later investigations have very largely gone to show that many gaseous reactions which hitherto were supposed to be homogeneous are in reality by no means so. Many of the curious phenomena encountered in the study of reactions in which gases take part are now discussed in terms of chain mechanisms.

The production of light in chemical changes may be due to rise of temperature resulting from a sufficiently great increase in the velocity of reaction, as happens in flames; or, alternatively, it may be the result of direct transformation of chemical energy into luminous energy. This latter process is true chemiluminescence, but it should be added that it is not always possible to distinguish between the two kinds of phenomena. The oxidation of certain classes of organic compounds at ordinary temperatures is sometimes accompanied with the emission of light, but there does not appear to be anything fundamentally different between the chemiluminescence of reactions of this kind and that of the longest known example, namely that of the slow oxidation of phosphorus. Although the literature on the oxidation of phosphorus is extensive, there has been little in the way of direct experimental study on the actual luminescence. In 1912 Centnerszwer and Petrikaln showed that the light from glowing phosphorus gives some bands in the ultra-violet as well as in the visible region of the spectrum. This subject received a thorough investigation by Emeléus and Downey in 1924 with the aid of a quartz spectrograph. Their object was to ascertain that the mechanism of the oxidation of the element was the same, whether the phosphorus burnt vigorously or slowly without appreciable rise of temperature. They found five bands present in the ultra-violet region under widely different experimental conditions, ranging from combustion in air enriched with excess of oxygen with a flame temperature of 800° C., down to the luminous glow obtainable at the ordinary temperature; they accordingly concluded identity in the mechanism of combustion.

The modern idea that many reactions—even apparently simple ones—proceed in terms of what have become known as chain mechanisms, appears to have originated in connexion with the photochemical union of hydrogen and chlorine. This reaction has been the subject of a great number of investigations ranging back to the time of Dalton, but the fundamental law of photochemical absorption, often wrongly attributed to Draper, who enunciated the principle in relation to this particular reaction in 1843, actually arose in a different connexion. In 1819 Grotthuss elaborated the law as the result of experiments which he carried out on the reduction of alcoholic solutions of ferric chloride in closed vessels under the influence of light. He concluded that only those rays of the spectrum which are absorbed by a substance sensitive to light can give rise to photochemical action. In giving expression to this law Grotthuss used phraseology from which it is apparent that he regarded light as having electrochemical characteristics; which is perhaps not surprising in view of his ideas on the mechanism of electrolysis; but, having regard to modern developments, it would appear justifiable to consider him as in a certain sense in advance of his time.

Draper's experiments on the union of hydrogen and chlorine were followed by the classical work of Bunsen and Roscoe in 1857. This work resulted in the confirmation of some, but not all, of Draper's conclusions. As regards the initial acceleration observed by these experimenters, often known as photochemical induction, it should be noted that Bunsen and Roscoe did not attribute it to any peculiar action of light, because they observed a precisely similar effect in the bromination of tartaric acid in darkness. On the contrary, they considered it to be a distinctive feature of the initiation of a chemical change. In viewing this subject historically, it should be remembered that the law of mass action was not clearly formulated at that time. This law was evolved gradually, and from more than one direction, extending over half a century from the publication of Berthollet's *Essai de statique chimique* to the precise expression which was given to it by Guldberg and Waage in 1867. Berthelot and Péan de Saint Gilles in their experiments on esterification in 1862 observed that the velocity of reaction was accelerated when the alcohol and acid were first mixed, and they remarked 'pour concevoir l'accélération initiale il faut admettre une sorte d'inertie, de resistance à vaincre qui retard la combinaison dans les premiers instants'. A contrary view, however, was expressed by Harcourt and Esson on this subject in 1866. They regarded the increase of velocity of reaction which they observed on the reduction of acidified potassium permanganate by oxalic acid as determined by secondary reactions. And van't Hoff produced convincing experimental evidence, drawn from the study of widely different types of chemical reactions, that disturbing effects of any kind are always traceable to the presence of impurities or to autocatalytic actions. All subsequent investigation has gone to show the accuracy of van't Hoff's fundamental ideas.

The reaction between hydrogen and chlorine was also studied by Bunsen and Roscoe from the point of view of actinometry. They were able to show that when various salts were introduced into a non-luminous flame, the rate of reaction could be varied accordingly: thus the flames coloured by lithium or strontium salts were practically devoid of activity, whereas a pronounced effect was obtained by introducing copper salts into a flame. Modern experimenters have confirmed and greatly extended these results; for instance, Allmand and his collaborators have shown direct proportionality between rate of reaction and intensity of light of specified wave-length. The effect of moisture on this reaction is very complicated. In 1887 Pringsheim observed that a dry mixture of hydrogen and chlorine was less sensitive to light than a moist one, and careful experiments by Baker in 1894 led to the same conclusion. But this conclusion has been disputed to some extent by later investigators. Thus Coehn and his collaborators showed in 1923 that under identical conditions of desiccation a mixture of the gases inert to visible light would nevertheless react when illuminated by ultra-violet light below 2540 Ångstrom units of wave-length. Regarding the effect of conditions which determine the period of induction observed by Draper and by Bunsen and Roscoe, Burgess and Chapman in 1906 showed that certain impurities, particularly traces of ammonia, had a marked effect in increasing the period of initial acceleration. They attributed this effect to the formation of a retarding catalyst, presumably nitrogen chloride, and the subsequent work of Chapman and of others has given general support to this view, but explanations have differed regarding the mechanism of the retarding action. This subject was considered, together with the role of water in the union of the gases, in a valuable research by Norrish in 1925.

The means of obtaining a satisfactory theoretical insight into the problems of the reaction between hydrogen and chlorine were forthcoming in 1912 when the quantum theory was introduced into photochemistry by Einstein. According to his law of photochemical equivalence, one light quantum, $h\nu$ (sometimes termed one photon), is absorbed for every molecule which is transformed. Since the frequency is inversely proportional to the wave-length, it is clear that the shorter the wave-length the larger must be the light quantum. When this principle was applied by Bodenstein in 1913 to the experimental results, it was found to be altogether at variance with them. It was observed—and confirmed by numerous other experimenters—that one photon effected the union of about 10^4 or 10^5 molecules of the reacting gases. A revision of the theoretical ideas was therefore necessary, and Bodenstein suggested the possibility of explaining the extremely high quantum efficiency of the reaction on the basis of what has since become known as a chain mechanism. In 1918 Nernst gave greater precision to this idea, and suggested that the primary action of light was to dissociate some of the chlorine molecules into atoms; these chlorine atoms would then react with hydrogen molecules forming hydrogen chloride and free hydrogen atoms, in some such manner as the following:

$$Cl_2 + h\nu = Cl + Cl, \quad Cl + H_2 = HCl + H, \quad H + Cl_2 = HCl + Cl;$$

and the chain would finally end with the direct union of the free chlorine and hydrogen atoms. All subsequent work has gone to show that this view is fundamentally correct. Thus Bowen in 1924, taking account of the heats of dissociation of the halogens and of the heats of formation of their hydrides, and correlating these values with the wave-lengths of the light absorbed as shown by the absorption spectra, was able to calculate whether a photon of specified value should be able to dissociate a given halogen molecule, and also whether the resulting atoms could react with hydrogen molecules and thus form a chain. He concluded that such would actually be the case with the hydrogen-chlorine reaction, and thereby obtained strong support for the Nernst chain mechanism. Direct evidence for the formation of chains has been obtained in other ways. Thus Rodebush and Klingelhoefer in 1933 obtained atomic chlorine by exposing the gas to the electrodeless discharge—an adaptation of a method previously used by Bonhoeffer for preparing atomic hydrogen—and found that the gas thus treated reacted at once with molecular hydrogen in darkness.

It has been pointed out by Nernst and by Warburg that deviations from the requirements of the Einstein law of photochemical equivalence may be in the opposite direction from that which has been observed for the hydrogen-chlorine reaction—the number of molecules which are activated being apparently *smaller*, not greater, than corresponds with the absorption of one photon per molecule which is transformed. This may arise either because the quantum which is absorbed may be too small to effect the primary change, or because the molecule, having absorbed the quantum, may lose it again by collision. However, a number of reactions have been shown to follow the law of photochemical equivalence. Thus Bowen in 1923 found that the decomposition of unstable substances, such as chlorine monoxide and chlorine dioxide in carbon tetrachloride solutions, when illuminated by violet light proceeds in accordance with the law. Another example is to be found in the action of light in producing the latent image in photography. The nature of this primary chemical change had long been recognized as in some manner connected with the partial loss of chlorine or bromine from the silver halides, and precautions to avoid this source of error were regularly taken by chemists concerned with atomic weight work, such as Stas. From 1887 onwards Carey Lea prepared a number of products, which he described as *photohalides*, and claimed that the primary product of the action of light was some form of sub-halide. The matter was finally settled about the year 1924 by Hartung with the aid of a sensitive micro-balance. He was able to demonstrate direct loss of the halogen, but without any evidence of the formation of any intermediate photohalides. Between 1921 and 1929 Eggert and Noddack demonstrated the validity of the law of photochemical equivalence for dry photographic plates.

The primary processes in photochemical reactions have also been considered in terms of what really consists in an elaboration of an idea put forward originally by Arrhenius in 1889, and considered to be applicable to the beginning of *any* chemical reaction. Activation, in terms of this idea, was supposed to consist in a certain fraction of the molecules becoming in some undefined manner endowed with additional chemical energy. In 1925 Victor Henri, as a result of studies on the absorption spectra of certain vapours when illuminated with light within a definite range of wave-length, directed attention to a broadening of the lines of the absorption bands, and elaborated a theory of *predissociation* to account for increased reactivity associated with this change in the spectra. It may be possible to regard the process of activation as something akin to incipient dissociation—to predissociation in fact. The concept of molecular activation has been elaborated, notably by Eyring, as an alternative hypothesis to the kinetic theory of molecular collisions favoured by Hinshelwood and by Moelwyn-Hughes as a basis for discussion of chemical change in general terms. The theoretical ideas of Eyring and others have sometimes been summarized in the *transition-state* theory, but, as Hammett has pointed out, both possess the idea of an energy of activation in common; 'whereas the collision theory has oversimplified the concept of activation, the other glosses over the necessity of collision.'

The classical division of chemical changes into various 'orders' according to the results of experiments on the velocity of reaction should be dated from the publication of van't Hoff's *Études de dynamique chimique*. The distinction between unimolecular and bimolecular reactions was regarded as fundamental, and in general terms van't Hoff laid down the principle that the time required for a given fractional transformation for an n-molecular reaction is inversely proportional to the $(n-1)$th power of the initial concentration of the reacting substances. It is undoubtedly true that there is a large mass of experimental evidence in support of this principle, but later work has gone to show that the distinction between first- and second-order reactions is one of degree rather than a fundamental one. The first step towards obtaining a satisfactory understanding of the mechanism of unimolecular reactions was taken in 1923 by Christiansen and Kramers. In a discussion of this subject in terms of the idea of molecular activation, they showed theoretically what conditions are necessary for a unimolecular reaction to take place, and also how departure from first-order procedure would arise. This subject was discussed independently by Hinshelwood in 1931, who pointed out very clearly that the distinction between first- and second-order reactions was a matter of the time elapsing between activation and reaction, and accordingly in the importance of the deactivation of active molecules before chemical transformation has occurred. The relation between the velocity constant of a reaction and the absolute temperature, suggested by Arrhenius to be of an exponential character, has received general support as the result of much later work both on gaseous reactions and on those which take place in solution. It should be noted that support for the collision theory has also been obtained from experiments on the comparatively few reactions the kinetics of which can be studied experimentally both in the gaseous phase and in solution.

When suitable 'inert' solvents have been chosen, it has been found that the energy of activation has approximately the same values for the reactions taking place in the liquid and in the gaseous phase. It has become well established that the energy of activation, E, is concerned with molecular collisions according to the general equation:

$$\frac{\text{number of effective collisions}}{\text{total number of collisions}} = e^{-E/RT},$$

in which the expression on the right-hand side involves the Boltzmann-Maxwell principle of the distribution of molecular velocities.

The course of chemical changes, which proceed with sufficient slowness to be suitable for experimental study, has been investigated by the isolation of substances, presumed to be intermediate products, from which it may be possible to obtain some insight into the nature of the mechanism of the reactions. While there can be no doubt that much information of real value has been obtained in this way, it has become recognized that such procedure may be attended with a certain amount of risk, because the isolation of such substances, which might be formed under the particular experimental conditions, provides no guarantee that the mechanisms necessarily involve the formation of such substances as intermediate products. The supposed intermediate compounds may be actually by-products of the main reactions. Nevertheless, when sufficient precautions have been taken, this sort of procedure has given rise to results which have secured general assent. Thus, for example, the elaborate experiments by which Bone and his collaborators were able to demonstrate the formation of aldehydes during the slow combustion of hydrocarbons in the early years of the present century, have resulted in establishing a satisfactory theory of the mechanism of the oxidation. It is recognized generally that the attack of oxygen upon a hydrocarbon takes place by hydroxylation, followed by decomposition of the unstable product into an aldehyde and steam, and not by any such process as preferential combustion of either carbon or hydrogen. Another example is to be seen in Chattaway's work in 1914 on the reactions between oxalic acid and glycerol. These reactions had for many years been employed for the preparation of formic acid and of allyl alcohol, but the nature of the mechanisms was not correctly understood, indeed erroneous explanations were to be found in standard text-books. Chattaway was able to show that when oxalic acid reacts with glycerol, both an acid and a normal oxalate are produced, the proportions of which vary according to the conditions. The decomposition of these two esters gives rise to all the products of the reaction; the monoxalate on heating giving rise to monoformin and carbon dioxide, and the dioxalate to allyl alcohol and carbon dioxide. By further action of oxalic acid upon monoformin the acid oxalate is reproduced together with formic acid. The production of formic acid by further additions of oxalic acid to the mixture thus received a satisfactory explanation.

Investigation of reaction mechanisms by modern physico-chemical methods has yielded results of great value; indeed it is no exaggeration to say that in many instances information obtained by such means could not have been obtained by the older methods. In this connexion the use of radioactive indicators has been of outstanding importance. This method of investigation, originally due to Paneth in 1918, resulted in the discovery of certain metallic hydrides, and has been greatly extended by the application of radioactive isotopes of the ordinary elements. Thus some aspects of the mechanism of the Walden inversion have been studied in this way by E. D. Hughes and his collaborators. A particularly impressive example of the value of investigation by the application of radioactive isotopes is to be seen in connexion with the well-known Friedel and Crafts ketone synthesis. Thus when benzene is allowed to react with acetyl chloride in the presence of anhydrous aluminium chloride, the products of the reaction are acetophenone and hydrogen chloride:

$$C_6H_6 + CH_3COCl = C_6H_5.CO.CH_3 + HCl.$$

The mechanism of the reaction, particularly as regards the function of the aluminium chloride, has been a subject of discussion for many years. Broadly speaking it was recognized that the action of aluminium chloride is somewhat different from that of an ordinary catalyst, since a comparatively large quantity of the compound is required, and there was general acceptance of the idea of the formation of an intermediate compound of some kind. In 1927 Meerwein suggested that the compound was a salt of the formula $[CH_3.CO]^+[AlCl_4]^-$ and an elegant verification of the correctness of this idea was given by Fairbrother in 1937. He used aluminium chloride containing a definite proportion of the radioactive isotope of chlorine to bring about the reaction between benzene and ordinary acetyl chloride without any radioactive chlorine. After the reaction it was found that the radioactivity of the hydrogen chloride which escaped was equal to that which remained in the residue, thus showing a complete exchange of chlorine atoms, the chlorine of the hydrogen chloride being derived in equal fractions from the aluminium chloride and from the acetyl chloride. This result is fully in accordance with the requirements of Meerwein's formula for the intermediate product, but cannot be explained on other principles.

Much information of real interest including many results of theoretical value has accrued from studies on the transformation of single substances, ranging from elements to molecules of considerable complexity. The study of polymorphic changes, or allotropic changes, as they have been more commonly termed when applied to elements, has attracted a great deal of attention. It has long been recognized that when a crystalline form of a substance can be transformed into another form, such a process may take place reversibly at a definite temperature, known as a transition point, or, in other cases, the process may be irreversible, one form being always less stable than the other, and there is no transition point realizable experimentally. The former class of substance is known as enantiotropic, the latter as monotropic; and Ostwald has assumed that the difference in behaviour between the two classes is a matter of the relative positions of the transition points and the melting points. In an enantiotropic substance the transition point is always below that of the melting-points of both allotropes, whereas in a monotropic substance that temperature has been assumed to lie *above* both melting-points. There are good grounds for regarding Ostwald's explanation of this difference in behaviour between the two classes of polymorphic substances as well founded. The whole subject is one of much importance, and in many instances it is of considerable complexity. It is very frequently to be observed among metals. Thus it has long been known that tin at low temperatures is liable to undergo transformation from the familiar white lustrous metal into a grey powder. Objects containing tin, such as organ pipes on old churches, have sometimes been observed to exhibit signs of deterioration, and this has been shown to be due to partial conversion to the grey modification. This phenomenon, to which the name of the *tin plague* has been given, was the subject of an elaborate investigation by Ernst Cohen and his collaborators between 1899 and 1908. He showed that tin is enantiotropic with the transition point between these two modifications at 18° C. As the average temperature in many parts of the world is frequently lower than this, it is clear that the conditions are such as to favour transformation into the grey allotrope. It has, however, been observed in this and in numerous other instances that transformation into the stable form is retarded, the substance under such conditions being in the *metastable* condition. A careful distinction has been drawn between conditions which have been termed metastable from those to which the word *unstable* is applicable, and broadly speaking the range between the two states is determined largely by the extent of departure from the condition of equilibrium. Thus when white tin is cooled below 18° C., the farther the metal is brought into the metastable region, the greater is the tendency for it to undergo change into the grey variety, but this is offset by a corresponding reduction of the reaction velocity. There is thus an optimum temperature at which the rate of transformation is a maximum, and this temperature is normally −50° C. according to Cohen and van Eyk. The optimum temperature is, however, dependent on various conditions, such as the previous history of the metal, and especially the presence of catalysts, among which a solution of ammonium stannichloride (pink salt) is highly efficient. In this, and in other cases of allotropy, contact with traces of the stable allotrope greatly facilitates transformation into the stable form.

The allotropy of iron is extremely complex and, in view of its bearing on the tempering of steel, has been extensively studied by metallurgists. As early as the time of Queen Elizabeth I it was observed by Gilbert of Colchester that the ferromagnetic properties of iron disappear on heating to high temperatures. This was confirmed by Coulomb in 1806, and has since been repeatedly verified. In 1873 it was discovered by Barrett that when iron is allowed to cool slowly from a temperature above 1000° C. evolution of heat takes place at certain temperatures, the phenomenon being known as *recalescence*. This subject was studied in detail by Osmond in 1887. He considered that there are three allotropes of iron, which were designated as α-, β- and γ-ferrite, with transition points at about 770 and 900° C. respectively. The possibility of a fourth modification of iron was suspected by Curie on certain evidence derived from magnetic phenomena, and later experimentalists, notably Ruer since 1913, assigned a transition point at about 1400° C. for the transformation of γ- into δ-ferrite. Still later it became recognized that there are only three, not four, varieties of iron, namely the α-, γ- and δ-ferrites, evidence having become available to show that the supposed β form is really identical with α-ferrite. Without entering upon any discussion on the subject, it can be readily appreciated how greatly the allotropy of iron is concerned with the tempering of steel.

The allotropy of sulphur has been a subject of a great many researches and two well-known crystalline forms, namely, the rhombic and monoclinic varieties have long been recognized. For the sake of brevity the former has been designated as α-sulphur and the latter as β-sulphur. The melting-points of these allotropes were determined by Brodie in 1854, which he gave as 114·5 and 120° C. respectively, and general agreement has been given to these figures by others. The transition point for the transformation of these modifications into each other was determined as 95·4° C. by Reicher in 1883, using a dilatometric method. The system is thus typically enantiotropic. But later work has shown that monotropic varieties are also to be obtained under suitable conditions, so that the allotropy of sulphur is really very complicated. The liquid state of sulphur is of great interest. It has long been known that, when the element is melted, the resulting liquid is of a pale yellow colour, but as the temperature is raised it darkens considerably and increases greatly in viscosity. Further application of heat causes the viscosity to diminish up to the boiling-point. Of the numerous researches which have been made on this subject, those of A. Smith and his collaborators, which were begun in 1902 and continued over several years, are of particular interest. According to Smith liquid sulphur is to be regarded as an equilibrium mixture of two allotropes, which have been designated as S_λ and S_μ respectively, the proportion of which depends on the temperature. This phenomenon has been termed dynamic allotropy, and is closely similar to tautomerism, and many of the peculiarities of liquid sulphur have been explained on this principle. Thus if liquid sulphur be quenched by pouring it into cold water, the resulting product is very different according to whether the sulphur has been heated just a little above the melting-point or has been heated to a considerably higher temperature. In the former instance the solid obtained is friable, but in the latter it is plastic. Again Smith and others have made a close study of the peculiarities of the melting-points of the various solid modifications, and a distinction has been drawn between the 'ideal' and the 'natural' freezing-points, the latter being always lower than the former. In general terms it may be stated that when a solid is melted and gives rise to a liquid consisting of only one molecular species—and such a substance has been termed a *unary* substance—there are no abnormalities about its freezing-point. But with sulphur the case is different: when the solid is melted the liquid at first consists primarily of S_λ, but some S_μ is also produced and this causes a lowering of the freezing-point; as the temperature of the liquid is raised the proportion of S_μ increases, and this circumstance provides an explanation of the variation in properties of the products obtained by quenching the liquid. It may be added by way of taking leave of this complicated and difficult subject that the molecular weight of sulphur has been the subject of a great deal of experimental study. Some of the older workers, having observed that solutions of rhombic and of monoclinic sulphur in various solvents gave rise to values corresponding to octatomic molecules, drew the unjustified conclusion that these crystalline allotropes were identical in molecular weight. The determination of molecular weights can only give rise to results which are valid within the limits of the experimental conditions. The identity of values for *dissolved* sulphur provides no information regarding the molecular condition of the solids from which the solutions were prepared. It is, however, of interest to note that X-ray methods of crystal study, which have been widely used in investigations on polymorphism, have been applied to the study of some of the allotropes of sulphur. In 1935 Warren and Burwell were able to show that the molecule of rhombic sulphur is octatomic, and that the molecules consist of puckered octagons with the atoms separated by distances of 2·12 Ångstrom units and a bond angle of 105·4°.

Of the very numerous instances of molecular rearrangements which are to be found among organic compounds, those involving migration of groups or of halogen atoms from the side chain into the nucleus of benzenoid compounds have formed subjects for many fruitful investigations. Such reactions are catalysed by acids, and the migrating group enters the *para* and usually also the *ortho* position in the ring, the hydrogen atom thus displaced taking the position in the side chain previously occupied by the halogen or group. Some of these reactions were discovered shortly after the nature of aromatic compounds had been established on a sound theoretical basis by Kekulé. Thus the transformation of diazoaminobenzene into *p*-aminoazobenzene under the influence of aniline hydrochloride was observed by Griess and Martius in 1866. And in 1871 Hofmann found that when alkylated anilines are heated the alkyl group enters the *para* position to the nitrogen atom, thus monomethylaniline is converted into *p*-toluidine. Similarly Bamberger in 1894 observed that phenylhydroxylamine is readily converted into *p*-amino-phenol under the influence of dilute acids. A great deal of later work has been done with the object of determining the mechanism of these and of other reactions of the same general type. An interesting review of these aromatic rearrangements was published in 1952 by Hughes and Ingold. At the outset they stated that, while reactions of this kind are *formally* all very similar, this similarity becomes less pronounced when the mechanism of the various processes is closely scrutinized. For the present purpose, however, the discussion will be illustrated with reference to a single example of much interest, namely the transformation of *N*-chloroacetanilide into *p*-chloroacetanilide:

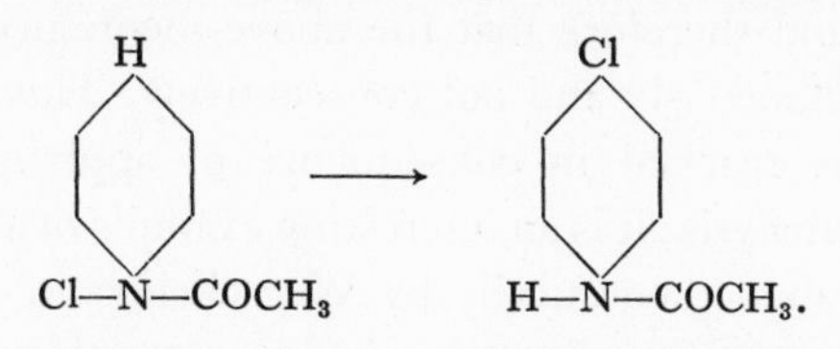

Bender first prepared *N*-chloroacetanilide in 1886, and the transformation into *p*-chloroacetanilide was discovered almost immediately afterwards. The velocity of this reaction was studied by Blanksma in 1902 and 1903, and the results were found to be in accordance with a unimolecular mechanism. There has been some discussion whether in this, and in other somewhat similar examples, the transformation should be described as *inter*- or *intramolecular*. When the migrating atom or group is known to become detached from the molecule the change is termed intermolecular, whereas it is described as intramolecular when the atom or group never becomes free. As might be imagined this has often been an extremely difficult question to decide. In the present example the work of Orton and others has shown that the reaction is fundamentally intermolecular. In 1900 it was shown by Armstrong, and independently by Orton, that hydrochloric acid is a specific catalyst for this reaction, and in 1909 Orton and Jones were able to show that the primary reaction is a reversible one which proceeds as follows:

$$C_6H_5.NClAc + HCl \rightleftharpoons C_6H_5.NHAc + Cl_2,$$

together with direct chlorination of the resulting acetanilide in the *ortho* and *para* positions:

$$Cl_2 + C_6H_5.NHAc = Cl.C_6H_4.NHAc + HCl.$$

This mechanism has been verified by numerous later experiments carried out by Orton and his collaborators and by others. Much of this work was concerned with the relative rates of isomerization of *N*-chloroacetanilide and of the *C*-chlorination of acetanilide by chlorine in various solvents, particularly in aqueous acetic acid. In 1928 Orton, Soper and Williams were able to show that when acetanilide is treated with chlorine in 40% acetic acid solution, the ratio of the *N*- to the *C*-chlorinated products was independent of the time, and therefore that the above-mentioned reactions take place simultaneously and not consecutively. This important conclusion was reached in consequence of applying an improved method of analysis; it is an interesting example of a principle which was established theoretically by Wegscheider in 1899, according to which the occurrence of simultaneous reactions can be demonstrated if the ratio between the various products is independent of the time. It should be added that Orton was one of the earliest workers on the mechanism of reactions to repudiate categorically the assumption that any particular reaction can have but one mechanism; and in this particular instance he pointed out that, while the available evidence gave clear indication that the reaction was intermolecular, he remarked in 1912 that under some conditions the possibility of its becoming intramolecular was not wholly excluded. In conclusion it is interesting to note that confirmation of the general results obtained by Orton was supplied by Olsen and his collaborators between 1935 and 1938. They effected the transformation of *N*-chloroacetanilide into *p*-chloroacetanilide using hydrochloric acid containing a known fraction of the radioactive isotope of chlorine, and found that the radioactivity of the resulting product was of the expected value.

The minute study of familiar reactions has been a profitable field of investigation, and there are good reasons for thinking that it is long likely to remain so, especially with the aid of modern methods. Although the mechanism of the union of hydrogen with chlorine is now fairly well understood, it is significant that in 1927 Hinshelwood remarked that 'this Mona Lisa of chemical reactions still smiles its bewitching smile, leaving us in doubt whether even yet the secret has been completely fathomed'.

REFERENCES

J. H. van't Hoff. *Studies in Chemical Dynamics*. Translated by T. Ewan. Amsterdam, 1896.

J. W. Mellor. *Chemical Statics and Dynamics, including the Theories of Chemical Change, Catalysis and Explosions*. London, 1904.

C. N. Hinshelwood. *The Kinetics of Chemical Change*. Oxford, 1940.

E. A. Moelwyn-Hughes. *The Kinetics of Reactions in Solution*. Oxford, 1933. Second edition, 1947.

E. J. Bowen. *The Chemical Aspects of Light*. Oxford, 1942.

Louis P. Hammett. *Physical Organic Chemistry*. New York, 1940.

Henri Moissan. *The Electric Furnace*. Translated by A. T. de Mouilpied. London, 1904.

Sir Edward Frankland. *Experimental Researches in Pure, Applied and Physical Chemistry*. London, 1877.

Sir I. Lowthian Bell. *Chemical Phenomena of Iron Smelting*. London, 1872.

F. Haber. *Thermodynamics of Technical Gas Reactions*. Seven lectures. Translated by Arthur B. Lamb. London, 1908.

T. Graham. *Chemical and Physical Researches*. Edinburgh, 1876.

J. J. Berzelius. *Lehrbuch der Chemie*. Fünfte umbearbeitete originale Auflage. Dresden und Leipzig, 1843.

Theodor von Grothuss. *Abhandlungen über Elektrizität und Licht*. Ostwalds Klassiker der exakten Wissenschaften, no. 152.

R. Bunsen and H. E. Roscoe. *Photochemische Untersuchungen*. Erste Hälfte, Ostwalds Klassiker der exakten Wissenschaften, no. 34; zweite Hälfte, no. 38.

F. Weigert. Die chemischen Wirkungen des Lichts. *Ahrens Sammlung*, Band XVII, 1912.

Victor Henri. *Structure des molécules*. Paris, 1925.

C. Moureu and C. Dufraisse. Catalysis and Autoxidation. *Chemical Reviews*, 1927, vol. III, p. 113.

C. E. Kenneth Mees. *The Theory of the Photographic Process*. New York, 1942.

C. H. Desch. The Le Chatelier Memorial Lecture. *J. Chem. Soc.* 1938, p. 139.

A. Smits. *The Theory of Allotropy*. Translated by J. S. Thomas. London, 1922.

E. D. Hughes and C. K. Ingold. Aromatic rearrangements. *Quarterly Reviews of the Chemical Society*, 1952, vol. VI, no. 1, p. 34.

C. K. Ingold. *Structure and Mechanism in Organic Chemistry*. London, 1953.

Annual Reports of the Chemical Society since 1904.

SELECT BIBLIOGRAPHY

Some Works on the General History of Chemistry

H. KOPP. *Geschichte der Chemie*. Vier Bänder. Braunschweig, 1843–7.

A. LADENBURG. *Lectures on the History of the Development of Chemistry since the time of Lavoisier*. Translated from the second German edition by L. Dobbin. Edinburgh, 1900.

E. VON MEYER. *A History of Chemistry*. Translated from the third German edition, with various additions and alterations by G. McGowan. London, 1906.

T. M. LOWRY. *Historical Introduction to Chemistry*. London, 1915. Reprinted with additions, London, 1936.

J. R. PARTINGTON. *A Short History of Chemistry*. London, 1937. Second edition, London, 1948.

H. E. FIERZ-DAVID. *Die Entwicklungsgeschichte der Chemie*. Basel, 1945.

INDEX OF SUBJECTS

INDEX OF NAMES